CENTRE FOR CO-OPERATION WITH THE ECONOMIES IN TRANSITION

SCIENCE, TECHNOLOGY AND INNOVATION POLICIES

FEDERATION OF RUSSIA

VOLUME II

BACKGROUND REPORT

ORGANISATION FOR ECONOMIC CO-OPERATION AND DEVELOPMENT

ORGANISATION FOR ECONOMIC CO-OPERATION AND DEVELOPMENT

Pursuant to Article 1 of the Convention signed in Paris on 14th December 1960, and which came into force on 30th September 1961, the Organisation for Economic Co-operation and Development (OECD) shall promote policies designed:

— to achieve the highest sustainable economic growth and employment and a rising standard of living in Member countries, while maintaining financial stability, and thus to contribute to the development of the world economy;
— to contribute to sound economic expansion in Member as well as non-member countries in the process of economic development; and
— to contribute to the expansion of world trade on a multilateral, non-discriminatory basis in accordance with international obligations.

The original Member countries of the OECD are Austria, Belgium, Canada, Denmark, France, Germany, Greece, Iceland, Ireland, Italy, Luxembourg, the Netherlands, Norway, Portugal, Spain, Sweden, Switzerland, Turkey, the United Kingdom and the United States. The following countries became Members subsequently through accession at the dates indicated hereafter: Japan (28th April 1964), Finland (28th January 1969), Australia (7th June 1971), New Zealand (29th May 1973) and Mexico (18th May 1994). The Commission of the European Communities takes part in the work of the OECD (Article 13 of the OECD Convention).

THE CENTRE FOR CO-OPERATION WITH THE ECONOMIES IN TRANSITION

The Centre for Co-operation with the European Economies in Transition (CCEET), was created in March 1990, as the focal point for co-operation between the OECD and the countries of Central and Eastern Europe. In 1991, the activities of the Centre were expanded to include the New Independent States of the Former Soviet Union and, the following year, Mongolia. In 1993, the Centre was renamed Centre for Co-operation with the Economies in Transition (CCET) to reflect its wider geographic coverage. Since 1991, the Centre has operated a "Partners in Transition" Programme for the purpose of providing targeted assistance to the countries more advanced in introducing market-oriented reforms and which desire to become Members of OECD. The "Partners" are now the Czech Republic, Hungary, Poland and the Slovak Republic.

Publié en français sous le titre :
POLITIQUES DE LA SCIENCE, DE LA TECHNOLOGIE ET DE L'INNNOVATION FÉDÉRATION DE RUSSIE
VOLUME II :
RAPPORT DE BASE

© OECD 1994
Applications for permission to reproduce or translate all or part
of this publication should be made to:
Head of Publications Service, OECD
2, rue André-Pascal, 75775 PARIS CEDEX 16, France.

Foreword

This report, prepared as part of the OECD review of science, technology and innovation policies in the Federation of Russia, describes the Russian science and technology system, recent developments, the Government's policies and current reforms. It provides information on the views held in the Russian Government on what should be done in the area of science and technology policy. This *Background Report* constitutes Volume II of the review and complements Volume I, the *Evaluation Report,* which was published earlier this year.

The review of science, technology and innovation policies in the Federation of Russia is designed to help Russian authorities to define a new policy in these areas. Undertaken by the OECD Directorate for Science, Technology and Industry, it follows the model adopted for OECD country studies. The review was included in the Centre for Co-operation with the Economies in Transition's (CCET) programme of activities following a request by the Minister of Science and Technological Policy of the Federation of Russia. The objectives and areas to be covered were defined at a meeting of representatives of the Russian Government and delegates of Member countries, held at the OECD Headquarters in December 1992.

The text of the background report was completed in the summer of 1993, having been prepared by a group of Russian experts under the supervision of A.G. Fonotov, First Deputy Minister of Science and Technological Policy. The evaluation report was prepared by a group of experts from OECD countries led by Professor J.-L. Lions, Collège de France, President of the International Mathematical Union. J.-E. Aubert of OECD's Directorate for Science, Technology and Industry co-ordinated the work on the study.

This report is published on the responsibility of the Secretary-General of the OECD.

Salvatore Zecchini
OECD Assistant Secretary-General
Director of CCET

Table of Contents

Acknowledgements 11

Introduction 13

I. Main geographical, political and economic characteristics of the Federation of Russia 15

1. Geographical and climatic features 15
2. Natural resources 16
3. Population 17
4. Political and administrative systems 19
5. National economy 22

II. The socio-economic situation and its influence on science and technology 31

1. Science and technology in Russia 31
2. Effects of the disintegration of the USSR on S&T in Russia 33
3. The economic situation in Russia 1991-92 34
4. Budgetary and monetary policies 35
5. Incorporation and privatisation 36
6. Conversion of military production and military science 36
7. The place of science in Russia's national priorities 37

III. Science and technology in Russia: main indicators 41

1. Introduction 41
2. Human R&D resources 42
3. R&D fixed assets 56
4. R&D expenditures 60
5. R&D output 74

IV. The organisation of science and technology 85

1. The principal sectors 85
2. The regional structure of science 102
3. Science cities: problems and perspectives 107

V. State science and technology policy: formation and implementation .. 115

1. Management of science and technology 115

5

		2. Contents and objectives of state science and technology policy	120
		3. Selection of S&T development priorities	121
		4. State S&T programmes	122
		5. S&T policy in key industries	125
		6. The evaluation of R&D	127
		7. Regional S&T policy and development prospects for regional R&D	128
		8. Legal framework for S&T and innovation activities	130
VI.	**The economic environment of R&D**		133
		1. Mechanisms for financing R&D	133
		2. Indirect stimulation mechanisms	136
		3. Reorganisation and privatisation in the R&D sphere	141
VII.	**The climate for innovation**		145
		1. Innovation activities prior to reform	145
		2. The innovation environment in Russia in 1993	146
		3. Small businesses	147
		4. Infrastructures	152
		5. Standardisation and certification	158
		6. Actors involved in shaping innovation policy	159
		7. Ways of shaping national innovation policy	161
VIII.	**Conversion of defence S&T**		165
		1. Defence R&D in the science and technology of the USSR and Russia	165
		2. Industrial and regional features of defence R&D	167
		3. Conversion programmes for defence science: the USSR experience	171
		4. R&D priorities in the defence complex and problems of technology transfer to civil industry	173
IX.	**Social problems in the S&T sector**		181
		1. R&D personnel: social status, employment and quality of living	181
		2. Advanced training and retraining	186
		3. Internal and external mobility	188
		4. Social policy in S&T: principles and directions	191
X.	**Russian science and technology in the international community**		195
		1. Scientific and technical co-operation with the CIS	195
		2. Co-operation in basic research	197
		3. International commercial scientific and technical relations	201
		4. Participation in international scientific and technical programmes and organisations	204
Annex 1:	Statistical addition to Chapter III		209
Annex 2:	The Russian R&D effort in an international perspective		245

List of Boxes

1.1	Administrative units of the Russian Federation	21
3.1	Categories of R&D personnel	42
3.2	Sectors of R&D performance in Russia	46
3.3	Problems of statistical information on "brain drain" from Russia	51
3.4	Characteristics of the higher education system in Russia	53
3.5	Data collection characteristics concerning R&D fixed assets in Russia	56
3.6	Qualitative indicators of R&D equipment	58
3.7	Gross national expenditure on S&T	61
3.8	Main forms of protection of author's rights in Russia	74
3.9	Use of inventions: main definitions	77

List of Tables

1.1	Land utilisation by type	16
1.2	Mineral resources: stocks and production	17
1.3	Main vital statistics	18
1.4	Total population by age and sex	18
1.5	Key economic indicators	24
1.6	Comparative indicators of living standards: 1989	24
1.7	Sectoral contributions	25
1.8	Industrial production by industry group	25
1.9	Agricultural production indicators	26
1.10	Equipment of housing units: 1991	26
1.11	Main trade indicators	26
3.1	R&D personnel	43
3.2	Share of R&D personnel in national employment totals	43
3.3	Total and R&D employment growth rates	43
3.4	Number of R&D researchers with advanced degrees	44
3.5	Percentage distribution by category of R&D personnel	44
3.6	Number of R&D personnel emigrating from Russia	51
3.7	Students in higher education in Russia and the major OECD countries	52
3.8	Higher education graduates in Russia and the major OECD countries	54
3.9	Fixed assets in the "science and scientific services" sector	57
3.10	R&D fixed assets by sector of R&D performance	58
3.11	R&D expenditure	62
3.12	Defence R&D appropriations in Russia	63
3.13	Current R&D expenditure by source of funds	64
3.14	Appropriations for R&D from the Russian Republic budget	65
3.15	Distribution of budget R&D appropriation by socio-economic objectives in Russia and major OECD countries	65
3.16	Percentage distribution of R&D expenditure by field of science: 1988	70
3.17	Current R&D expenditure by type of costs	71

3.18	R&D capital expenditure by type of costs and source of funds	73
3.19	Percentage distribution of inventions by technical level	77
4.1	Structure of costs for R&D in the Russian Academy of Sciences by type of research	91
4.2	R&D funding in some Russian colleges in 1991	97
4.3	The R&D share of some regions in Russia in 1991	103
4.4	Change of specialisation of small business enterprises in Novosibirsk in 1991	107
4.5	Russian science cities	108
5.1	Russian S&T programmes	123
7.1	Activities of small ventures in science and science services	148
7.2	Employment in R&D small ventures by the end of 1991	149
7.3	Performance of small ventures in St. Petersburg region at mid-1992	150
7.4	Objectives of small ventures for the near future	151
7.5	Competition strategies of small ventures	151
7.6	Level of competition in main sphere of activities of small ventures	151
7.7	Volume of transactions on stock exchanges in Russia	155
8.1	Defence enterprises according to the number of industrial employees	169
8.2	Expenditure on defence R&D in the USSR (1990) and the Russian Federation (1992)	174
8.3	Estimated defence expenditure in the Russian Federation	174
9.1	Average monthly wages in branches of the Russian national economy in March, 1993	185
9.2	Remuneration categories envisaged by the United Wage Scale for workers of science and science services	186
9.3	Number of emigrants who left Russia for permanent resettlement, by countries	190

List of Figures

1.1	Structure of the main state bodies of the Russian Federation	20
1.2	Administrative system of the Russian Federation	21
1.3	Economic regions of the Russian Federation	23
1.4	Trade by group of countries	27
1.5	Exports and imports in 1992 by commodity group	28
3.1	Researchers by gender	45
3.2	R&D personnel by sector of performance	47
3.3	Distribution of researchers by field of sciences	50
3.4	Post-graduate students enrolment and output: 1986-92	55
3.5	Percentage of major regions of Russia in the total value of fixed assets of the "science and scientific services" sector: 1991	57
3.6	Percentage distribution of personnel and fixed assets of R&D institutions by field of science	59

3.7	Trends in gross national expenditure on S&T in the former USSR and in Russia.	61
3.8	Annual growth rates of gross national S&T expenditure in the former USSR and in Russia	62
3.9	Value of R&D performed within R&D institutions by sector of performance	68
3.10	Value of R&D performed within R&D institutions by type of activity	69
3.11	Average monthly salaries of R&D personnel by sector	72
3.12	Resident applications and author certificates granted	76
3.13	External applications and protective documents granted abroad	78
3.14	External patenting	79
3.15	Geographical distribution of exports of licences	81
3.16	Payments for and receipts from trade in licences	82
5.1	State-Public regulation in the science and technology sphere in Russia	116
9.1	Dynamics of mobility of personnel in branches of the national economy of Russia (employment and discharge) in December 1992	182
9.2	Structure of monthly salaries in various branches of the Russian economy in March 1993 (percent of the average salary)	184

Acknowledgements

The original report was prepared under the overall supervision of A.G. Fonotov, First Deputy-Minister of Science and Technological Policy. The co-ordination of the work was ensured by B. Yourlov, Head of Department in the Ministry and V. Kisselev, consultant.

Expert groups worked on the report included personnel of:
- the Analytical Centre of the Russian Academy of Sciences, led by professor D. Piskunov (Chapters II, IV, VIII and X);
- the Centre of Science Research and Statistics of the Ministry of Science and Technological Policy of the Russian Federation and the Russian Academy of Sciences, led by Professor L. Mindeli (Chapters I, III and Statistical Annex);
- the Science and Technology Policy Division of the Ministry of Science and Technological Policy of Russia, led by I. Nikolaev (Chapter V);
- the Science and Technology Organisational and Economic Management Division of the Ministry of Science and Technological Policy of Russia, led by A. Kulaghin (Chapters VI and VII);
- the Science and Technology Social Problems Division of the Ministry of Science and Technological Policy of Russia, led by V. Valiukov (Chapter VIII).

Published works of many academic and branch research institutes of Russia were used for drafting this report.

The English version is based on the translation of the original report. This translation was furnished by the Russian authorities and edited by the OECD Secretariat.

Introduction

The present report on the current state of Russian science was prepared by Russian analysts with the assistance of OECD experts. It appears to be the first of its kind for Russia, and it is hoped that it will encourage systematic Russian participation in the monitoring of science and technology as practised internationally.

The report has two purposes: first, to expose the Russian and world scientific communities to problems of science and technology development in Russia; and second, to provide analytical background for science policy decision makers and international organisations interested in obtaining an unbiased view of the situation of and prospects for S&T research. The report may also improve the understanding of Russia's role in international S&T co-operation.

The experts who drafted the report faced a task of unusual scope and complexity. The present political and economic situation in Russia is unique; today's social changes and the ensuing difficulties have no parallel. In addition, in Russia, the process of resource allocation, the priorities for applying S&T, and the climate for innovation differ considerably from Western patterns.

The authors of the report considered that, to be properly understood by a Western reader, the data should be reported in a form that is as close to OECD conventions as possible. However, the transitional processes in Russia defy efforts to present data in such a form.

These considerations account for the framework and methodology of the report.

The indicators now employed in Russian statistics do not fully reflect current developments in the field of science owing both to objective factors and to recent subjective approaches to statistical theory and practice. Averaged estimates, such as those conventionally used for studying trends in national S&T development, can hardly reflect the minor fluctuations which, in the transition period, may be more telling. Consequently, the report makes extensive use of information on individual regions, scientific trends and institutions. It also draws on survey data and expert evaluations of the latter.

The indicators of S&T development formerly used in the USSR and still used, virtually unaltered, by various statistical bodies in Russia, make use of unified statistical accounting forms supplemented by ad hoc surveys of particular R&D components.

The accounting procedures used since 1990 allow for developing indicators concerning the number of R&D personnel, the volume of R&D work performed on a self-supporting basis, and the volume of R&D work by type of research. This is a major step towards bringing Russian accounting practice up to world standards. At the same time, the current system of accounting suffers from incomplete and disparate data, the persistent incompatibility of certain indicators with international practice, and the non-comparability of the new data with previous data.

Because information is supplied annually, with quarterly and monthly data available only for a few indicators, R&D statistics are difficult to analyse. This has always been true of the Russian statistical accounting system and explains why several important trends are inadequately represented in this report. These trends are: mobility of R&D personnel, part-time employment, new sources of R&D financing, the conversion of military R&D, development of regional science centres and cities, and the social dimension of these processes.

The dissolution of the All-Union statistical service and the reduction (in some cases, disappearance) of statistical services in some of the former Soviet republics have had a severe impact on the integrity of the statistical accounting system. Nonetheless, the report takes account of the developments of the 1990s that have had a major impact on S&T development in Russia:

- changes in the functioning and structure of the R&D sphere, following market-oriented reform efforts and the restructuring and conversion of military industry and science;
- the "regionalisation" (regional fragmentation) of the R&D sphere owing to the collapse of the USSR and to the increased autonomy of different areas of the Russian Federation;
- the sharp increase in the openness of Russian science and the broadening of Russian participation in international co-operation.

The main contributors to the report were the experts of the Analytical Centre on Science and Industrial Policy (attached to the Ministry of Science and Technological Policy, the State Committee on Industrial Policy, and the Russian Academy of Sciences) and the Centre on Science Research and Statistics (attached to the Ministry of Science and Technological Policy and the Russian Academy of Sciences). A wide range of studies concerning R&D activities and state science policy has been conducted in certain fields, with the assistance of experts of the Central Economic-Mathematical Institute, the Institute for Economic Forecasting, the Institute of World Economy and International Relations, and the Institute of Economics of the Russian Academy of Sciences. Official documents and working materials of various institutions, including the Supreme Soviet of Russia and the Ministry of Science and Technological Policy, were also extensively used in the preparation of this report.

The Russian contributors greatly appreciate the decisive contributions of the OECD experts to the methodology of the report, which considerably helped set the overall analytical framework and bring sometimes divergent approaches closer together.

Thanks to all those joint efforts, the report as it stands takes a balanced approach to evaluation of current developments, an approach largely free from the subjective political biases that are so typical of present-day life in Russia.

Chapter I

Main geographical, political and economic characteristics of the Federation of Russia

1. Geographical and climatic features

The Russian Federation (RF, Russia) is one of the largest countries in the world by its area (17.1 million square km, 76 per cent of the former USSR) and population (148.6 million as of 1 January 1993). Its territory is situated in the eastern and north-eastern part of Europe and the northern part of Asia and extends between 2 500 and 4 000 km from north to south and 9 000 km from west to east. The territory of the Russian Federation occupies one-eighth of the world's total land surface.

The borders of the Russian Federation touch Belarus, the Ukraine, Norway, Finland, Poland, Lithuania, Latvia, Estonia, Georgia, Azerbaijan, Kazakhstan, Mongolia and China, and conventional lines connecting the Rybachiy Peninsula and Ratmanov Island with the North Pole form the Arctic border. Russia also borders on the Barents, Baltic, North, Black, Caspian, Bering and Okhotsk seas and the Sea of Japan.

The Russian Federation has a favourable geographical location and has convenient transport and economic connections with all continents and countries of the world. It possesses enormous national resources and many unique mineral, fuel, energy, water and forest resources. Its agricultural potential is substantial.

Russia's climate is predominantly continental, and in the eastern part it is extremely continental. The southern part of the far eastern section has a typical monsoon climate, and the Black Sea coast has a subtropical maritime climate.

In winter, cold and comparatively dry weather prevails. The average temperature in January is below zero everywhere (except on the Black Sea coast of the Caucasus): from -1 to $-5\,°C$ in the West of the Russian Plain to -35 to $-50\,°C$ in eastern Siberia. In June, the average temperature ranges from $+1$ to $+2\,°C$ in the Far North to $+24$ to $+25\,°C$ in the steppe and semi-desert regions. Precipitation is abundant (up to 600-650 mm per year) in the western Russian Plain, and to the east it decreases in some areas up to 100-150 mm (in the south-eastern European area). The severe climate and poor snow cover in Siberia and the Far East contribute to the formation of permafrost.

2. Natural resources

Russia has enormous land resources (Table 1.1). Soils and vegetation are distributed by zones that are clearly marked from north to south: Arctic deserts, tundra, forest-tundra, forest, forest-steppe, and, in the south-east, semi-desert.

Possibilities for increasing land areas suitable for agriculture are rather limited. About 60 per cent of land resources are located in the tundra and taiga zones (only 2 per cent of this land is occupied by fields and meadows). It would be very difficult to extend the agricultural land area within the most fertile lands of the forest-steppe and steppe zones (25-28 per cent of the total land area). In fact, more and more land is marked by "industrial" (or "technological") erosion, *i.e.* developed agricultural land, including arable land, is being increasingly taken over for non-agricultural needs.

Russia is one of the most densely forested countries in the world, with 771.1 million ha of forests, covering 45 per cent of the territory. It has 81.6 billion cubic metres of timber stock. There are, on average, 5 ha of forest land and over 550 cubic metres of timber stock per capita. By comparison, the United States has 0.8 ha of forest land per capita, Sweden has 2.6, Finland, 4.1, and Canada, 7.3.

The average annual volume of river water withdrawals in Russia is 4 270 cubic km (over 90 per cent of the former USSR figure). The potential exploitable stock of underground water is 228 cubic km per year, of which 21 per cent is approved for exploitation by the State Commission on Reserves. Total annual water consumption reaches 117 cubic km, or 2.7 per cent of renewable resources.

Mineral resources

The Russian Federation possesses rich and exceptionally diverse mineral resources of: brown and bituminous coal (in the eastern part of the Donbass, the Kuzbass, the Kansk-Achinsk, Moscow, Pechora, Kizel, South Urals, Irkutsk, Tunguska, Minusinsk, Lena, and South Yakutia basins); oil and gas (the Timano-Pechora, Volga-Urals, and

Table 1.1. **Land utilisation by type**
As of 1 November 1991

	Million ha	Per cent
Total land area	1 707.5	100
Land use:		
Agriculture	643.6	37.7
State reserve and forestry enterprises	1 006.6	59.0
Other	57.3	3.3

Source: State Committee on Statistics of the Russian Federation.

Table 1.2. **Mineral resources: stocks and production**

	Total stock billion	Total stock percentage of the former USSR	National production as a per cent of:	
			Production of the former USSR	World production
Oil	–	64	92	17.0
Gas	–	80	76	29.6
Coal	275.0	70	57	9.1
Iron ores	100.0	60	46	16.4
Shales	2.6	37	15	–
Phosphorite ores	3.6	56	72	–
Potassium salts	140.0	62	48	–

Source: Central Institute for Economic Research; CIS Statistical Committee; *The Economist Atlas: The Share of the World Today*, Hutchinson Business Books, London, 1993.

Western Siberian oil and gas fields, the off-shore shelf of the northern and eastern seas and of the Caspian Sea); and iron ore (the region of the Kursk magnetic anomaly, the Urals, western and eastern Siberia). Deposits of manganese, non-ferrous and rare metals are numerous (the Urals, Siberia, the Far East, Kola peninsula). Of non-metallic mineral resources there are deposits of potassium salts (the Urals, the Astrakhan region), of apatite (Khibiny), of asbestos (the Urals, the Orenburg region), of mica (the Irkutsk region, Yakutia), and of diamonds (Yakutia, Northern Urals, the Arkhangelsk region).

Russia's shares of the mineral resources and production facilities of the former USSR are significant (Table 1.2). Some three-quarters of the country's territory is likely to have exploitable oil and gas resources. In the European part of Russia, large new fields of oil and gas, deposits of ores of ferrous and non-ferrous metals, titanium, bauxite, agrochemical and building raw materials have already been discovered.

3. Population

As noted above, the population of the Russian Federation as of 1 January 1993 is 148.6 million. The average density is 8.7 inhabitants per sq km, but it varies from 1.3 in the Far East and 2.2 in eastern Siberia to 62.6 in central regions of the country.

The population is multinational, and Russians represent more than four-fifths of the population, with 119.9 million. There are 5.5 million Tatars, 4.4 million Ukrainians, 1.8 million Chuvashes, 1.3 million Bashkirs, 1.1 million Moldovians, 1.2 million Byelorussians, 0.9 million Chechens, 0.8 million Germans, 0.7 million Udmurts, 0.6 million Maris, 0.6 million Kazakhs, 0.5 million Jews, and 1.7 million Daghestan nationalities.

Table 1.3. **Main vital statistics**

Per thousand population

	1980	1985	1990	1991	1992
Birth rate	15.9	16.6	13.4	12.1	10.8
Death rate	11.0	11.3	11.2	11.4	12.1
Infant* death rate	22.1	20.7	17.4	17.8	18.0
Natural growth rate	4.9	5.3	2.2	0.7	−1.3
Marriage rate	10.6	9.7	8.9	8.6	7.1
Divorce rate	4.2	4.0	3.8	4.0	4.3

* Infants under one year of age.
Source: State Committee on Statistics of the Russian Federation.

According to forecasts, the population of Russia will be 148.3 million at the end of 1993, due to the negative balance of births and deaths (Table 1.3). The drop in population would be even greater, but the population is being stabilised and may even grow due to immigration of the Russian-speaking population from the countries of the CIS. Immigration is increasing and may reach an average of some 0.8 to 1.0 million over the next few years. The decline in birth rates has led to an ageing of the population (Table 1.4).

Almost 74 per cent of the population live in urban settlements,[1] one-third live in towns of over 500 000 inhabitants. There are 13 towns with populations of over 1 million, the largest being Moscow (about 9 million inhabitants) and St. Petersburg (5 million).

Table 1.4. **Total population by age and sex**

Per cent

	1989	1990	1991	1992
Sex:				
Male	47	47	47	47
Female	53	53	53	53
Age				
Under 16 years	24.5	24.3	24.0	23.7
Working age population*	56.9	56.6	56.6	56.6
Over working age	18.5	19.0	19.4	19.7

* Women: 16 to 55 years; men: 16 to 60 years.
Source: State Committee on Statistics of the Russian Federation.

4. Political and administrative systems

Political system

The Russian Federation is a sovereign, democratic, federative state, with a republican form of government. The citizens of Russia express their will both directly and through the system of state bodies and local self-administration in the forms and under the limits set by the Constitution and federal laws.

The highest legislative body is the Congress of People's Deputies which elects the Supreme Council of the Russian Federation, a permanent body which meets in regular sessions, its Chairman, and the Praesidium (Figure 1.1). The Supreme Council consists of two chambers: the Council of the Republic and the Council of Nationalities. The chambers are presided by Chairmen, and they establish both permanent and temporary commissions, as well as joint committees.

The President of the Russian Federation is elected by the people and heads the federal executive, represents the Russian Federation in domestic and foreign relations, heads the activities of the government, and exercises general leadership over other bodies of the federal executive branch. The Vice-President of the Russian Federation is elected together with the President and is assigned to perform some of the President's duties.

The Council of Ministers is the Government of the Russian Federation and executes domestic and foreign policy under the leadership of the President. It reports back to the Congress of People's Deputies and to the Supreme Council of the Russian Federation. The structure, composition and competence of the government are determined by the Federal Law. The government acts as a collegial body under the leadership of its Chairman.

The organisational and legal forms of the central bodies of the federal executive power are ministries, state committees, federal services, Russian agencies, and federal inspectorates. The President, the government, the ministries and other bodies establish co-ordination and advisory bodies.

Judicial power in Russia belongs only to courts set up by the Federal Law. The Constitutional Court is the highest judicial body for the protection of the Constitution. The Supreme Court is the highest body of the judicial power and renders justice on civil, criminal and administrative cases. The Supreme Arbitration Court is the highest judicial body for economic cases.

Administrative structure

The administrative structure of the Russian Federation is based on the principle of federalism and is composed of 21 republics, six territories, 48 administrative regions, Moscow and St. Petersburg (Figure 1.2). It includes one autonomous region, ten autonomous districts, 1 857 districts, including 1 057 towns, 2 164 urban and 23 848 rural settlements (see Box 1.1).

Figure 1.1. **Structure of the main state bodies of the Russian Federation**

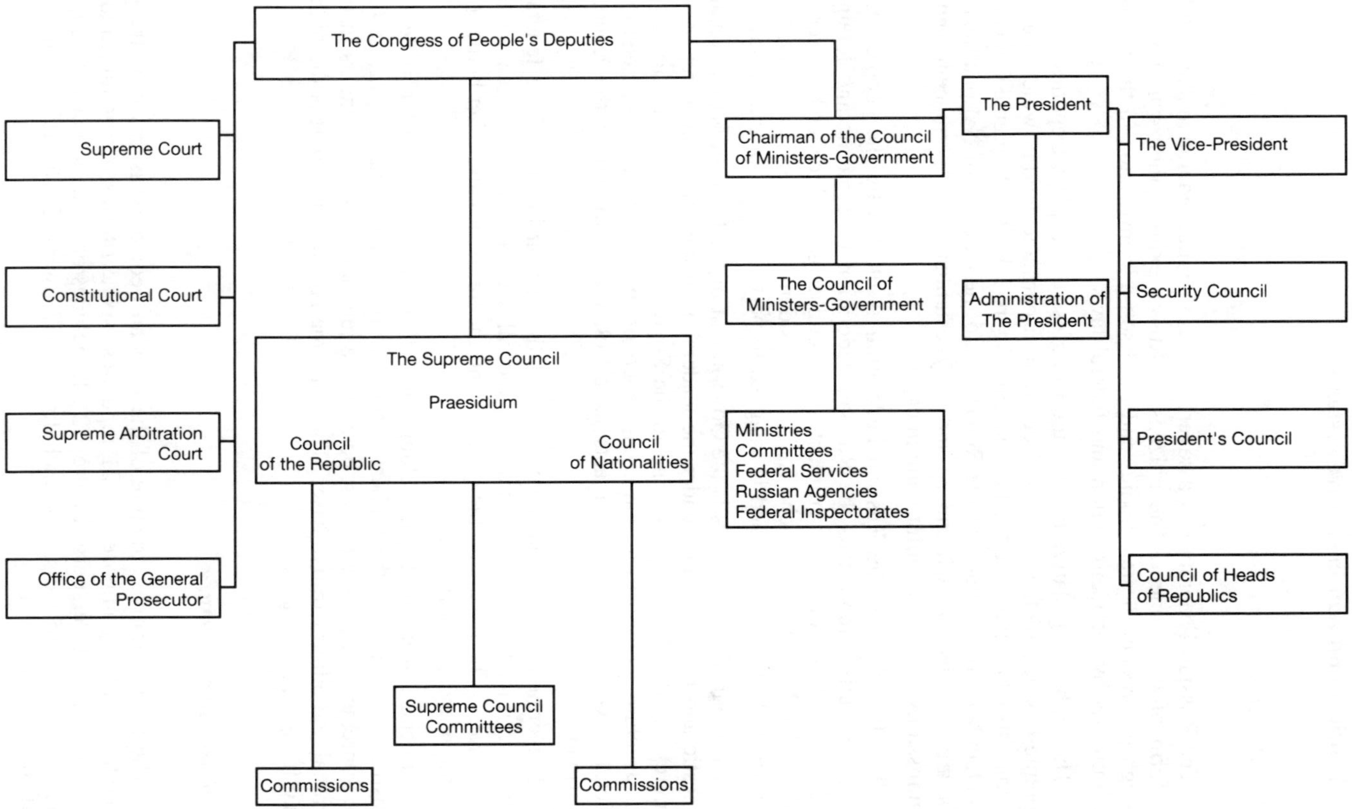

Figure 1.2. **Administrative system of the Russian Federation**

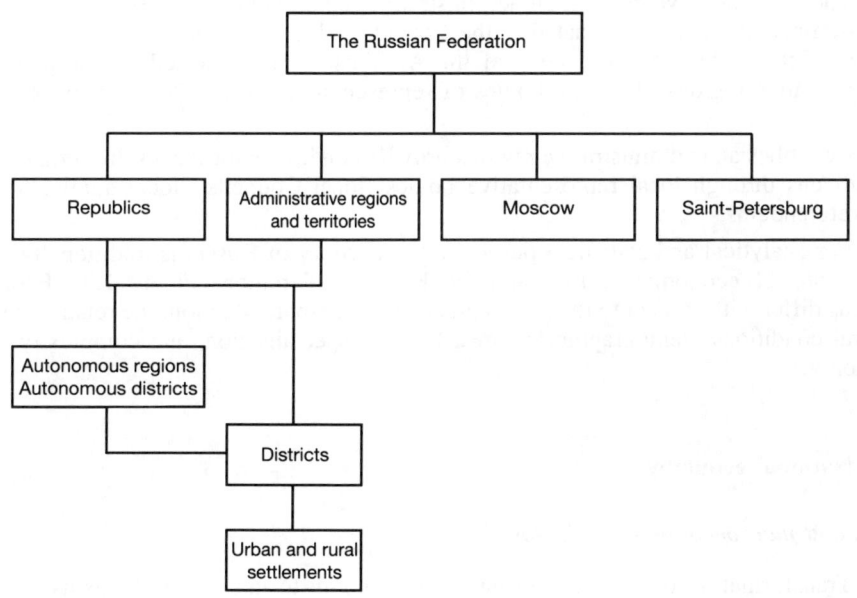

Box 1.1

Administrative units of the Russian Federation

A *republic* is a sovereign national state within the Russian Federation.

An *administrative region* is a territorial unit of the Russian Federation formed on the basis of natural, economic, and historical circumstances. The largest administrative regions are also called *territories*.

An *autonomous district (or autonomous region)* is a part of an administrative region (or territory) and is distinguished by the ethnic identity of its population.

A *district* is a territorial unit of a republic, an administrative region (or territory), or an autonomous district or region.

In the republics, the highest legislative body is the Supreme Council of the Republic. The executive power is represented by the Council of Ministers, which is part of the system of executive power of the Russian Federation.

The representative body in an administrative region is the Council of Deputies, and the Administration is subordinated to the Council and is part of the system of executive power of the Federation. The head of the Administration is elected by the people. In administrative regions, there are bodies of representatives of the President of Russia as well.

Republics and administrative regions provide conditions for local self-administration by citizens through local representative bodies (local Councils), local administrations, and referendums.

For analytical and statistical purposes, the territory of Russia is traditionally subdivided into 11 economic regions and the Kaliningrad region (Figure 1.3). Economic regions differ with respect to the geographical and transport situation, the relative unity of natural conditions, demographic features, level of specialisation, and complexity of the economy.

5. National economy

Principal macroeconomic indicators

Transformation of the Russian national economy to market mechanisms has radically altered the country's political and economic situation. Transition to the market economy is a difficult but irreversible process.

The principal macroeconomic indicators (Table 1.5) give a clear picture of the current economic situation. The Russian economy is in deep crisis. In 1992, GDP fell by 18.5 per cent and industrial production by 18.8 per cent. Inflation reached almost 1 600 per cent in 1992. Nevertheless, the employment level remains high, as employment fell by only 1.1 per cent in 1992. By the beginning of 1993, the number of unemployed registered at employment agencies was 0.6 million (only 0.7 per cent of the total labour force). Thus, the economic recession is evidenced more in wage decreases than in growth of unemployment. At the same time, there is increasing partial unemployment (incomplete work weeks, additional unpaid holidays, etc.), which in 1992 concerned 2 million workers in industry (9 per cent of the total number of workers).

Real income[2] decreased by 44 per cent during 1992, consumers purchased 39 per cent fewer goods than in 1991. (For an international comparison for 1989, see Table 1.6).

Structure of the economy

The Russian national economy largely depends on industry, which, together with agriculture and construction, contributes 67 per cent and 55 per cent, respectively, to GDP and employment, while trade and services account for 23 per cent and 37 per cent, respectively (Table 1.7).

Figure 1.3. **Economic regions of the Russian Federation**

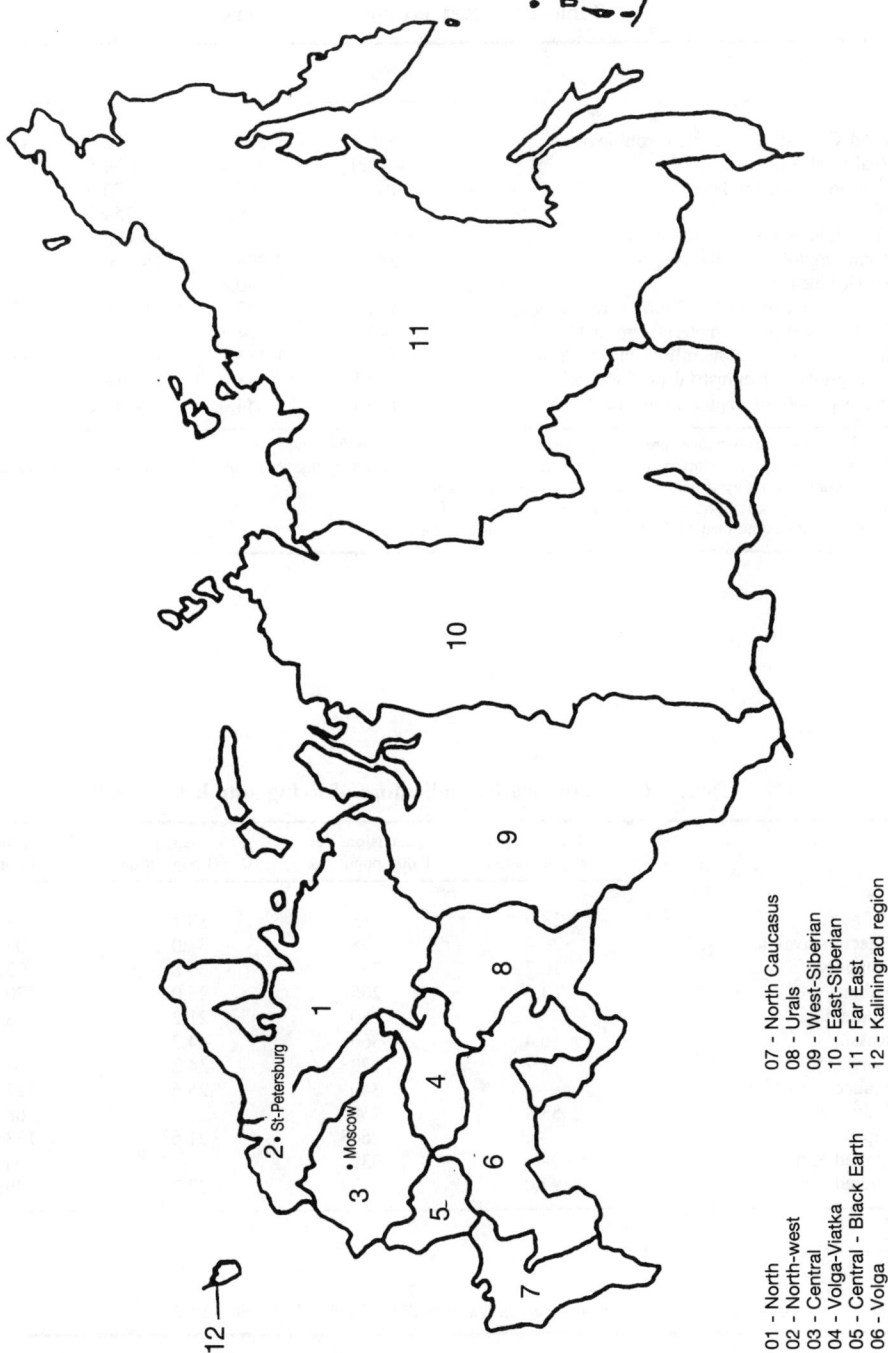

01 - North
02 - North-west
03 - Central
04 - Volga-Viatka
05 - Central - Black Earth
06 - Volga
07 - North Caucasus
08 - Urals
09 - West-Siberian
10 - East-Siberian
11 - Far East
12 - Kaliningrad region

Table 1.5. **Key economic indicators**

	1990	1991	1992	1993 (at 1.07.93)
Total GDP (billion current roubles)	626.3	1 300.0	19 992.0	41 786.0
Real GDP growth[1]	−11.0	−12.9	−18.5	−14.0
Consumer price indices[1]	105.3	200.3	1 570.0	344.1
Wage rates[1]	118.0	216.7	754.2	930.0
Total labour force (thousands)[2]	86 809.0	86 666.0	86 200.0	n.a.
Total employment (thousands)	74 383.0	73 809.0	73 000.0	n.a.
Employment growth[1]	−1.0	−0.8	−1.1	n.a.[3]
Net material product (billion current roubles)	444.6	942.0	1 310.0	32 270.0
Real growth of net material product[1]	−4.0	−14.3	−22.0	84.0
Industrial production (billion current roubles)	556.0	1 183.0	16 135.0	31 500.0
Real growth of industrial production[1]	−0.1	−8.0	−18.8	−16.6
Fixed growth of capital investment[1]	100.1	84.0	55.0	−6.0

1. Percentage growth over previous year; first half of previous year for 1993.
2. Working age population, excluding unemployed invalids and persons receiving pensions on preferential terms, but including employed persons under or over working age.
3. Unemployment (thousands officially registered): 716.8.

Source: State Committee on Statistics of the Russian Federation.

Table 1.6. **Comparative indicators of living standards: 1989**

	Telephones per 100 population	Televisions per 1 000 population	Physiciens per 10 000 population	Hospital beds per 10 000 population
Bulgaria	28.0	185	38.1	99.9
Czechoslovakia	26.4	298	37.0	103.0
Hungary	16.7	278	34.8	93.6
Poland	13.3	265	26.0[3]	70.0[3]
Romania	–	160	21.2	88.9
Russia[1]	16.4	366	44.3	134.7
Germany	71.7	379[2]	34.2	107.0
France	–	340	25.6	127.0[2]
Italy	53.4	258	–	68.1[2]
Japan	–	266[2]	21.6[2]	133.0[2]
United Kingdom	–	339	–	64.9[2]
United States	97.0	812[2]	27.7[4]	49.8[4]

1. 1991.
2. 1988.
3. 1990.
4. 1987.

Source: Rossija i strany mira. State Committee on Statistics of the Russian Federation, 1992.

Table 1.7. **Sectoral contributions**

	Total	Industry	Agriculture	Construction	Transport and Communications	Trade	Services
GDP[1]	100	40	17	10	10	5	18
Employment[2]	100	28	13	14	8	8	29

1. 1990.
2. 1991.
Source: State Committee on Statistics of the Russian Federation.

The decrease in industrial production in 1991-92 was not due to structural changes. Disproportions in the structure of industry are being maintained (Table 1.8). In comparison with the major Western countries, it has high shares of metallurgy, textile and food products, whereas the share of chemicals and machinery is rather low.

Agricultural output fell by 18 per cent in 1992 because of the decrease in production by public enterprises (Table 1.9). By the beginning of 1993, the number of private farms reached 184 000, with land totalling 7.8 million ha. The share of agricultural production from private farms and households accounted for over one-third of the national total in 1992, including 80 per cent of potatoes, 55 per cent of vegetables, 36 per cent of meat, 31 per cent of milk, and 26 per cent of eggs. Information on housing can be found in Table 1.10.

Table 1.8. **Industrial production by industry group**
Per cent

	Russia	United States[1]	West Germany (1989)
Total industrial production	100.0	100.0	100.0
Fuel and electricity	9.9	5.3	13.9
Ores, metals and fabrication	10.6	5.2	5.7
Chemicals, fertilisers and rubbers	6.8	14.2	14.5
Machinery and equipment	23.9	41.3	42.7
Stone, clay and glass products	4.0	2.5	2.8
Wood, furniture, paper products	5.6	7.9	4.8
Textiles, clothing and leather	16.6	5.2	4.0
Food products	17.8	14.4	10.4

1. Manufacturing.
Source: Rossija i strany mira, State Committee on Statistics of the Russian Federation, 1992, p. 99.

Table 1.9. **Agricultural production indicators**

	1990	1991	1992
Real agricultural production growth[1]	−12.8	−10.1	−18.0
Production:			
Grain (million tonnes)	116.7	98.1	106.8
Meat[2] (million tonnes)	10.1	9.4	12.7
Milk (million tonnes)	55.7	52.0	47.0
Eggs (million)	47.5	47.1	42.6
Potatoes (million tonnes)	30.8	34.3	37.8
Vegetables (million tonnes)	10.3	10.4	9.9
Sugar beets (million tonnes)	31.1	24.3	25.5

1. Percentage growth over previous year.
2. At slaughter weight.
Source: CIS Statistical Committee.

Table 1.10. **Equipment of housing units: 1991**

	Towns and other urban settlements	Rural settlements
Percentage of housing equipped with:		
Water	94	50
Sewerage	92	38
Central heating system	93	38
Gas supply	72	78
Electric stoves	21	4
Hot water	80	10
Baths	87	33

Source: CIS Statistical Committee.

Table 1.11. **Main trade indicators**
Billion dollars

	1990	1991	1992
Total trade	147.8	95.4	73.1
Exports	78.7	50.9	38.1
Imports	69.1	44.5	35.0
Trade balance	9.6	6.4	3.1

Source: CIS Statistical Committee.

Trade

The decrease in trade (Table 1.11) is due, first, to reduction of trade with the former CMEA (Council for Mutual Economic Assistance) countries, which dropped by 43 per cent in 1992, due to the introduction of world market prices and hard currency payments, while reduction of trade with developing and industrially developed countries was 27 per cent and 17 per cent, respectively.

The structure of foreign trade has been changing due to the collapse of economic relations between enterprises and regions within the former USSR, the reduction of oil and fuel production, difficulties in the food supply, blockage of the financial and credit systems, and increasing inflation. Shares of exports and imports have changed significantly (Figure 1.4).

Total trade with OECD Member countries dropped by 17 per cent in 1992, but trade with the Unites States increased by 56 per cent, mainly due to grain purchases. Trade also

Figure 1.4. **Trade by group of countries***

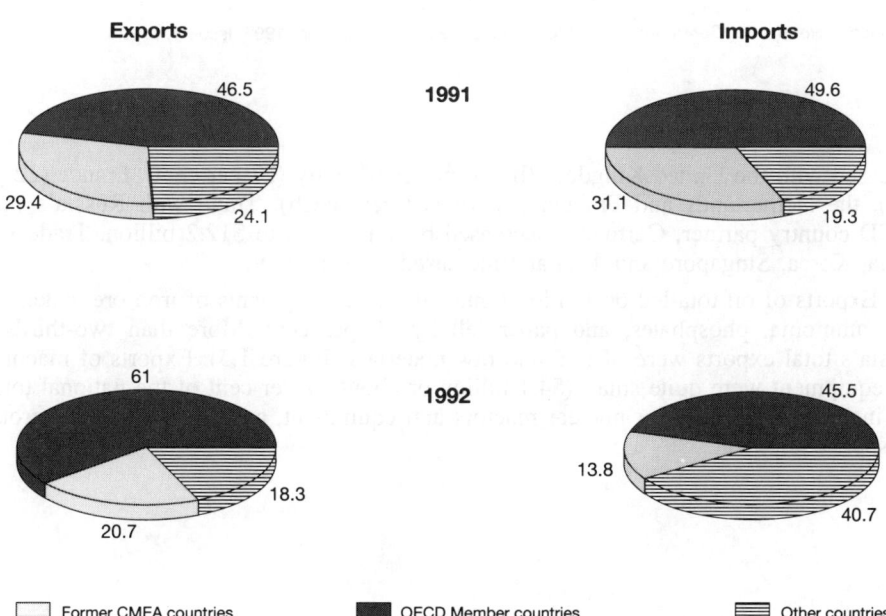

* Estimated by CSRS using data of the State Committee on Statistics of the Russian Federation.

Figure 1.5. **Exports and imports in 1992 by commodity group**
(percentage)

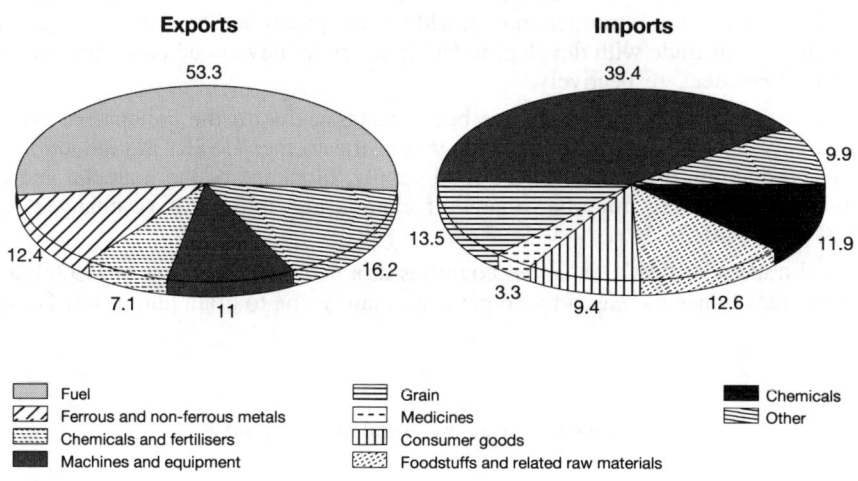

Source: *Rossija-93*, Centre for Economic Conjuncture and Forecasting, 1993, Issue 1, p. 228.

increased with the United Kingdom (by 80 per cent), Italy (27 per cent), France (22 per cent), the Netherlands and Finland (by 14 per cent each). Trade with Russia's main OECD country partner, Germany, decreased by 7 per cent to $12.2 billion. Trade with China, Korea, Singapore and Thailand increased considerably.

Exports of oil totalled 66 million tonnes in 1992. Shipments of iron ore, coke, cast iron, ammonia, phosphates, and paper fell by 50 per cent. More than two-thirds of Russia's total exports were of fuel and raw materials (Figure 1.5). Exports of machines and equipment were quite small ($4.1 billion or about 11 per cent of the national total), and included $1 billion for nuclear reactors and equipment, and $1.5 billion for ground transport equipment.

Notes

1. In Russia, settlements are considered as urban when the population exceeds 3 000 persons (3 000 to 12 000 for urban settlements and over 12 000 for towns). These settlements also carry out specific, non-agricultural, functions (in industry, transport, administration, etc.).
2. Income, minus obligatory payments and dues, corrected for the index of consumer prices.

Chapter II

The socio-economic situation and its influence on science and technology

1. Science and technology in Russia

The science and technology (S&T) sector in Russia in 1991 was part of the S&T complex of the former Soviet Union; as such, it inherited the main characteristics and problems of Soviet science, which it is useful to recall here.

The major goal of Soviet science was to create a powerful R&D sector appropriate to a socialist state, in a context in which economic development was oriented to large-scale industrialisation. This created a particular S&T and innovative climate. Scientific schools for basic research were founded (in physics, mathematics, biology, etc.) and engaged in research of world-calibre level, but they developed in isolation. At the same time, industry evolved in a climate favourable to labour-intensive and resource-intensive, but not capital-intensive, production processes. Thus, from the beginning, there was autonomous development of important science and an unfavourable climate for using its findings. As a result, monopolistic structures formed in science and in industry, there were few research groups in a given discipline, and there was little competitiveness.

The next stage followed World War II. It was characterised by a period of rapid and extensive growth, which continued throughout the 1960s. R&D expenditure grew, on average, 10 to 12 per cent annually and for S&T personnel, 7 to 8 per cent.[1] Many factors were involved, but the primary ones were the high rates of overall economic growth, the "cold war", the nuclear and conventional arms race, prestige, the extensive development of higher education, and the social climate of the "thaw" in the 1960s.

Thus was formed an S&T complex suitable to a large industrial country, with a broad spectrum of research and high-quality scientific personnel. The S&T sector fully shared the aims of the Soviet State. During this period, many important results were achieved in areas such as aerospace research, physics, mathematics, chemicals and biology. High economic growth allowed R&D resources to grow independently of economic needs.

The innovation climate of the "developed socialist economy" was such that the transfer of an invention or innovation to industrial firms, although free, was usually restricted to a single firm. Lack of interest on the part of both industry and research made the diffusion of new technologies extremely difficult. Some 90 per cent of innovations were used by only one or two enterprises. This resulted in a deformation of the structure of S&T, with a large amount of applied research and relatively little development. Central planning and regulation for a growing number of research institutions became more and more difficult. The so-called State Plan for R&D was, in practical terms, formed on the basis of the demands of ministries and organisations which were then formally approved by central bureaucrats.[2] It was a top-down decision-making process. The State Committee of Science and Technology USSR, for example, was the central financing and planning body for civilian S&T, and all ministries played a similar role in the planning and financing of their own research and development.[3] The major share of military R&D was placed under the Ministry of Defence and the Ministry of "Nine", or the nine ministries that produced military goods and services, which elaborated their R&D policy essentially in isolation.

The sharp increase in R&D funding allowed ministries to create S&T networks oriented to their own production goals. This strategy had negative consequences. Ministry and regional barriers protected S&T from competition. The lack of real links between R&D organisations and enterprises meant that R&D had little effect on production. There were no mechanisms for selecting new research projects and for ending those that had outlived their usefulness. Structural changes were determined by the availability of surplus resources and were thus only possible in a framework of growth of R&D resources. It became increasingly difficult to maintain the necessary rates of growth during the stagnation of the 1970s.

During this period, science and engineering gradually became a mass profession with average and later less than average wages. As wages declined, the social status of researchers fell; the quality of S&E personnel dropped as well, and signs of a crisis appeared.

Despite continued relatively high growth in R&D expenditure (5.1 per cent annually in 1975-85),[4] even traditionally strong areas of research began to lag behind leading research elsewhere. The number of author's certificates dropped by 20 per cent in 1980-85,[5] reducing the USSR's world share of inventions by nearly half. From 1980 to 1988, R&D results in industry superior to those achieved elsewhere dropped from 9.1 per cent to 4.1 per cent; those certified as equal to the best achieved elsewhere declined from 33.9 per cent to 21.9 per cent.[6] At the same time, new science and technology areas developed (*e.g.* in microelectronics and informatics), but due to inadequate organisation and management, this did not lead to changes in the economic structure.

In the 1980s, decreasing overall economic growth and declining state expenditure for R&D had a distinctly negative impact on science and technology. Fewer new research directions were explored, the share of younger researchers fell, and the renewal of research equipment slowed drastically. The situation was aggravated by differences in the rate of decline in different R&D sectors. Resource shortages revealed the priority accorded by the State, the main "sponsor" of S&T, to military R&D, which continued to receive the largest share of high-quality resources. As a result, the gap widened between military and civil R&D, the USSR Academy of Sciences and the academies of other republics, and between R&D in the centre and the provinces. Non-priority areas lagged behind not only in terms of research, but also in terms of production. In some areas, decisions to import technology (*e.g.* chemical machinery paid for with income from exports of crude oil) led to decreasing use of national S&T.

The government tried to implement some institutional and organisational reforms (to make civil industrial R&D organisation self-supporting, to merge industrial enterprises and R&D organisations, to reform the wage system in science, etc.). However, it failed to solve the problems and in some respects made them worse.

Thus, in the beginning of the 1990s, R&D in the USSR and then in Russia had the following main characteristics:
- the main organisational form was the research institute, which was government-supported and had very weak links with industrial enterprises and their needs;
- the large resources involved (3.6 to 3.9 per cent of overall national employment and annual expenditures of about 5 per cent of national income) were of relatively low quality and were used ineffectively;
- there was a stagnant and backward structure and low level of research in most civil industries;
- it depended on budget or other centralised sources of resources and lacked mechanisms for adapting to the changes in the economic environment.

R&D expenditure increased by 36.7 per cent in 1985-90, while GDP increased by approximately 28.7 per cent.[7] The idea of *khozraschet* (economic efficiency) was extended to the R&D sphere, and by 1988 had been implemented in nearly 2 000 research institutes and design bureaus. Results of scientific activity were recognised as goods, contract prices for scientific and technical products appeared, and the right of scientific organisations to choose research directions and to use their own financial resources was expanded. In spite of this, results continued to decline (for example, the number of innovations and of samples of new technical hardware dropped dramatically). One reason was a shortage of funds, and the government's intention to increase growth rates in industry was not supported by any real stimulus to innovation, so that residual resources for growth in the economy were exhausted, thus making future shifts in the economy and in the S&T sphere difficult.

2. Effects of the disintegration of the USSR on S&T in Russia

The disintegration of the USSR and the emergence of new sovereign states within its borders led to a partitioning of a formerly integrated scientific sector. The greatest share was located on what is now Russian territory: nearly 68 per cent of the specialists performing research and development (R&D); nearly 64 per cent of the R&D expenditure; 58 per cent of all scientific organisations, and almost all the main research directions of Soviet science. Nevertheless, isolation from former republics and the disintegration of the relations among them have had a negative impact on science and technology in Russia.

Among the most significant problems caused by the breaking up of the integrated science sector is the fact that the scientific sectors in the new states do not correspond to their economic needs. Their scientific organisations were decided by the USSR as a function of its overall needs, and they therefore did not develop in directions useful for their own economic development. The former republics consider national R&D an obligatory attribute of sovereign states, and its ranking among priorities has therefore increased, but only with respect to their "own" R&D, not to the part that served the needs of the USSR as a whole.[8]

The breakup of the USSR caused the destruction of both formal and informal S&T networks. Owing to the territorial division of labour in S&T in the former USSR, scientific research, design and project organisation, as well as technology transfer took place in different republics (*e.g.* research was performed in Russia, development in Belarus, and technology transfer in Ukraine). Elements of scientific research were spread across the territory of the entire URSS. For instance, the RAS Institute of Engineering Technology and the Kurchatov Institute of Atomic Energy (located in Russia) and the Institute for Strength and Resistance Studies and the Physical and Mechanical Institute (both in Ukraine) were engaged in a programme for ensuring reliability, safety and longevity of highly sensitive equipment, including nuclear installations. Research related to unique natural phenomena on the territory of the former Soviet republics in Transcaucasia and Central Asia may have to be eliminated, as may neutrino telescope investigations in the Balkan observatory (Kabardino-Balkaria), where the most important results of 1991 in the field of cosmic rays and neutrino astrophysics were obtained.

The sharp increase in the migration of scientific personnel in the republics of the former USSR, largely in the direction of Russia, has caused reduction of S&T personnel in these republics and deterioration of the social situation in Russian S&T.

3. The economic situation in Russia 1991-92

The state of the economy is the key factor for developing S&T. In 1991-92, the economic situation was characterised by a deepening structural-technological crisis which resulted in an economic depression and stagflation. GDP dropped by 12.4 per cent in 1991, and by 20 per cent in 1992. On 1 January 1993, industrial production had declined about 30 per cent with respect to 1 January 1992. Industry wholesale prices increased 34 times in 1992 and 2.1 times in the first quarter of 1993, while consumer prices increased 26 and 1.9 times, respectively.[9]

In 1991-92, there was a shift in the balance of production in the key economic sectors. In mid-1992, the greatest decline in output volume was in industries producing goods for final demand, investment and consumption goods. In 1992, fuel and energy output declined differently for different types of resources, from 0.4 (coal) to 13 per cent (crude oil); production of consumer goods dropped overall by 15 per cent, including foodstuffs (18 per cent). In the machine-building sector, with the most science-intensive products, output of different types of machinery and equipment fell from 20 to 50 per cent, the decrease in total fixed capital investment was 48 per cent in one year, and there was, in particular, a sharp decline in high-technology machinery and equipment, which affected the demand for S&T.[10]

These trends continued during the first quarter of 1993. Crude oil output was reduced by 4 per cent, there were faint but unstable signs of recovery in light industry (textiles, etc.) and foodstuffs, and machine-building continued to decline at the previous rate. Overall, in 1992-93, high-technology industries were most severely affected, and non-state demand for R&D was consequently reduced.

At the beginning of 1993, about one-third of the population was below the poverty line (8 000 roubles in March), and, according to official statistics, the median per capita income of the very rich was eight times that of the very poor. A sociological survey of scientific personnel in Moscow has shown that 71.3 per cent of scientific personnel have average income of less than 2 000 roubles a month (the standard of living minimum is estimated at 1 900 roubles).[11]

Official statistics on unemployment first appeared in Russian in 1991. In 1992, nearly 1 million Russian citizens applied to employment offices in search of employment, and there are 600 000 officially unemployed (or 0.8 per cent of the total labour force), 2.2 times the amount in the previous year.[12] In the first quarter of 1993 the figures rose to 1.1 million and 730 000, respectively.

4. Budgetary and monetary policies

In 1991, administrative economic regulation in Russia was abruptly discontinued, and the first step in economic reform was price liberalisation. The main instrument of the new economic policy was fiscal and monetary policy, a traditional tool in developed countries. Unsatisfied demand on a large scale and the absence of competition led prices to increase by a factor of ten, far more than the disparity between supply and demand appeared to warrant.

Under conditions of tight budgetary and monetary policy, enterprises found themselves without funds to make payments and no possibilities for obtaining commercial credit: this resulted in increased debt and a non-payment crisis. Consumer demand also declined markedly.[13] At mid-1992, non-payment was 8.7 per cent of GDP; the Central Bank then began to allocate credit for half of their debts to firms (1.5 billion roubles). Sums allocated by the government for minimal wages, pensions and social outlays increased.

On 1 September 1992, the state budget deficit reached 13.2 per cent of GDP, but it dropped to 4.2 per cent at the end of the year. For the first quarter of 1993, it was estimated at 10.1 per cent.[14] The government therefore decided to tighten restrictions on outlays, and those projected for social programmes were cut by about 36 per cent. The severe budget policy has meant that all federal budget expenditures have been cut similarly, including those for R&D. Lags in budget confirmation or between allocation and spending also mean cuts in real expenditures, because of inflation rates.

The share of state budget allocations for the R&D sphere has increased to 85 to 90 per cent, which means that R&D remains dependent on the State.[15] Increased budget allocations for R&D in current prices have not compensated for the decrease in industrial demand for R&D.

Monetary policy in 1992-93 has been characterised by increasing interest rates, and this has meant less credit for scientific organisations and a huge and rapid growth in the money supply, causing a decline in the standard of living of scientific personnel.

The radical economic reforms led to substantial deterioration in the situation of the sectors of the economy that were financed from the state budget, which suffered, to a large extent, from the government's finance and credit policy, which combined a deficit-free budget strategy with social concessions.

5. Incorporation and privatisation

Institutional reforms are very important to Russia's transition to a market economy. Until now, reforms have generally been restricted to changes in the structure of government regulatory bodies. The only other reform process that concerns the relationships between R&D and the economy is the process of incorporation and privatisation in industry.

At the end of 1992, 4 per cent of Russia's industrial enterprises were privatised. The privatisation programme for 1993 plans for 50 to 60 per cent of the total number of trade and food enterprises to become private property and for 5 000 to 6 000 of the largest state industrial enterprises to be incorporated.

The lack of free private capital, high inflation rates and a sharp decline in investments will present serious obstacles to changing the current production technology in most incorporated and private enterprises. The main way to increase effectiveness will therefore be intensification of labour and reductions in long-term expenditures (*e.g.* investment and R&D expenditure). This could result in high rates of unemployment (particularly among scientists and engineers). In the process of incorporation and privatisation, some industrial enterprises try to shed their R&D units. In other cases, pilot plants of large R&D organisations try to separate themselves from their parent structure, become private, and change their activity.

6. Conversion of military production and military science

The structural changes in industrial production resulting from the demilitarisation of the economy and the conversion of military enterprises has had a great impact on R&D in Russia. The goal is to increase economic efficiency and to adapt to market conditions.

The military-industrial complex's share of GNP in the USSR was 30 per cent, according to expert estimates, and its share of R&D appropriations was over 80 per cent (in 1990, according to official estimates, half of all science appropriations were for military R&D). From 1991 to 1992, defence production was reduced by half, and civil production in the defence sector (dual-use production) rose by 9 per cent.[16] In most cases, conversion led to production of less complex goods, using simpler technology. As a result, defence sector demand for R&D fell sharply. The transfer of military technologies to the civil sector proved to be generally impossible, for a number of reasons. First, civil enterprises lacked funds to purchase them, but even more important is the great technological gap between the civil and military sectors of industry. Civil enterprises are unprepared to use the results of the R&D organisations of the military sectors and the latter often have too little understanding of the needs of civil production, especially in a market economy, because they never were concerned with low production costs and because exploitation of results was not the a primary goal.

7. The place of science in Russia's national priorities

The peculiarities of Russia's socio-economic and political development have largely determined national priorities for science, which have changed over time, as was noted above. Today's new economic and political reality has made it impossible to preserve the old system of organisation and management, and the time appeared ripe in 1992 for deep changes in the Russian R&D system. However, science did not occupy a very high position among the priorities of the Russian government, because it did not offer ways to solve the main political and economic problems that were the centre of attention.

Appropriations for science offer an indicator of the decreasing importance of science: as a share of national income, in real terms, science allocations declined by 5.1 per cent in 1990, by 3.1 per cent in 1991, and in 1992 they were reduced further. During 1990-92 R&D expenditure as a share of GDP decreased from 3.1 per cent to 1.2 per cent. In 1992, the federal budget expenditure for civil science was 102 billion roubles out of a total expenditure of 178 billion roubles. In 1991 prices, this was only 40 per cent of the amount of the previous year's budget.[17] The projected level of state budget financing of R&D for 1993 – 686 billion roubles for civil and military R&D – again means a reduction in science appropriations in real terms.[18]

It should be noted that indicators presented in relative terms obscure the essence of the problem: nominal growth of R&D expenditure does not take account of the decline in the amount of national income used for consumption and investment. Increases of 3 to 4 per cent in the relative share of the state budget, along with absolute and relative declining outlays from other sources, really means the worsening of the financial position of science. In 1992, the share of state budget expenditure in national income was estimated at 50 per cent (against 73 per cent in 1990), and national income decreased by 20 per cent. Thus, in 1992 the state was distributing a much smaller part of resources than previously, and the amount itself was substantially reduced, so that the volume of resources allocated was also reduced in real terms.

Due to the reduction of government support to R&D, the distribution and use of resources had to be changed considerably. Resources allocated for science in 1992 were sufficient for maintaining a minimum standard of living for scientists remaining in the sector, but not for producing science or using the results in the economy. In 1990, the impact of labour and capital factors in the total volume of scientific output was estimated at 0.75 and 0.25[19] but already in 1991 the estimate for capital stock had declined to zero. Practically the entire sum was spent on wages and salaries, overhead and operating expenses.

The necessary legislative base was not created, although the government did implement several measures concerning, in particular, the regulation of relations in the area of industrial and intellectual property, non-budget sources of R&D financing (Technological Development Foundation), and the introduction of tax benefits for scientific organisations. The contradictory and inconsistent character of the government programme for transformations in the field of science largely discredited it in the eyes of the scientific community. The government was criticised less for proclaiming unpopular policy than for not taking real steps to implement it, for accepting, in essence, a principle of unregulated survival of the fittest. Overall science was "allowed" to survive, and state budget resources were allocated to this end.

Despite recognition of the need to save the scientific capacity of Russia, science decreased markedly in the hierarchy of national goals. The legislative and the executive were not in control of the situation in the field of science, and the legal regulations proved to be very imperfect.

Notes

1. *Narodnoe Kchozyastvo SSSR*, 1970, 1975; Moscow, *Finansy i statistika*, 1971, 1976.
2. According to the data of State Committee of Science and Technology, more than 70 per cent of R&D was controlled by ministries.
3. The so-called SCST sphere (all organisations subordinated to the State Committee on Science and Technology) included more than 100 ministries subordinated to the government of the Soviet Union and about 50 ministries, subordinated to both Union and Republic authorities.
4. Data from Centre of Science Research and Statistics, Russian Academy of Sciences, and Ministry of Science and Technological Policy.
5. Data from Centre of Science Research and Statistics, Russian Academy of Sciences, and Ministry of Science and Technological Policy.
6. Nauchno-tehnichesky progress, Moscow, *Finansy i Statistika*, 1990, p. 35.
7. *USSR in Figures*, 1991, p. 192.
8. For example, the Government of Ukraine decided to reduce scientific personnel in military scientific organisations by 50 per cent.
9. *O razvitii ekonomicheskih reform v rossiyskoy federatzii v 1992*, Moscow, Goskomstat, 1993.
10. For example, in 1992, the production of digital programmable machine tools was reduced by two-thirds, and in the first quarter of 1993 by three-fourths.
11. *Nauka i rynok*, Russian Academy of Sciences, 1993.
12. *Nauka i rynok*, Russian Academy of Sciences, 1993.
13. In 1992 and early 1993 prices rose, respectively, 2.3 and 1.3 times faster than nominal personal income.
14. Alternative expert estimates suggest as much as 30 per cent of GDP.
15. Similar trends are typical for all countries of the former USSR. For example, in Ukraine and Moldavia, the share is 50 per cent, in Kazakstan and Belarus, it is 60 to 70 per cent, according to estimates of the Centre for Scientific and Technological Potential and Science History Studies of the Ukrainian Academy of Sciences.
16. Estimates of State Committee on Statistics (Goskomstat).
17. Data from Goskomstat and the Centre of Science Research and Statistics.
18. Taking account of a 20-30 per cent monthly price increase at the beginning of 1993.
19. Calculation by the Analytical Centre RAS. This ratio corresponds approximately to the normal ratio in manufacturing.

Chapter III

Science and technology in Russia: main indicators

1. Introduction

The present chapter describes the current status and recent trends of the R&D capacity of Russia, measured in terms of resources and output.

Extensive growth in numbers of R&D institutions, researchers and expenditure until the late 1970s resulted in the creation of an extremely large R&D base, greater than that of most OECD countries. In particular, it generated the highly-qualified human resources which made Russia famous in basic research and military technologies.

The Russian (and ex-USSR) S&T system developed under pressures from a centrally planned economy, ideological dogma, and a dominant military sector. Together with the absence of an adequate structural policy and market regulators, it led to a waste of R&D resources and to low efficiency in the S&T system as a whole.

The Soviet bureaucratic system of centralised S&T planning and funding strongly influenced the formulation of R&D statistics. They were based on gross ("macro") indicators and were badly suited to analysis. Even if efforts are now underway in Russia to adopt OECD statistical standards (as laid down in the Frascati Manual for the measurement of R&D resources) many of the indicators and classifications used below may still be rather specific to Russia, as well as to other ex-USSR republics.

Data on R&D specifically in Russia (as opposed to the former USSR) are available from 1989 when the new national R&D survey was launched. As a result, the national categories of R&D personnel, types of R&D, etc., are broadly comparable with those of the Frascati Manual. This chapter will use both indicators traditional in Russian statistics and indicators compatible with the OECD standards. Annex 1 presents additional statistical information to complement this chapter.

All personnel data are, however, expressed as head counts and not in full-time equivalence as recommended by the OECD. Growth rates reported for expenditures, unless separately indicated, have been calculated from series expressed at current prices.

2. Human R&D resources

Trends in R&D personnel employment

At the beginning of 1992, the total number of R&D personnel reached 1.68 million including 52.4 per cent researchers, 11.9 per cent technicians, and 35.7 per cent supporting staff (Box 3.1). At the beginning of 1992, doctors of sciences accounted for 1.8 per cent and candidates of sciences for 13.4 per cent of the total number.[1]

Box 3.1

Categories of R&D personnel

The following categories of R&D personnel are considered in R&D statistics in Russia:

Total R&D personnel – all persons employed in R&D and in direct services to R&D (such as administrators and clerical staff) on a full-time basis.

Researchers – scientists and engineers (including postgraduate students) engaged directly in R&D and having higher education (university or equivalent) degrees.

Technicians – personnel with special secondary education performing technical tasks within R&D projects.

Supporting staff – personnel performing support services associated with R&D: staff of planning, financing, S&T information and patent units, S&T libraries, workers installing and maintaining research equipment and instruments, workers in experimental units, secretarial and clerical staff without special (post-secondary) training. Other personnel distinguished in Russian R&D statistics (staff of personnel, sale and purchase services, accounting staff, etc.) are also included here.

Table 3.1 shows the general trend of decreasing employment in R&D caused by the closing of research institutes, decreasing R&D expenditure, fall in the prestige of R&D work, and low R&D salaries. In spite of decreasing R&D personnel numbers, Russia still has a relatively high level of R&D employment compared to national employment totals (Table 3.2).

The number of R&D personnel fell by almost one-quarter in 1989-91, compared to 1.8 per cent for total employment and 7.5 per cent for industry (Table 3.3). The reduction especially concerned supporting staff. It reflects the urge to reduce general expenditures, deterioration in the quality of R&D infrastructure, and the introduction of institutional changes. Under the pressure of financial difficulties, technicians and supporting staff are laid off in order to preserve the stock of researchers. Not surprisingly, labour conditions of researchers have deteriorated and they have become less productive.

Table 3.1. **R&D personnel**

	1989	1990	1991	Percentage change over previous year	
				1990	1991
Total R&D personnel	2 210 363	1 943 432	1 677 784	−12.1	−13.7
Researchers	1 115 738	992 571	878 482	−11.0	−11.5
Technicians	269 561	234 817	200 606	−12.9	−14.6
Supporting staff	825 064	716 044	598 696	−13.2	−16.4

Source: Centre of Science Research and Statistics.

Table 3.2. **Share of R&D personnel in national employment totals**

	R&D personnel per 10 000 labour force		R&D personnel per 10 000 employment	
	Total	Researchers	Total	Researchers
1989	255	129	294	148
1990	224	114	261	133
1991	194	101	227	119

Source: Centre of Science Research and Statistics.

Table 3.3. **Total and R&D employment growth rates**
Per cent

	1990	−1991	−1992
Total employment	−1.0	−0.8	−1.1
Industry	−3.4	−4.2	−5.2
R&D	−12.1	−13.7	−

Source: Centre of Science Research and Statistics.

Against the general background of reduced R&D employment, the situation of highly qualified researchers looks different. The number of new doctors of sciences engaged in R&D grew in 1991 (Table 3.4), principally as a result of simplified procedures for defending dissertations. The uneven decreases in categories of R&D personnel and the absolute growth in the numbers of doctors of sciences in R&D have led to an increase in the share of highly qualified personnel (Table 3.5).

Table 3.4. **Number of R&D researchers with advanced degrees**

	1989	1990	1991	Percentage change over previous year	
				1990	1991
Doctors of sciences	15 609	15 475	16 165	–0.9	4.5
Candidates of sciences	138 952	126 975	118 011	–8.6	–7.1

Source: Centre of Science Research and Statistics.

In the absence of regulations aimed at needed structural changes, the reduction of S&T personnel and the appearance of a new type of S&T labour market are occurring spontaneously.

In this connection, there has been an increasing outflow of researchers, especially highly qualified ones, to the business sector (internal "brain drain"). Widening opportunities for business and the revival of private property make entrepreneurship more and more attractive to qualified and enterprising people. Higher revenues in the business sector are a very important reason for the outflow from R&D. Finally, many of the high-level managers of large business enterprises (banks, industrial groups, joint ventures, etc.) have doctoral degrees.

Personnel discharged from R&D institutions constitute the principal source of unemployment among scientists, engineers and technicians. According to Centre of Science Research and Statistics (CSRS) survey data, engineers and supporting staff are being cut back more severely than other categories of R&D personnel. Among applicants at unemployment offices previously employed at R&D institutions, most are engineering and technical personnel (48.7 per cent) and supporting staff (23.7 per cent). The share of researchers is low (8.2 per cent). Furthermore, only half of the unemployed who have registered at employment offices find a new job, and 25 per cent of them only with a change of profession and a notable decline in social status.

Table 3.5. **Percentage distribution by category of R&D personnel**

	Total R&D personnel	Researchers	Of whom:		Technicians	Supporting staff
			Doctors of sciences	Candidates of sciences		
1989	100	50.5	0.7	6.3	12.2	37.3
1990	100	51.1	0.8	6.5	12.1	36.8
1991	100	52.3	1.0	7.0	12.0	35.7

Source: Centre of Science Research and Statistics.

Demographic structure

The age structure of researchers has for many years been characterised by ageing of personnel, due to the reduction of the 30 to 40 years age group. In the former USSR, the share of scientific and teaching staff[2] in this age group decreased from 33.1 per cent in 1983 to 28.6 per cent in 1988.

The problem is especially acute for the most highly qualified personnel. In 1988, among doctoral researchers and university teachers below 40 years of age only 25 per cent were candidates of sciences and 2 per cent doctors of sciences. In the Academy of Sciences and universities these indicators were even more alarming. At the beginning of 1991, there were 550 600 female researchers in Russia, or some 51 per cent of the national total (Figure 3.1); they constituted only some 28 per cent of the highly qualified group of doctors and candidates of science (29.8 per cent of candidates and 14.8 per cent of doctors).

At the beginning of 1992, the greatest shares of female researchers were in the pharmaceutical sciences (77.1 per cent), philology (72.6 per cent), and economics (65.2 per cent). Their share was lowest in physics and mathematics (33.4 per cent) and in philosophy (43.8 per cent).

Sectors of R&D employment

Russia's R&D personnel is found in four major sectors (see Box 3.2): academies, higher education, industrial R&D institutions, and enterprises (Figure 3.2, and Table A1.1).

Figure 3.1. **Researchers by gender**
(as of 1 January 1992)

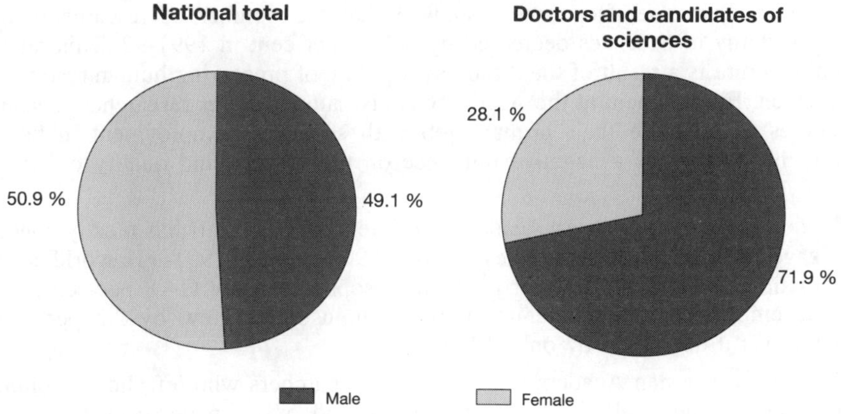

National total

50.9 %   49.1 %

Doctors and candidates of sciences

28.1 %

71.9 %

■ Male   □ Female

Source: Centre of Science Research and Statistics.

> Box 3.2
>
> **Sectors of R&D performance in Russia**
>
> The **academy sector** consists of the Russian Academy of Sciences (RAS), the Russian Academy of Agricultural Sciences, and the Russian Academy of Medical Sciences.
>
> The **higher education sector** includes R&D units of higher education institutes.
>
> The **industrial R&D sector** covers all research institutes, design bureaus, project and experimental organisations working independently of industrial enterprises. This sector traditionally also includes R&D units serving government.
>
> The **enterprise sector** consists of R&D units of industrial enterprises.

The academy sector

At the beginning of 1992 the academy sector consisted of 586 research institutes of the Russian Academy of Sciences and the academies of agricultural and medical sciences. The total number of R&D personnel was 190 000.

The real potential of the academy sector manifests itself not only in numbers but also in the professional structure of its personnel. The largest number of academy researchers are in physics and mathematics, engineering, and biology (Table A1.2). In this sector 42.6 per cent of the researchers hold a doctoral degree.

The academy sector has been less affected than others by the large-scale reduction of personnel. A survey undertaken by the Centre of Science Research and Statistics together with the RAS Personnel Department showed that the number of researchers in the Russian Academy of Sciences decreased by only 8 per cent in 1991-92. This relatively favourable picture is a result of the Academy's policy of preserving human resources for basic research. Employment at the Academy is also attractive for researchers because of opportunities to combine their primary job with secondary employment in business. However, this factor has a negative influence on the volume and quality of Academy research.

The decrease in the Russian Academy of Sciences R&D staff has mostly concerned those engaged in research in economics (down 17.9 per cent in 1991-92), world economy and international relations (14.9 per cent), philosophy and law (14.8 per cent). At the same time employment in mathematical research institutes grew by 2.3 per cent. In nuclear physics it decreased by only 0.1 per cent.

Most of the Russian Academy of Sciences' researchers who left did so voluntarily (85.8 per cent of the total): 7.6 per cent retired, and only 6.6 per cent were laid off because of direct staff reduction.

Figure 3.2. **R&D personnel by sector of performance**
(as of 1 January 1992)

**Total R&D personnel
= 1 677 800**

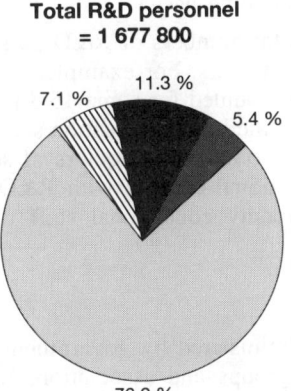

Researchers = 878 500

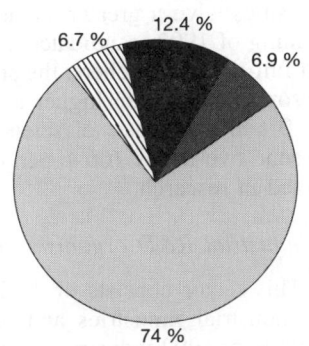

**Doctors of sciences
= 16.2 thousand**

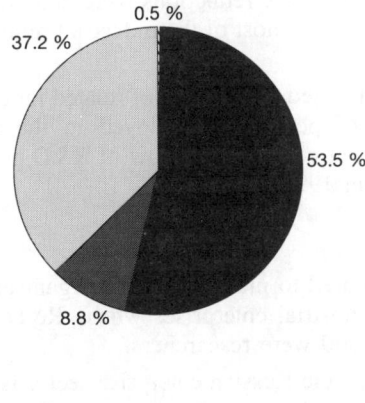

**Candidates of sciences
= 118.0 thousand**

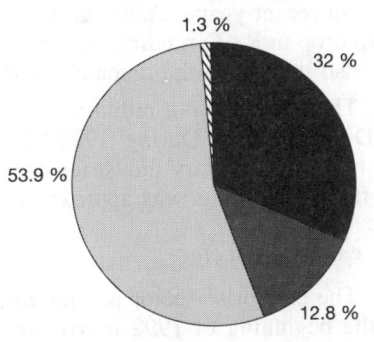

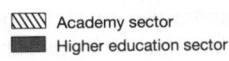 Academy sector
Higher education sector

 Industrial R&D organisations
Enterprise sector

Source: Centre of Science Research and Statistics.

The higher education sector

The higher education sector included 450 R&D units at the beginning of 1992. Full-time R&D personnel numbered 90 600, including 65 800 researchers. Furthermore, some 89 100 educational staff were engaged in R&D on a part-time basis.

Lagging behind industrial R&D organisations in total numbers of R&D personnel, universities have a greater share of highly qualified researchers. For example, if, at the beginning of 1992, candidates and doctors of sciences accounted for some 15.3 per cent of all full-time researchers, the share was 27.1 per cent in the higher education sector and the proportion is even higher among the teaching staff. Some 8 600 doctors of science and 50 600 candidates of sciences combine their educational activity with R&D; they represent two-thirds (66.4 per cent) of the total university educational staff directly engaged in research.

The industrial R&D organisations

This sector consists of 3 128 R&D institutions administered by government agencies, industrial ministries and departments, industrial groups and associations. At the beginning of 1992 industrial R&D organisations employed some 1.3 billion R&D personnel, including 650 000 researchers (74 per cent of the national total). This sector's shares of doctors and candidates of sciences in the total number of researchers were considerably lower, 1 per cent and 10 per cent, respectively.

The number of personnel in industrial R&D organisations has decreased substantially in recent years (Table A1.1). To a large extent, these reductions were caused by a sharp drop in R&D funding, following the liquidation of most of the industrial ministries and also the fall in the demand for defence R&D.

The conversion of military-oriented R&D concerned 44 per cent of related industrial R&D institutions. During 1989-92 the number of personnel employed in the R&D institutions of military industries decreased by 25 per cent. The outflow of R&D personnel from these units was approximately 250 000 in 1992.

The enterprise sector

The enterprise sector is relatively small compared to industrial R&D organisations. At the beginning of 1992 it covered some 400 industrial enterprises whose R&D units employed 118 400 R&D personnel, of whom 59 000 were researchers.

Due to economic and institutional peculiarities, the Russian enterprise sector is, as a rule, only able to adapt innovations to production in order to modernise current products. This sector is characterised by the relatively low level of qualifications of its researchers: the share of doctors of sciences is some 13 times less than the average elsewhere in the research sector and that of candidates of sciences is some seven times less.

The general reduction in R&D personnel has markedly affected the enterprise sector. The difficult financial position of industrial enterprises and the decline in (already low) product renovation rates have led to a situation in which many firms have stopped all R&D financing. During 1991 the number of researchers in industrial enterprises decreased by 14 per cent, and the number of candidates of sciences by 37.5 per cent.

Researchers by field of science

As shown in Figure 3.3, engineering employs some 60 per cent of the national stock of researchers. A second group, each having between 11 and 2 per cent of the national total, includes physics and mathematics, chemistry, biology, geology and mineralogy, agriculture, economics, and medicine. This professional structure appears to be very stable with only relatively slow changes over time.

As far as the most qualified researchers (doctors and candidates of sciences) are concerned, the distribution is rather similar to that of the national stock, with engineering, physics, mathematics and medicine dominating (Table A1.3).

Regional distribution of the R&D personnel

Two economic regions – Central and North-West – account for more than half of the R&D personnel. The Central region's share of national researchers in 1991 was 42.9 per cent (doctors, 62.2 per cent; candidates of sciences, 54.4 per cent). The North-West region accounts for 16.8 per cent, 16.0 per cent and 16.4 per cent, respectively. The dominating role of these two regions is related to the fact that they include the most prominent R&D cities of Russia, Moscow and St. Petersburg.

Trends in the reduction of R&D personnel vary in the regions of Russia. The greatest decreases occurred in the Far East (17.8 per cent), in the North-West (15.7 per cent), and in the North Caucasus (15.1 per cent).

The data on trends of different categories of R&D personnel by regions are provided in Table A1.4.

Emigration of R&D personnel

Emigration of scientists and engineers is one of the factors influencing the trends in Russia's S&T human resources (see Box 3.3).

A recent special study of emigration of researchers conducted by the Centre of Science Research and Statistics using data of the Ministry of the Interior of the Russian Federation made possible a statistical evaluation of the numbers of R&D personnel who have emigrated (Table 3.6). R&D personnel account for some 2 per cent of the total number of emigrants. This analysis seems to indicate that the process of "brain drain" has not yet taken serious dimensions. The main part of the emigrant flow, as previously, is driven by ethnic factors; the labour market plays a less significant role.

Furthermore, jobs in R&D abroad on contract are gaining importance. This concerns the most highly qualified specialists, often those with recognised scientific achievements. This form of "brain drain", even if not so significant in scale, may represent the main problem for the development of Russia's future S&T human resources.

Figure 3.3. **Distribution of researchers by field of sciences***
(as of 1 January 1991)

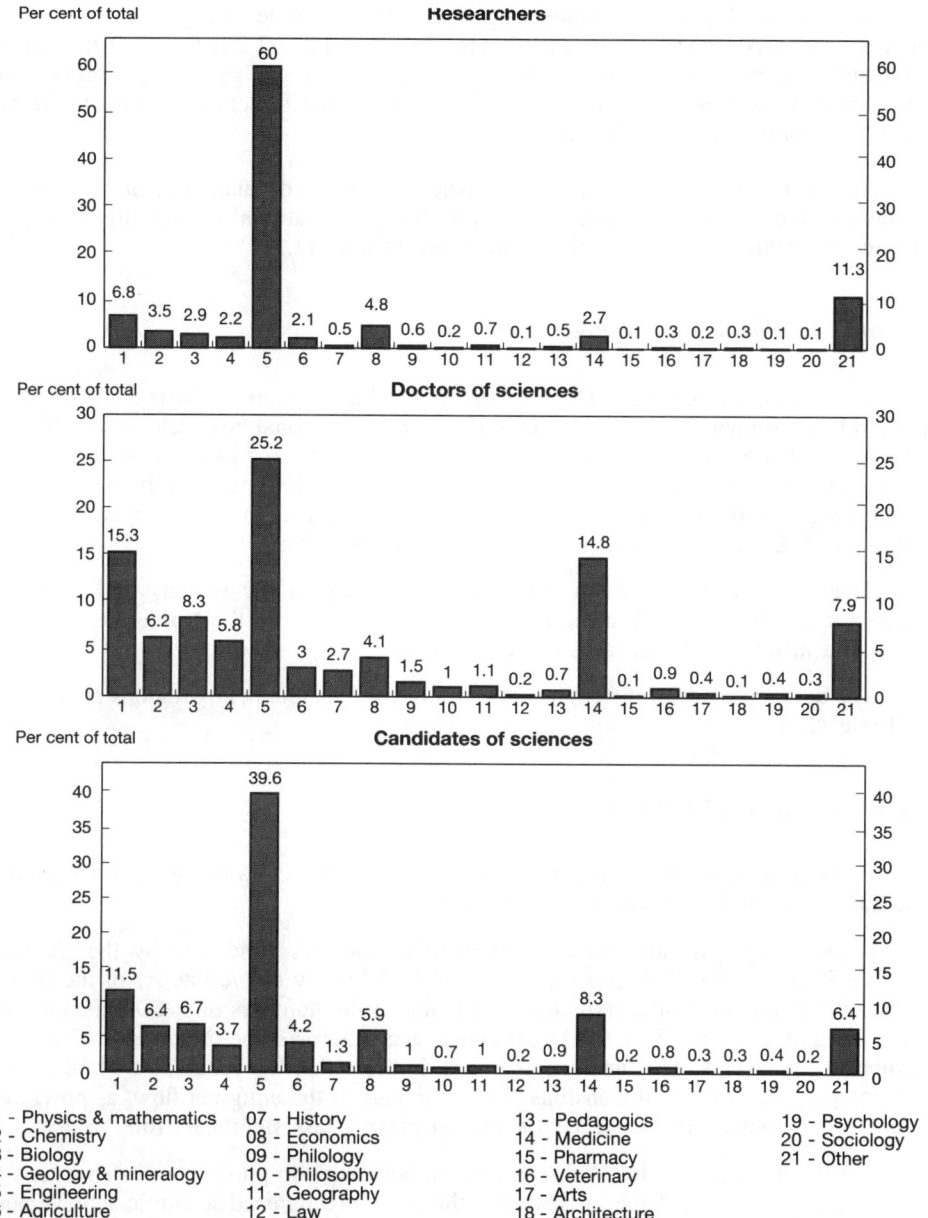

01 - Physics & mathematics
02 - Chemistry
03 - Biology
04 - Geology & mineralogy
05 - Engineering
06 - Agriculture
07 - History
08 - Economics
09 - Philology
10 - Philosophy
11 - Geography
12 - Law
13 - Pedagogics
14 - Medicine
15 - Pharmacy
16 - Veterinary
17 - Arts
18 - Architecture
19 - Psychology
20 - Sociology
21 - Other

* Including higher education teaching staff working as part-time researchers.
Source: *Science and Technology in Russia: 1991,* Data Book, Centre of Science Research and Statistics.

> Box 3.3
>
> **Problems of statistical information on "brain drain" from Russia**
>
> The main source of statistical information on emigration in Russia is a personal history form which is completed when applying for visas.
>
> The emigration procedure was simplified within the framework of human rights policy actions undertaken in the former Soviet Union in 1985-86. Questions on qualification and occupation were deleted from the personal history form. As a result, official statistics contain only data on the total number of people who received emigration permits, their distribution by gender and age, region, and country of destination.
>
> The Russian Federation Emigration Law promulgated in 1993 prohibits questions in the personal history form concerning information that is not necessary for a passport. Furthermore, the abolition of departure visas under the new law and the delivery of passports for five-year periods make it impossible to collect even the general information on emigration which was previously available.
>
> This situation has resulted in inaccurate and contradictory estimations in the mass media of the numbers of emigrating scientists and engineers. That is why *ad hoc* statistical studies are urgent.

According to the Centre of Science Research and Statistics survey of employment in the Russian Academy of Sciences institutes, undertaken together with the Russian Academy of Sciences Personnel Department, 508 researchers left the Russian Academy of Sciences institutes in order to emigrate in 1991-92. This represents some 0.8 per cent of the total stock of the Russian Academy of Sciences researchers: 13.2 per cent of the emigrants were employed in general physics and astronomy, and 11.6 per cent in biochemistry, biophysics and chemistry of physiologically active compounds. Most of the emigrants had the degree of candidate (55.9 per cent) or doctor of sciences (16.2 per cent). Half of the researchers who emigrated were under 40 years old. Israel and the United States dominate among receiving countries: 42.1 per cent and 38.6 per cent, respectively, of the total number of emigrants.

Table 3.6. **Number of R&D personnel emigrating from Russia**
In thousands

1980	1989	1990	1991	1992
0.14	0.95	2.1	1.8	2.1

Source: Centre of Science Research and Statistics.

Besides emigrants, 1 701 researchers of the Russian Academy of Sciences were working on long-term missions (lasting over half a year) or under contracts abroad: 81.5 per cent had scientific degrees and 60 per cent were under 40 years old.

Russian Academy of Sciences' researchers working abroad are in the fields of mathematics (12.1 per cent), followed by biochemistry and biophysics (9.2 per cent), nuclear physics (4.9 per cent), and general physics and astronomy (4.1 per cent). A significant share of these researchers work in the United States (38.2 per cent), followed by Germany (16.2 per cent), France (8.9 per cent), the United Kingdom (5.7 per cent), Canada (5.2 per cent), and Japan (4.1 per cent).

Training of S&T personnel

The system of S&T personnel training in Russia consists of higher education and post-graduate training.

Higher education

Higher education in Russia is ensured through a widely developed system of educational institutions. There were 535 public higher education institutes and 2.6 million students in Russia at the beginning of the 1992/93 academic year. By the end of 1992, 40 private higher education institutes had been established.

The number of students per 10 000 population in Russia is decreasing, but it remains comparable to that of the major OECD countries (Table 3.7). Between 1985 and 1992 the higher education student population in Russia decreased by 11.1 per cent, mostly due to the decrease (29.8 per cent) in the number of part-time students and in education by correspondence (Box 3.4, Table A1.5).

The most important reduction in the student population from 1985 to 1992 occurred in the higher education institutes of industry and construction (11.1 per cent), transport and communications (19.7 per cent), economics and law (14.5 per cent). The number of

Table 3.7. **Students in higher education in Russia and the major OECD countries**
Per 10 000 population

	1980	1985	1991
Russia	219	206	186
United States	268	322	319
Japan	148	153	155[1]
Germany	111	. .	147[1]
France	156	. .	164[2]

1. 1989.
2. 1987.

Source: *Rossija i strany mira*. Russian Federation State Committee on Statistics, 1992, p. 77; *Vysshaja shkola v 1991*, Annual report on higher and post-secondary education, State Committee on Higher Education of the Russian Federation, 1992, p. 166.

> *Box 3.4*
>
> **Characteristics of the higher education system in Russia**
>
> The higher education system consists of full-time, part-time and correspondence education. Part-time and correspondence students combine training with their work activity. The reduction in the volume of the two last types of education can be explained by their relatively low quality.
>
> The main characteristic of higher education is its sectoral orientation, which includes the following groups: industry, construction, agriculture, transport, communications, health services, education, economics and law, physical training and sports, arts and cinema. The education sector includes both pedagogical institutes and general universities.

students increased in higher education institutes of health services, physical training and sport (2 per cent), education (12 per cent), arts and cinema (4.8 per cent). The student population in the higher education sector increased mainly due to "traditional" university students; this confirms that university education in Russia continues to maintain its traditionally high prestige. Somewhat similar changes took place in the higher education institutes of all economic regions of Russia (Table A1.6).

The overall number of higher education entrants decreased over 1985-92 by 19 per cent, particularly in higher education institutes of industry and construction (by 33.5 per cent), transport and communications (25.6 per cent), agriculture (17.2 per cent), economics and law (18.4 per cent), health services, and physical training and sport (5.4 per cent). In the education sector institutes there was some growth in the number of entrants (5.9 per cent), whereas arts and cinema institutes remained unchanged.

The number of higher education graduates decreased by 10.9 per cent between 1985 and 1992. The greater reduction concerned higher education institutes of industry and construction (21.4 per cent), of transport and communications (18.5 per cent), agriculture (16.7 per cent), economics and law (14.6 per cent). In the education sector, the number of graduates increased by 6 per cent. The current number of high school graduates in Russia is well under half that of the United States and somewhat greater than in Japan (Table 3.8).

The professional orientation of graduates in Russia differs significantly from that in the developed countries. For example, engineers constitute the largest single category of higher education graduates in Russia (46 per cent in 1992); the shares are much lower for Germany (24 per cent in 1988), Japan (20 per cent in 1988), and the United States (13 per cent in 1987).[3] This is mainly the result of the priority given to engineering education in the former USSR. On the other hand, the share of graduates in high technologies is quite small (Table A1.7).

Table 3.8. **Higher education graduates in Russia and major OECD countries**
Thousands

	1980	1985	1991
Russia	459.6	476.6	406.7
United States	929.4	979.5	991.3 [1]
Japan	378.7	373.3	382.2 [2]
Germany	108.2	132.1	141.9 [2]

1. 1987.
2. 1988.

Source: *Vysshaja shkola v 1991*, Annual report on higher and secondary education, State Committee on Higher Education of the Russian Federation, 1992, p. 167.

With the current trends in higher education, further reductions are expected in the inflow of qualified personnel to R&D. Available information indicates that interest in R&D careers among graduates is constantly decreasing. The share of higher education graduates intending to work as researchers was 6 per cent in 1976-80, whereas in 1986-90 it fell to 2 per cent.

The teaching staff of the higher education sector in Russia was 28 000 in 1992, 58 per cent of whom had a scientific degree. On average, higher education teachers with a doctor of sciences degree are currently over 58 years of age.

According to the sample survey data, 46 per cent of the teaching staff in engineering and 36 per cent in economics (mainly in the under 40 age group) intended to leave the higher education institutes. One of the main reasons is that teaching staff salaries are comparable to those of little-qualified workers. Thus, at the end of 1992 a professor's monthly salary was 5 000 roubles, or only about a quarter of salaries in industry.

Higher education in Russia is mostly financed from the government budget, in proportion to the student population. In recent years the deficits in budget allocations have risen due to inflation and the low priority given to education in the government budget. Higher education budget funding in 1992 was some 46.4 billion roubles. Measured at constant prices, this sum provided only some 40 per cent of needed appropriations. Non-budget funding does not exceed 10-15 per cent of the total.

The new "Law on Education" of the Russian Federation was adopted in 1992. It provides for tax reductions, increased budget appropriations according to the rate of inflation, and for improving the social security of public higher education institutes, and it guarantees teachers' and students' medical services, nourishment, transport, pensions and holidays.

Postgraduate training

The postgraduate training of highly qualified S&T personnel includes two levels: postgraduate courses and doctoral courses oriented towards candidates' and doctors' degrees. Between 1986 and 1992 the postgraduate student population fell by 22 per cent while the numbers graduating decreased by 12 per cent (Figure 3.4).

The main decreases occurred in the fields of science connected with technology (physics and mathematics, chemistry, engineering) and in the social sciences (economics, philosophy, law), whereas in geology, medicine, pedagogy and psychology, growth was notable (Table A1.8).

The effectiveness of postgraduate courses is low, as, annually, only about 20 per cent of postgraduate students finished their candidate dissertation in 1990-92.

The final stage in the training of researchers is the system of doctoral courses. In 1992 there were 338 institutions in Russia with such courses, including 198 research institutes (516 students) and 140 higher education institutes (1 128 students). Some 40 per cent of students in doctoral courses graduate with a doctoral dissertation. The Supreme Certification Commission of the Russian Federation confirms some 35 000 scientific degrees (both candidate and doctor) annually in different fields of science (Table A1.9).

Figure 3.4. **Post graduate student enrolment and output: 1986-92**

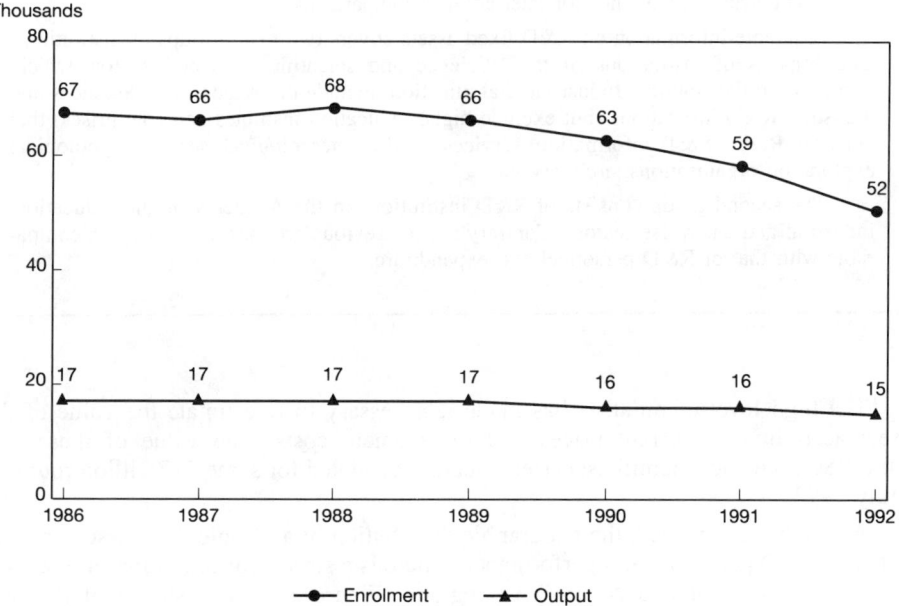

Source: Centre of Science Research and Statistics.

3. R&D fixed assets

General situation

Trends in R&D fixed assets of the "science and scientific services" sector (Box 3.5) are characterised by decreasing rates of replacement. Rates of the R&D fixed assets indicators varied from year to year and have tended to decrease (Table 3.9). The total value of the fixed assets of R&D-performing institutions, which reached 34.7 billion roubles in 1991 (Table A1.10) is somewhat lower than that of the "science and scientific services" sector.

Box 3.5

Data collection characteristics concerning R&D fixed assets in Russia

Data on fixed assets in use in the economic and R&D systems belong to the traditional Russian S&T indicators but are not commonly used for R&D analysis in OECD countries, at least not for international comparisons.

Available information on R&D fixed assets covers two main groups of institutions. One consists of institutions of the "Science and scientific services" sector, which, according to the National Industrial Classification, include the Academy of Sciences and industrial R&D institutions (but exclude higher education institutes and enterprises) that perform R&D, S&T information services, hydrometeorological services, geological exploration organisations, archives, etc.

The second group consists of R&D institutions of the Academy, higher education, industrial and enterprise sectors. Contrary to the previous group, the coverage is comparable with that of R&D personnel and expenditure.

The high level of inflation has made it necessary to re-estimate the value of these assets according to current prices and replacement costs. The value of these assets in the "Science and scientific services" sector accounted for some 717 billion roubles on 1 July 1992.

As might be expected, the geographic distribution of available fixed assets is similar to that of R&D personnel and performance. There is a strong concentration of R&D fixed assets in the Central and North-West regions (Figure 3.5). The shares of the West-Siberian, Ural and Volga regions are also notable, while those of other regions vary between 0.9 per cent (North) and 4.1 per cent (North Caucasus) (see Table A1.11).

Table 3.9. **Fixed assets in the "Science and scientific services" sector**

	1986	1991
Billion roubles (at constant 1972 prices):	33	40
Previous year = 100	105.4	102.9
Rate of depreciation of fixed assets (per cent)	46.0	45.0
Renewal coefficient [1] (per cent)	7.8	7.2 [3]
Withdrawal coefficient [2] (per cent)	5.3	3.5

1. Fixed assets placed in operation during the year as a percentage of total value at year end.
2. Fixed assets withdrawn during the year as a percentage of total value at the beginning of the year.
3. 1990.

Source: Centre of Science Research and Statistics.

The most informative indicator of the provision of fixed assets in R&D institutions is the ratio of fixed assets to labour (Table A1.10). Trends in this ratio are currently influenced by two factors: general price increase and reduction of R&D personnel. A re-estimation of fixed assets at constant 1991 prices indicated that the real value per employee decreased by 11 per cent during 1991.

Figure 3.5. **Percentage of major regions of Russia in the total value of fixed assets of the "science and scientific services" sector: 1991**

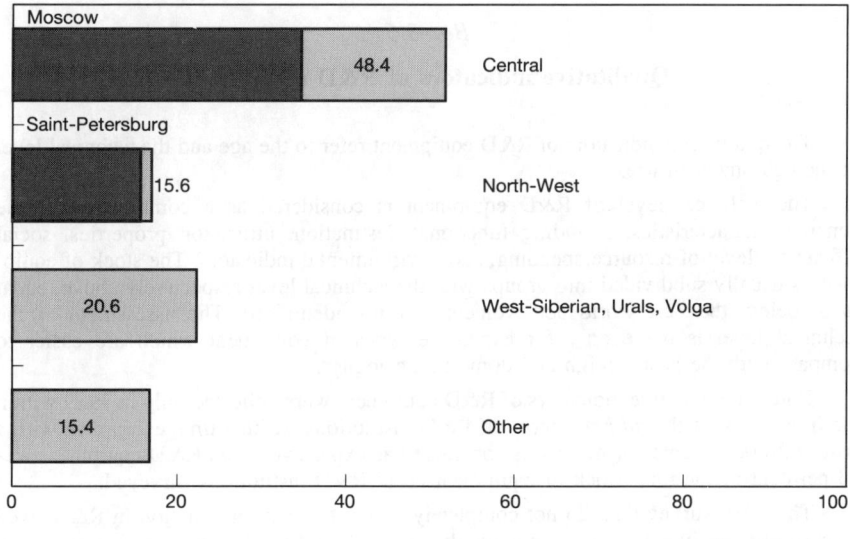

Source: Centre of Science Research and Statistics.

Table 3.10. **R&D fixed assets by sector of R&D performance**
Per cent

	1990	1991
Total, all sectors	100	100
Academic sector	20	21
Industrial R&D organisations	68	69
Higher education sector	7	7
Enterprise sector	4	3

Source: Centre of Science Research and Statistics.

Fixed assets by sector of R&D performance

Two-thirds of the total stock of R&D fixed assets are concentrated in industrial R&D organisations (Table 3.10). Data show general nominal growth in the stock of fixed assets in 1991, with the exception of the enterprise sector which saw a decrease even at current prices as a result of a decrease in the R&D activity of enterprises.

Box 3.6

Qualitative indicators of R&D equipment

The qualitative indicators of R&D equipment refer to the age and the technical level of the equipment in use.

The technical level of R&D equipment is considered as a combination of the concrete characteristics, including functional destination, utilisation properties, social efficiency, level of resource spending, and environmental indicators. The stock of equipment is usually subdivided into groups with the technical level respectively above, equal to or below the best world achievements (or not identified). The assessment of the technical level is made only for expensive types of equipment which are easier to compare with the best foreign and domestic analogues.

Data on qualitative indicators of R&D equipment were collected only in 1989 within the framework of the *ad hoc* survey of R&D institutions. At that time equipment with a cost of 30 000 roubles or more was considered as expensive. Such R&D equipment was 23 per cent of the total stock of equipment in all R&D institutions surveyed.

The 1989 survey data do not completely reflect the current situation in R&D fixed assets, but they show the situation at the threshold of the transition to a market economy.

As far as the qualitative characteristics of R&D fixed assets are concerned, no sector appears to be in a privileged position (see Box 3.6). The Academy research institutes have a more complete supply of expensive and unique equipment. However, in those institutes performing more than half the total volume of basic research, nearly a quarter of all equipment is obsolete, and more than 30 per cent is not to world state-of-the-art level. The age structure of fixed assets in industrial R&D institutions is the best in comparison with other sectors, while indicators of technical level are below average. The higher education sector has less expensive equipment, but its age structure and technical characteristics are rather high (Tables A1.12 and A1.13).

R&D fixed assets by field of science and technology

The field of engineering accounts for 62.3 per cent of the total stock of R&D fixed assets (Figure 3.6).[4] However, the natural sciences are relatively better provided with fixed assets. The R&D fixed assets-to-labour ratio in the natural sciences was twice the average and equal to that of engineering.

High quality equipment, which by its technical level exceeded the best available elsewhere, was mainly concentrated in the natural sciences (69.5 per cent of the total stock of such equipment). Engineering's share was notable as well (27.7 per cent). The most up-to-date equipment was in the field of information and information systems. Medical sciences took last place (Table A1.14).

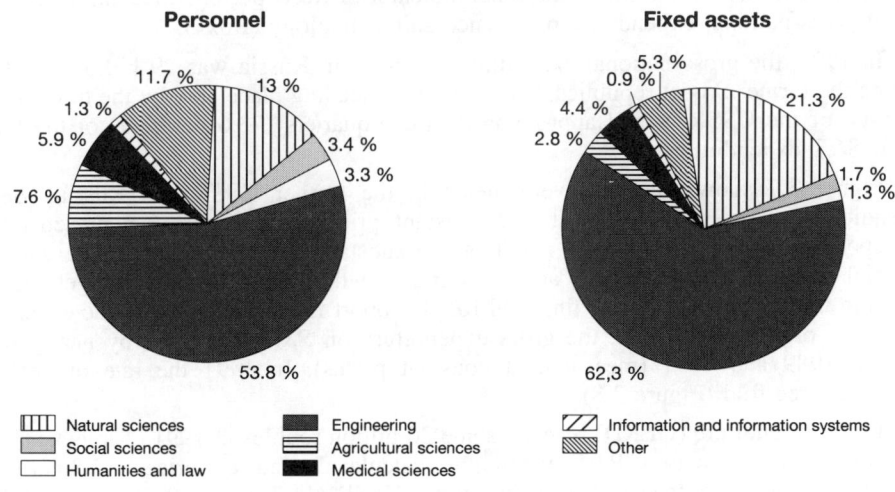

Figure 3.6. **Distribution of personnel and fixed assets of R&D institutions by field of science**
(as of 1 July 1989)

Source: Centre of Science Research and Statistics.

Problems of ageing R&D equipment

For a long time, R&D institutions were not able to replace obsolete machines and equipment. The annual fixed assets renovation ratio was only some 2-3 per cent a year, so that large stocks of ageing equipment accumulated. As indicated above, the rate of depreciation of fixed assets in the "Science and scientific services" sector reached 45 per cent in 1991 (Table 3.9).

According to available data, one-fifth of machinery and equipment in use in R&D institutions is more than ten years old, and 5 per cent is more than 20 years old (Table A1.12). The average age is seven years, and fears are expressed that, given the decline in replacement of fixed assets, the age structure of R&D equipment is worsening.

On average, about half (51 per cent) of the total stock of machinery and equipment could be considered "new" (under five years), 22 per cent very new (under two years of age). Computer hardware accounts for some 44 per cent of the cost of all R&D equipment under five years of age.

Only an insignificant part of expensive R&D equipment – 0.5 per cent of the total stock – is superior to the best world technical standards (Table A1.13). This research equipment and instruments are mostly concentrated in R&D institutes of military industries, with some in the Academy and higher education institutes.

4. R&D expenditures

General situation

In the national statistics the traditional indicator of R&D performance and finance is that of gross national expenditure on science and technology (Box 3.7).

In 1991, the gross national expenditure on S&T in Russia was 29 billion roubles. Among the former Soviet republics, Russia held the leading place and, by the time of the break-up of the USSR, it had approximately three-quarters (73.6 per cent) of the total USSR S&T expenditure.

Figure 3.7 shows recent developments in the former USSR and Russian S&T expenditures, expressed at current and constant prices, and Figure 3.8 presents the corresponding growth rates. As a result of the substantial deterioration of the general financial situation, budget deficits and declining growth rates of research budgets, difficulties in finding supplementary financial R&D support from ministries, agencies, enterprises and organisations, etc., the gross expenditure on S&T decreased by nearly half between 1989 and 1991 (measured at constant prices). In 1991 the rate of decline increased three-fold (Figure 3.8).

R&D expenditure (GERD) reached some 20 billion roubles in 1991 (Table 3.11). In Russia the annual growth of R&D expenditure calculated at current prices (12.8 per cent in 1989-91) slightly outpaced that of the former USSR (11.7 per cent), but was insufficient to compensate for accelerating inflation.

Box 3.7

Gross national expenditure on S&T

Official statistics on R&D expenditure in the former USSR have been based on estimation of the so-called "gross national expenditure on S&T". This indicator was created by the centralised planning system to demonstrate the overall value of R&D institutions' activity, and it is not comparable with that used in the OECD area ("GERD", which is limited to R&D expenditures).

The gross national expenditure on S&T is calculated as the total value of work performed by R&D institutions (including both expenditures and profits received during the year), and R&D capital expenditure (excluding investment by R&D institutions in housing, personnel facilities and other installations not connected with R&D). Expenditures on the implementation of innovations are excluded.

Figure 3.7. **Trends in gross national expenditure on S&T in the former USSR and in Russia**

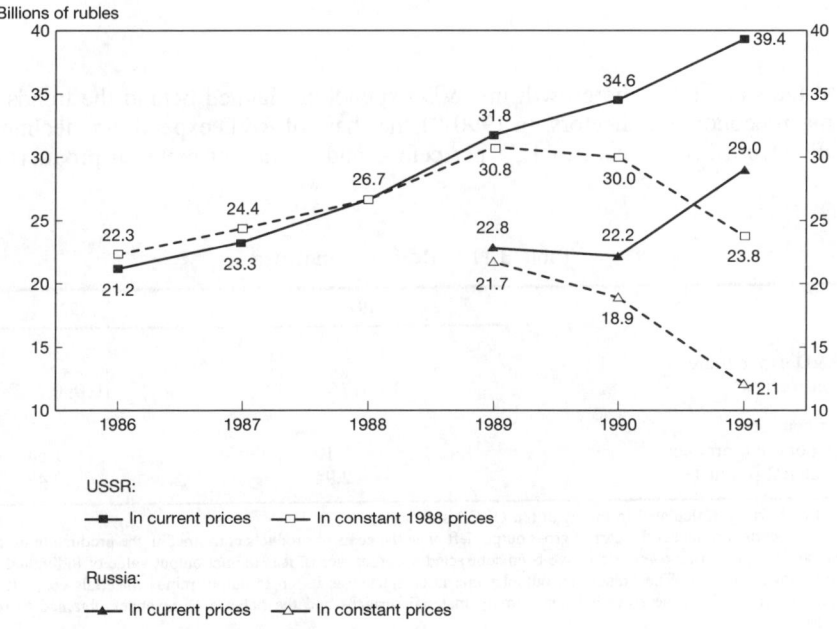

Source: Centre of Science Research and Statistics.

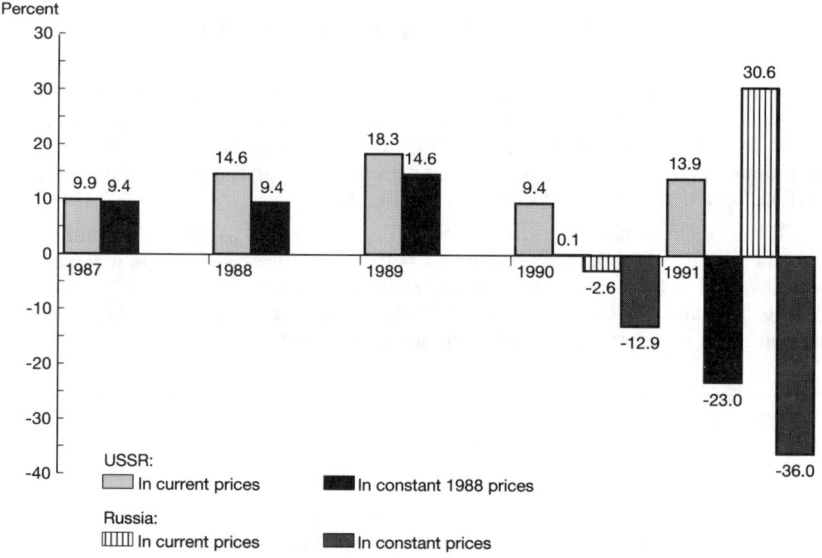

Figure 3.8. **Annual growth rates of gross national S&T expenditure in the former USSR and in Russia**

Source: Centre of Science Research and Statistics.

At the same time, the growth in R&D expenditure lagged behind the trends of the main macroeconomic indicators. In 1990-91 the share of R&D expenditure declined both in GDP – from 2.1 per cent to 1.54 per cent – and in the net material product – from

Table 3.11. **R&D expenditure**

	1990	1991
Total R&D expenditure, million roubles[1]	13 077.7	19 990.7
As a per cent of:		
Gross domestic product	2.10	1.54
Net material product[2]	2.94	2.47

1. At current prices. Calculated in line with the OECD standards.
2. The net material product is the part of gross output left once the costs of products consumed in the production process (raw materials, fuel, electric power, etc.) have been subtracted. In other words, it is the net output value of individual branches of material production. The branch net output value is calculated as its gross output minus materials costs. It does not include revenues from the so-called non-primary material services and the balance of revenues obtained from foreign countries.

Source: Centre of Science Research and Statistics.

2.94 per cent to 2.47 per cent. Compared with OECD data for this indicator, Russia falls at the median level, in the group of countries with medium R&D potentials, such as Belgium, Denmark, Austria and Canada.

Defence vs. civil R&D expenditure

An important aspect of R&D expenditure concerns the breakdown between civil and military R&D. In the last years of the USSR, expenditure for defence R&D was reduced. In 1989-90, it decreased from 15.3 to 14 billion current roubles. In 1988-91, total USSR defence expenditure was projected to drop by 14 per cent, including a reduction of 15 per cent in defence R&D expenditure.

The sharp inflationary growth in military industry costs made it necessary to raise appropriations for military R&D, which in Russia were multiplied by more than 18 at current prices (1991-93) to reach 224.7 billion roubles (Table 3.12). In terms of constant prices, this indexation was clearly insufficient. In 1992 the value of military R&D did not exceed 4.3 billion roubles (in 1991 prices). The share of R&D in total military expenditure decreased in 1989-92 from 19.8 per cent (USSR) to 10.6 per cent (Russia). This situation threatens the existence of many big R&D research institutions of military industries.

Nevertheless, by international comparison, Russian R&D remains excessively militarised. Defence R&D programmes account for some 43 per cent of the gross national expenditure for S&T. In 1991, the share of civilian R&D expenditure did not exceed 1.1 per cent of Russian GDP (in 1989 the value of this indicator was: 1.21 per cent in Italy, 1.83 per cent in France, 1.85 per cent in the United Kingdom, 1.93 per cent in the United States, 2.67 per cent in Germany, and 3.04 per cent in Japan.[5]

Regional distribution of R&D

The strengthening of regional economic independence and national statehood in the republics of the Russian Federation make the analysis of regional contributions to R&D especially important. The uneven geographical distribution of R&D institutions and differences among economic regions in terms of scientific capacity by size and specialisation influence the regional R&D financial resources.

Table 3.12. **Defence R&D appropriations in Russia**
At current prices

	1991	1992	1993[1]
Total, billion roubles	12.4	75.7	224.65

1. Estimates as of 1 July 1993.
Source: Russian Federation Budget Laws for relevant years.

Nearly two-thirds of national R&D[6] is performed by institutions of the Central and North-West economic regions, among which Moscow and St. Petersburg account for 30.5 per cent and 15.1 per cent, respectively. The Urals, West-Siberian and Volga regions have shares in the range of 7-8 per cent (Table A1.15) of the national total.

The financing of R&D

General situation

The trends in R&D allocations from different funding sources are influenced by the recent substantial transformations of the S&T management system. Among the major measures to reorganise R&D financing in the late 1980s, the introduction of new management principles in R&D institutions and the increased importance of contract research should be mentioned. Table 3.13 presents R&D expenditure by source of funds since 1986.

The role of the government budget

The government budget is the largest source of R&D funding. According to CSRS estimates, it covered in 1991 approximately 95 per cent of current R&D expenditures. The situation did not change in 1992, *i.e.* the extremely centralised system of R&D funding is being maintained.

In the former USSR, budget allocations for R&D (excluding fixed capital investment) grew from 15.2 to 24.6 billion roubles from 1986 to 1990, *i.e.* by nearly 62 per cent (in current prices). From 1991 to 1993, R&D budget appropriations grew from 25.8 billion to 909.3 billion roubles (Table 3.14), but in 1991 prices, the 1992 budget allocations for R&D decreased by nearly two-thirds.

R&D spending as a whole was considered a low-priority objective in the former USSR government budget and is also so considered in Russia today. The share of R&D

Table 3.13. **Current R&D expenditure by source of funds**[1]

Per cent

	Total	Budget funds	Centralised (non-budget) funds	Own funds of organisations
1986	100	86.4	11.4	2.2
1987	100	85.8	12.0	2.2
1988	100	78.8	16.8	4.4
1989	100	78.1	19.5	2.4
1990	100	79.4	18.0	2.6
1991	100	95.0	2.6	2.4

1. Data for 1986-90 refer to the ex-USSR and for 1991, to Russia.
Source: Centre of Science Research and Statistics.

Table 3.14. **Appropriations for R&D from the budget of the Russian Republic**
Excluding capital expenditure [1]

	1991	1992	1993 [3]
Billion roubles (at current prices)	25.84	177.95	909.28
Per cent of the total republic budget appropriations	7.42 [2]	3.0	4.86

1. Data on budget appropriations for R&D for Russia are available only from 1991 when, due to the break-up of the USSR, Russia and other republics initiated their own full-scale national budgets.
2. The data seems to be overestimated by half, because the major part of the budget spending on the territory of Russia came from USSR federal government budget resources, not the republic budget. The real volume of the total budget appropriations in the national economy of Russia (including both the USSR's and Russia's budgets) was therefore overestimated at least by half.
3. Estimate as of 1 July 1993.

Source: Centre of Science Research and Statistics.

in total USSR government budget appropriations in 1970-90 is in the range of 3.4-4.8 per cent. In Russia it is projected to be 4.86 per cent for 1993.

R&D objectives of the government budget

Since 1988, there has been a provision for goal-oriented distribution of government budget R&D allocations for national and international S&T programmes and intersectoral S&T problems of national importance.

The functional orientation of budget allocations for R&D in Russia has traits both similar to and different from those of the leading industrial countries (Table 3.15). In

Table 3.15. **Distribution of budget R&D appropriation by socio-economic objectives in Russia and in major OECD countries**
Per cent

	Russia [1]	United States [2]	Japan [2]	Germany [2]	France [2]	United Kingdom [2]
Promotion of industrial development	10.7	0.2	4.6	12.8	13.3	8.5
Production and rational use of energy	0.8	3.9	22.2	6.4	3.5	3.3
Health	1.7	12.9	2.7	3.5	3.3	5.1
Defence	48.0	65.5	5.1	12.8	37.0	45.5
Other not elsewhere specified	38.8	17.5	65.4	64.5	42.9	37.6

1. 1991. *Source:* Centre of Science Research and Statistics.
2. 1989. *Source:* National Science Board, *Science and Engineering Indicators – 1991*. Washington, 1991, p. 344.

particular, the share of defence-oriented R&D, although behind that of the United States, is close to the level in other countries with nuclear armaments, such as the United Kingdom and France. It is some 3.8 times higher than in Germany. Allocations for energy R&D seem to be relatively low in Russia.

Principal orientations of public R&D spending

The financing of R&D from the Republic budget takes two main directions:
- work co-ordinated by the Ministry of Science and Technological Policy of the Russian Federation (MSTP);
- R&D of a defence-oriented character.

In 1991-93 the allocations for R&D under the auspices of the Ministry of Science and Technological Policy (MSTP) grew from 13.4 to 684.6 billion roubles (see Table A1.16), but, in fact, the real value of these funds in 1992, at constant prices, was some 2.5 times lower than in 1991. Budget allocations from the MSTP account for 75.3 per cent of total R&D budget financing. In 1993, 175.9 billion roubles, or 25.7 per cent of the civil R&D budget, is designed to permit research institutions of military industries under conversion to perform R&D.

The budget allocations co-ordinated by MSTP emphasise three main orientations:
1. R&D performed by R&D institutions of ministries and Russian public agencies and integrated in the programme for maintaining the R&D potential. In 1991-92, approximately one-quarter of these resources were intended to finance the institutes of the Russian Academy of Sciences and its regional branches. In 1992, the trends in resources allocated for Academy R&D outpaced general budget allocations for R&D. In 1993, a slowdown is expected in the growth rate of Academy R&D budget financing. As a result, the share of the RAS in the programme for maintaining the national R&D potential will be reduced to 19.6 per cent.
2. Financing, by the Russian Fund for Fundamental Research, of basic research in the RAS, the academies of medical and agricultural sciences, higher education institutes and industrial R&D institutions. The resources of this fund are some 3 per cent of R&D budget financing, used as grants to finance basic research performed by small teams of researchers and individual scientists, to subsidise the development of the material and equipment bases of R&D institutions, the acquisition of scientific literature, fellowships, etc.
3. Financing of federal S&T programmes, intersectoral and industrial R&D in priority S&T areas, and also the participation of the Russian Federation in important international programs.

In 1993, the allocations for these projects will total some 277.8 billion roubles (40.6 per cent of the budget allocations of the MSTP). The continued growth in these funds and in the shares of R&D in federal programmes, from 17.8 per cent in 1991 to 40.6 per cent in 1993, as expected, shows the strengthening of the goal-oriented approach in R&D budget financing and the effort to concentrate limited financial resources on the most important objectives.

The government S&T programmes have great importance for scientific, economic and social development. Table A1.17 shows budget appropriations including those planned for 1993. In 1993, besides space and civil aviation, the major programmes are: new materials, future agricultural technologies, high-energy physics, high-temperature superconductivity, exploration of the Arctic and Antarctic oceans and seas, ecologically clean power engineering, technologies of the future, and future technologies for food production. Funds allocated for each of these programmes exceed 1 billion roubles. The financing of a large-scale programme on the creation of new pharmaceuticals was launched in 1993.

It should be mentioned that these programmes generally coincide with those established in the former USSR in 1989-90. At the same time, the shares of the principal programmes are now approximately a tenth of what they were then. The dissipation of resources among specific programmes does not provide for real growth of funds, especially in light of the accelerating inflation. Thus, the funding of research on superconductivity grew only 8.9 times at current prices during 1989-93.

Non-budgetary and private R&D funding

The restructuring of the S&T mechanisms along principles of self-financing was accompanied by gradual growth of non-budget sources. In 1989, in the former USSR, self-financing reached a maximum of 21.9 per cent. The deterioration of the financial situation and certain negative traits of self-financing of enterprises and research institutions (absence of interest on the part of enterprises in spending their own money on R&D, their orientation being towards maximum income) contributed to the decrease in R&D finance. For example, from 1989 to the beginning of 1992, the allocations for R&D from own resources of enterprises and R&D institutions in Russia remained at a constant 0.65 per cent, or 0.8 billion roubles. At the same time, in 1989-90, the volume of spending for R&D from centralised funds of ministries and agencies remained practically unchanged.

In 1991, allocations from remaining centralised reserves accounted for not more than 2.6 per cent of R&D spending in Russia, and the share of budget resources rose to 95 per cent of total national R&D expenditures. In 1992 a new practice of using non-budget funding to finance industrial R&D and to favour the use of new products was introduced. But, according to MSTP data, in 1992 the volume of these resources was only 5-6 billion roubles, *i.e.* approximately 25 times lower than forecasted. The major part is spent on financing additional costs of enterprises for absorbing new products.

In 1992 non-budget funds accounted for 4-5 per cent of current spending on R&D, at most. It continued to prove impossible to interest enterprises, organisations and commercial structures in financing R&D from their own resources.

In search of supplementary finance, R&D units started to raise the volume of activities not directly relevant to their work: services to other organisations, enterprises, consumer services, etc. In 1990 the volume of these activities increased 1.6 times and, by the end of the year, reached 1.9 billion roubles.

R&D by sectors of performance and types of activity

The various sectors (academies, industrial R&D organisations, higher education institutes, enterprises) play different roles in performing different types of R&D (basic and applied research, experimental development).

Table A1.18 shows the distribution of R&D performance by sector and by type of activity. In 1991, the Academy sectoral institutions accounted for 64.6 per cent of the total volume of basic research, *i.e.* 5.5 times higher than their share in the total national R&D effort (Figure 3.9).

The shares of the higher education sector in the volume of basic (17 per cent) and applied research (9.3 per cent) are some 3 and 1.7 times higher than their shares in the total volume of R&D. In the industrial sector, the shares of basic and applied research are lower than their shares in the total volume of R&D (by 60.4 and 3.5 percentage points), and the volume of development is higher by 11.9 points. Enterprises proper account for only 4.2 per cent of the R&D volume, their share in the total volume of development being 1.5 times higher.

Due to increasing short-term economic considerations, there are signs in all sectors of decreasing interest in long-term investments such as R&D, and especially in basic

Figure 3.9. **Value of R&D performed within R&D institutions by sector of performance**

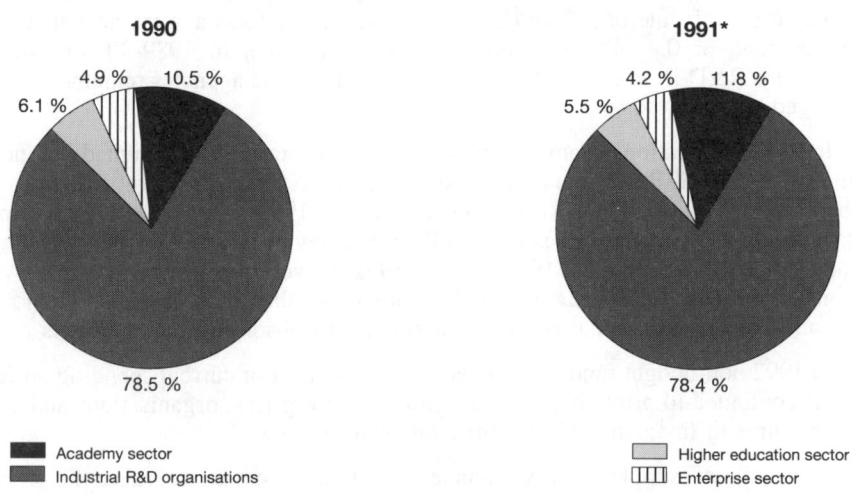

* Detail may not add to total because of rounding.

Source: *Science and Technology in Russia: 1991*, CSRS, 1992, p. 79.

research, which in 1991 only accounted for some 9.3 per cent of the total (though with a minor relative increase since 1990) (Figure 3.10).

As a result, Russia starts to lag behind the leading industrial nations in terms of shares of basic research in the national R&D total: 13 per cent in the United Kingdom and Japan, 14 per cent in the United States, 19 per cent in West Germany, and 23 per cent in France.[7]

The share of basic research is highest in the Academy sector, at 51.5 per cent. Here, the leaders are the institutes of the Far Eastern and the Ural branches of the RAS, with 74 per cent and 60.8 per cent, respectively. The research institutes of the Agricultural Academy and the Medical Academy are to a greater extent oriented towards applied research (73.9 per cent and 57 per cent, respectively). The R&D institutions of the Siberian branch have considerable applied research (37.1 per cent) and a relatively high share of experimental development (17.8 per cent).

Development also dominates in the industrial R&D organisations and in the enterprise sector, where the share of basic research is very low (2.1 per cent and 0.8 per cent, respectively). In the higher education sector basic research accounts for only 28.8 per cent of the total value of R&D.

R&D by fields of science

The analysis of R&D spending by fields of science shows disproportions due to the traditionally technical orientation of Russian R&D (Table 3.16). For many years, the

Figure 3.10. **Value of R&D performed within R&D institutions by type of activity**

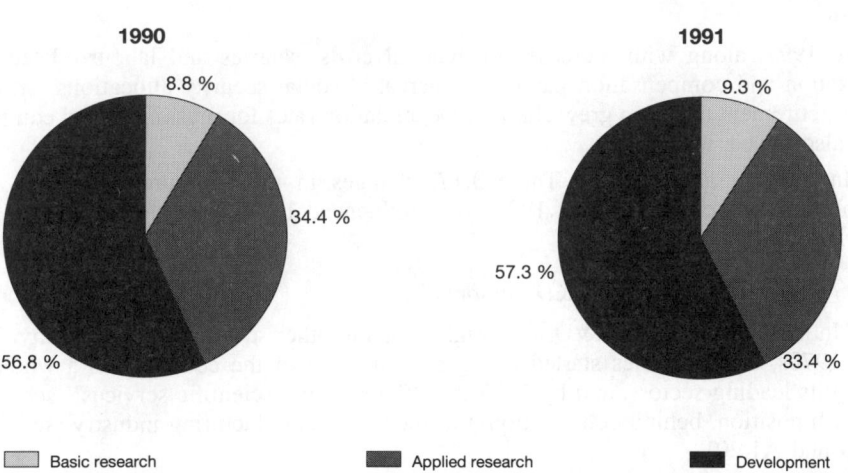

Table 3.16. **Percentage distribution of R&D expenditure by field of science: 1988**

	Research and development	Basic research	Applied research	Development
Total	100.0	100.0	100.0	100.0
Natural sciences	14.7	49.8	19.7	5.5
Social sciences and humanities	3.1	7.1	4.1	2.0
Engineering	71.3	28.8	63.1	83.4
Agricultural sciences	1.8	3.0	3.0	1.1
Medical sciences	2.0	5.5	3.4	0.6
Information and information systems	1.0	0.9	1.3	0.9
Other	6.0	4.9	5.4	6.5

Source: Centre of Science Research and Statistics.

main emphasis was on engineering, which still, according to the estimates, accounts for some three-quarters of the total: in the United States it does not exceed 50 per cent. R&D is especially low in medicine (2 per cent in Russia against some 10 per cent in the United States) and in the natural sciences (14.7 per cent and 30 per cent, respectively). The natural sciences dominate basic research in Russian R&D institutions.

In general, research is insufficiently oriented towards the solution of social and ecological problems and problems of human life. The shares in total R&D of medical and agricultural sciences and of informatics are very low, only 1-2 per cent. Within engineering, the share of pilot, future-oriented work is also very small.

R&D expenditure by type of costs

General

In 1991, along with increases in material costs, salaries and labour-related costs (indexation and compensation payments, increased social security allocations, introduction of retirement tax) also grew sharply. Depreciation rates for machinery and equipment were also raised.

In general, as shown in Table 3.17, changes in the structure of current R&D expenditure between 1990 and 1991 were influenced by developments in wages and material costs.

Recent trends in salaries of R&D personnel

Until 1970 salaries in R&D were higher than in other sectors of the economy. In the early 1970s, R&D salaries started to lag behind those of the economy as a whole and among its leading sectors, and by 1987 the "Science and scientific services" sector was in fourth position, behind construction, transport and manufacturing industry (see Tables A1.19 and A1.20).

Table 3.17. **Current R&D expenditure by type of costs**
Per cent

	1990	1991
Total	100.0	100.0
Material costs (including depreciation)	37.0	29.5
Wages	30.4	34.6
State social security	5.8	9.8
Obligatory medical insurance	0.1	0.1
Other costs	28.7	26.0

Source: Centre of Science Research and Statistics.

The 1988 introduction of new management mechanisms in most R&D institutions provoked a sharp increase in R&D salary levels. At the beginning of 1989-90, the average monthly salary in R&D rose above that in industry for the first time in many years. From this moment, R&D wages slowed in comparison to wages in the economy as a whole and in its leading sectors.

In 1992 this trend began to threaten R&D itself. If in 1990 the average monthly salary in the "Science and scientific services" sector was still 118.6 per cent of that for the economy as a whole, and 113.2 per cent of that in industry, in 1991, it decreased to 105.3 per cent and 96.2 per cent, and, in 1992, to 70.9 per cent and 59.9 per cent, respectively. According to CSRS calculations, by December 1992 it had declined to 62.4 per cent (Table A1.19). These trends refer to the R&D system as a whole, but there were considerable variations among institutional sectors and fields of science.

In 1990 the highest wages were in the Academy sector, the lowest in universities and enterprises (Figure 3.11). Since then the Academy has lost its leadership to enterprises and industrial R&D institutes, as a result, primarily, of an accelerated growth in contract prices for R&D projects in sectors with high shares of applied research and development (and not basic research which is mainly financed from the budget). The higher education sector found itself in an even more difficult situation, as average monthly salaries of researchers and technicians were 15 per cent lower than the average in 1991 and minimal in comparison with other sectors.

As concerns wages in different fields of science, a sample survey by the Centre of Science Research and Statistics shows that the highest level was in the geological and mineralogical sciences (80 per cent higher than the average). In physics and mathematics and in engineering, salaries of researchers were only 5.3 per cent and 1.2 per cent, respectively, higher than average, and they were lowest in geographical and agricultural sciences and the humanities at 70 per cent of the average.

In the absence of an effective mechanism of social protection, galloping inflation and the deteriorating consumer market situation means that wages can hardly retain personnel in R&D institutions. By the beginning of 1993, wages in joint enterprises were

Figure 3.11. **Average monthly salaries of R&D personnel by sector**

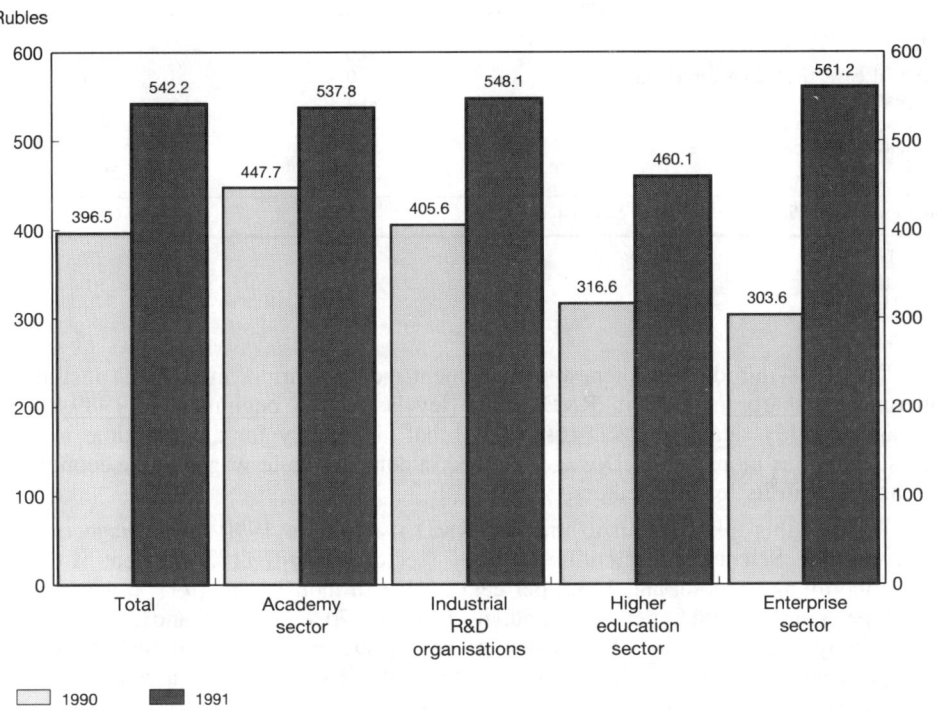

Source: Science and Technology in Russia: 1991, CSRS, 1992, p. 90.

2.5 times higher, and in private firms 1.8 times higher, than the average attained in the "Science and scientific services" sector.

Since 1990, efforts to compensate for the sharp inflationary rise in the cost of living by increased wages have been made at the expense of other costs, notably materials costs. In 1991, wages rose to 37 per cent of current R&D expenditure. As a result of indexation measures, the share of wages in 1992, according to preliminary estimates, reached 46.7 per cent and, if social security fees are taken into account, 64.4 per cent of the total current R&D expenditure.

Other current R&D expenditure

The reduction in the shares of "materials costs" in current R&D expenditures, which are also decreasing in absolute terms, is further aggravated by a very large rise in prices for small equipment, materials, fuel, electric energy, etc. In nominal terms, prices for some types of instruments and materials for R&D increased 30 to 50 times between 1990 and 1992, and prices for fuel and energy grew by 80 times in 1992.

The lack of foreign currency and the fall in the exchange rate of the rouble have reduced to nothing imports of research equipment and acquisitions of foreign scientific and technical literature.

The maintenance costs of buildings and premises also rose substantially. According to a sample survey of R&D institutes, conducted by the Centre of Science Research and Statistics together with the Institute of Sociology of the RAS, the volume of equipment supplies decreased in 1992 by ten times at constant prices, and that of chemical reagents and other materials by 25 times. Many advanced capital-intensive research institutions with expensive equipment and modern premises found themselves in a most precarious situation. In 1990 only 3.6 per cent of the current spending of R&D institutions went for purchases of research instruments.

Financial difficulties also caused a sharp reduction in spending for information support. According to sample survey data, from the beginning of 1990 to April 1992, some Academy institutes experienced, on average, an eight-fold reduction of the number of participants in scientific conferences. Visits abroad were practically cancelled. Spending for information materials decreased three times at constant prices and, for information networks services, 20 times.[8]

Capital R&D expenditure

In 1991 the volume of capital R&D expenditure was 1.8 billion roubles. It represented only some 6.2 per cent of the gross national expenditure on S&T (Table 3.18).

The 1989-91 decline in investment activity had a negative influence on the dynamics of fixed capital investment in R&D, which decreased faster than that of investments in the Russian economy as a whole. In 1991 the volume of capital investment in R&D decreased by 42 per cent measured at constant prices. This decline is accompanied by

Table 3.18. **R&D capital expenditure by type of costs and source of funds**
In millions of roubles[1]

	Total	Type of costs			Source of funds	
		Construction and installations	Equipment	Other	Centralised funds	Own funds of public enterprises
1990	2 174.8	353.4	1 628.3	193.1	941.9	1 232.9
1991	1 793.0	508.0	898.1	386.9	908.1	885.0

1. May not add to total because of rounding.
Source: Science and Technology in Russia: 1991, CSRS, 1992, pp. 96-97.

unfinished construction, which in 1991 was already 29.3 per cent higher than that of capital R&D expenditure.

The investment situation in R&D is characterised by changes in the structure of fixed capital investment. In 1990-91 the share of construction and installations decreased considerably, *i.e.* the reduction in the scale of investment is accompanied by a relative deterioration in the way it is used.

The development of R&D fixed assets is financed nearly entirely from state sources: centralised funding from the budget and own funds of public enterprises. The absence of additional sources of finance further aggravates the situation. In 1991 the amount of non-public fixed capital R&D investment (funded by non-government associations, collective enterprises and firms, consumer co-operatives) was only some 3.4 million roubles, or 0.2 per cent of public investment.

5. R&D output

The legal mechanisms for protection of industrial property in Russia were directly dependent on the political, economic and social situation in the country. The "war communism" policy, which rigidly regulated the national economy in 1917-19, abolished the institution of private property including property of inventions. The Soviet decree "The Statute of Inventions" (1919) announced an "author certificate" as the only legal form of invention protection. During the thaw of the new economic policy (1924-31), patents were also recognised as a form of legal protection of inventions (Box 3.8).

Since 1931 only these two forms of protection have existed, but the author certificates were most commonly used until 1991. Thus, author certificates have represented some 95.4 per cent of all applications for invention protection and 98.2 per cent of domestic applications.

A new step in industrial property protection is the Law "On Inventions in the USSR", implemented on 1 July 1991. The law states some basic principles to be accepted

---

Box 3.8

Main forms of protection of author's rights in Russia

An **author certificate** is a document certifying the invention, its priority and authorship, as well as the exclusive rights of the state to use and take charge of an invention. It also secures the rights and the privileges of the author as specified by legislation.

A **patent** is a document approving the invention, its priority, authorship and the exclusive right of the patent owner to the invention.

within the framework of the transition to the market economy, including the abolition of taxes on income and currency receipts for enterprises that own patents over a five-year period from the beginning of the use of the invention, as well as the abolition of taxes related to sales of licences during the validity of the patent. In addition, the Law guarantees authors of inventions, when they are not the owners, at least 15 per cent of annual income from patent use during the period of patent validity and at least 20 per cent of the gains from sales of licences.

The Patent Law of the Russian Federation of 23 September 1992 could be mentioned as another positive step. It declares patents a unique form of legal protection of inventions, introduces a useful model, and provides legal protection in the form of a certificate.

Discoveries and inventions

From the beginning of the registration of discoveries in the USSR in 1957 up to 1992, some 92 per cent of all discoveries were made by Russian scientists alone or as co-authors with researchers from the other former USSR republics. Most of the discoveries registered in Russia in 1991 were in the fields of biology, biophysics, biochemistry and medicine (Table A1.21).

Figure 3.12 shows the fluctuation in invention activities. Following the rise between 1985 and 1987, there has been a progressive decline. The average annual rate of applications from 1987-91 in the USSR decreased by 14.5 per cent. In 1991 the total number of domestic applications decreased by 35.4 per cent.[9] At the same time the number of patent applications increased some 11 times, whereas author certificates decreased by 53.8 per cent. The abrupt changes can be explained by the fact that the patent was recognised as the form of legal protection of inventions (Tables A1.22 and A1.23).

The distribution of inventions by categories of the International Patent Classification (IPC), which reflects the technological objectives of domestic R&D, changed slightly in 1991, essentially owing to the conversion of military research. The shares of inventions in the classes "physics", "chemistry and metallurgy", "mechanics, lighting and heating; engines and pumps"; "weapons and ammunition, explosive works" decreased, whereas those of inventions aimed at human needs increased by 2.8 per cent (see Table A1.24).

In the second half of the 1980s, there was an abrupt decline in the introduction of inventions in the national economy (Box 3.9). Thus, in 1990 the number used in the former USSR was 39.7 per cent of that in 1985, and 73.8 per cent of the level of 1989. The situation in Russia is similar: the number of inventions used for the first time in 1990 was 55.2 per cent of the 1985 level. Furthermore, the decline is increasing, and the value of this indicator in 1992 was only 47.5 of that in 1990. In general, the decrease in the number of inventions introduced is connected with the reduction, by 85 per cent, of small-scale inventions. Nevertheless, small inventions, which neither have a strong economic effect nor lead to essentially new goods and technologies, still dominate (Table 3.19).

More than 70 per cent of the total number of inventions are for insignificant improvement in existing, mostly obsolete, technologies. Many inventions introduced, in fact, do not improve on models already in use. In 1989, in the ex-USSR, only 105 inven-

Figure 3.12. **Resident applications and author certificates granted**

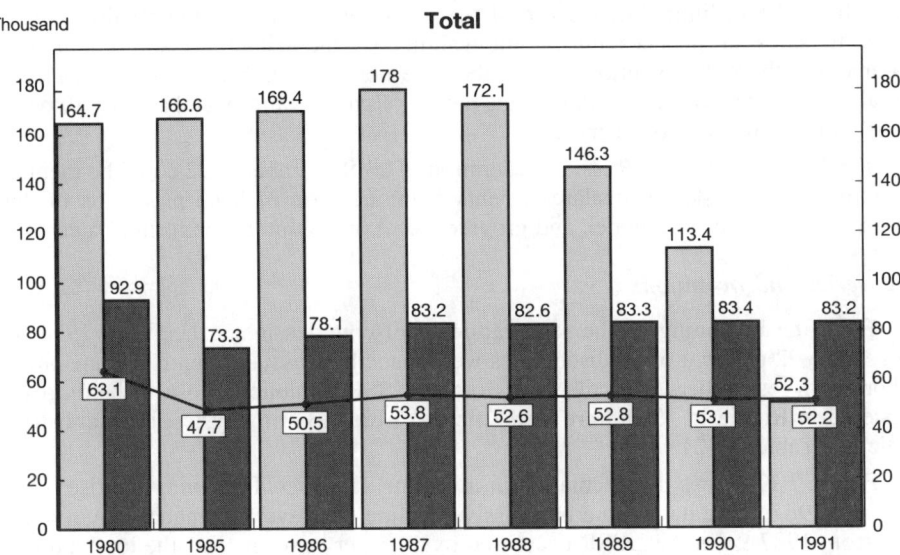
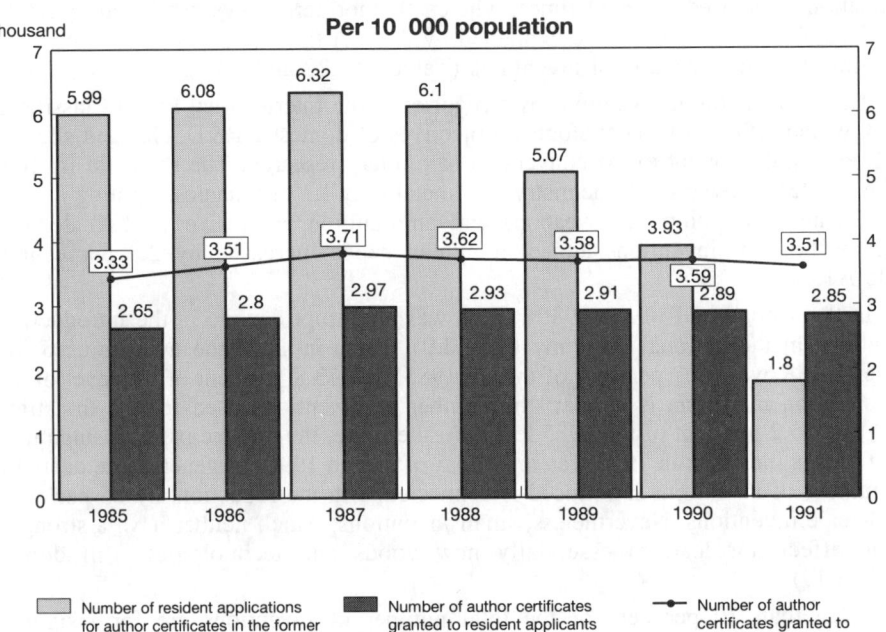

Number of resident applications for author certificates in the former USSR

Number of author certificates granted to resident applicants in the former USSR

Number of author certificates granted to resident applicants in Russia

Source: CNRS, Russian Patent Office.

> *Box 3.9*
>
> **Use of inventions: main definitions**
>
> An invention is identified as used, if: 1) it is used in manufactured or consumed products or technology; 2) it is transferred abroad in accordance with established procedure (licences); 3) it is used to transfer a prototype to exploitation.
>
> The technical level of the invention is the relative indicator of the quality of the object, based on a comparison of its technical characteristics with those of a basic pattern.
>
> Ageing is the process caused by the invention and introduction into production of new, technically or technologically improved objects. It is reflected in the indicators of changes in technical level.

tions having no analogies were used for the first time, or 0.6 per cent of the total. Large-scale inventions were essentially introduced only in Russia and in the Ukraine.

In the first three years following initial registration, 57 per cent of the total number of inventions introduced were in use, 80 per cent for the first eight years, and 6.5 per cent after 16 years. The last figure concerns the most valuable technological inventions, which do not rapidly lose their significance.

The rapid implementation of most of the inventions during the first years after registration is explained by the fact that enterprises generally prefer inventions that do not require restructuring of large production facilities, long-term preparation, or technology changes. These inventions are implemented quickly, but after two or three years they are no longer useful. Furthermore, data available show that only 13 per cent of the inventions

Table 3.19. **Percentage distribution of inventions by technical level** [1]

Technical level	Percentage of the total number of inventions
1. Improvement of minor characteristics of technical products (processes)	40.2
2. Improvement of major technological characteristics	30.8
3. Achievement of qualitative leaps in main technological characteristics	16.0
4. Development of new products with improved main characteristics	10.5
5. Development of essentially new products	2.5

1. Estimated for 1989.
Source: *Nauka v SSSR: analyz i statistika*, CSRS, 1992, p. 131.

are used a second time, mainly in allied enterprises. As a whole, the lag between first and second use is so great that inventions become obsolete (Box 3.9).

External patenting[10]

Unfortunately, the negative trends in invention activity mentioned have also been reflected in the international protection of S&T output. In 1990 only 38.7 per cent of the number of applications were granted patents (Figure 3.13). At the same time, after a significant drop in 1988, the number of patents lapsed doubled (Figure 3.14).

The extremely low level of external patenting of domestic inventions is clearly shown by the rate of diffusion (Table A1.25). In the former USSR in 1990, this coefficient was only 0.04, while in the United States it was 3.58, in the United Kingdom 4.03, in Germany 4.93, in France 5.25.

In 1990 domestic inventions were patented in 63 countries (see Table A1.26 and A1.27). OECD Member countries obtained 69.4 per cent of the total number of protection documents[11] granted, the former socialist countries 28 per cent, and developing countries only 2.6 per cent.

External patenting of domestic inventions is based on international agreements, such as the Patent Co-operation Treaty (PCT), the European Patent Convention (EPC), and the Agreement on Mutual Recognition of Author Certificates and Other Protective Documents. In accordance with the PCT there were 265 external applications in 1990 (83.3 per

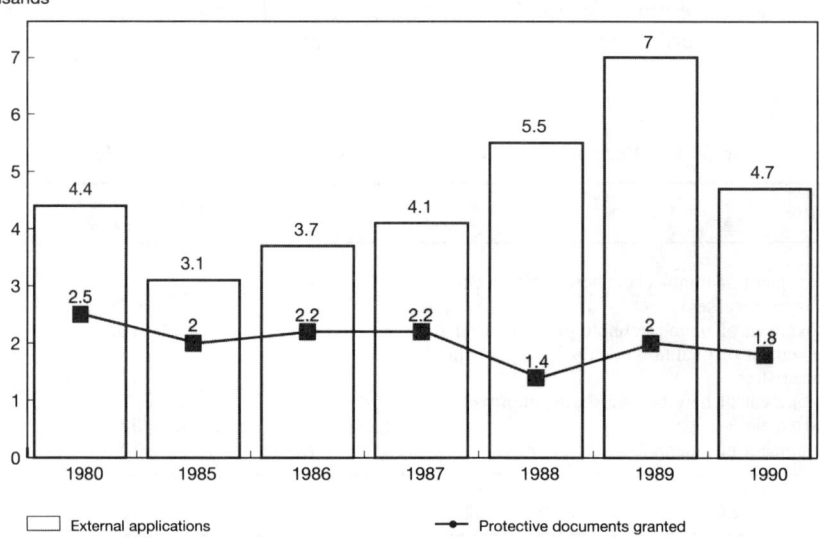

Figure 3.13. **External applications and protective documents granted abroad**
(data for the former USSR)

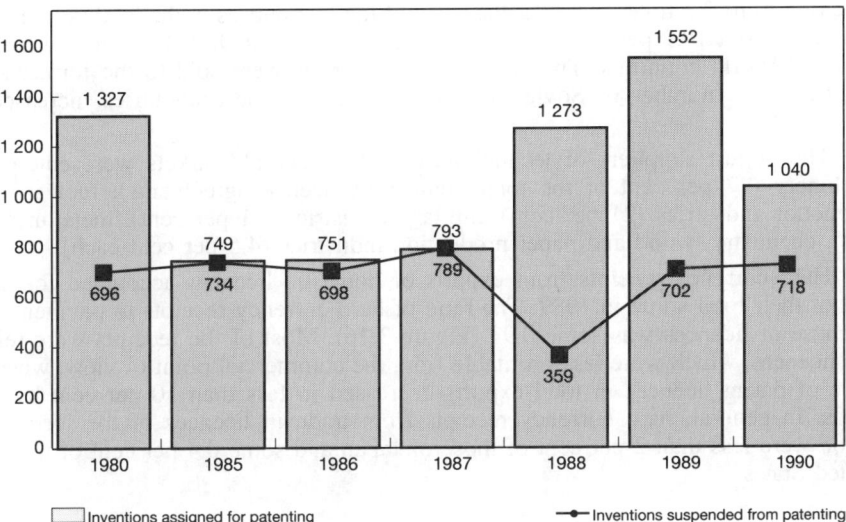

Figure 3.14. **External patenting**
(data for the former USSR)

Source: Research and Development in the USSR. Data Book: 1990, CSRS, 1992, p. 50.

cent of those in 1989) on 452 inventions of the former USSR (see Table A1.28). These applications included 2 754 designations of countries of patenting. There were 214 applications for the European patent, with 1 354 designations of countries. According to the EPC, 12 applications were submitted to the European Patent Office (83.3 per cent of those in 1989), including 84 designations of countries. In accordance with the Agreement on Mutual Recognition of Author Certificates, 847 applications were submitted in 1990 (46.1 per cent of those for 1989), and 585 patents were granted, 11.2 per cent more, than in 1989.

The trends in patents and licences in Russia continue those of the former USSR. For the last ten years, some 60 per cent of the annual external applications and half of all those granted abroad for the ex-USSR were for Russia.

Trade in licences

A notable reduction in the number of licences exported (45.8 per cent) took place in 1989 (Table A1.29). Besides the general situation in the country, it was caused by the disarray in the state mechanism for licence exports, inadequate financing and credit mechanisms, lack of necessary research and experience in penetrating external markets.

The largest licensees among the OECD countries were Japan (185 licences), Finland (175), West Germany (150), Italy (144), the United States (98), France (82) (see

Table A1.30). OECD Member countries accounted for 25.8 per cent of the total number of licences exported (Figure 3.15).

The number of Soviet licences exported to developing countries in 1976-89 increased some 3.5 times, whereas the share of these countries in the total volume of sales decreased from 10.9 per cent to 7.7 per cent. In all, to 1989, 431 licences were sold to 36 Third World countries. Two-thirds of the licences were sold to the former socialist countries. The number of Soviet licences exported to these countries increased some 3.3 times.[12]

The largest suppliers of technologies to the external markets were enterprises of machinery (27 per cent of the total number of licence agreements), fuel and energy production industries (21 per cent), military industries (11 per cent), metallurgy (9 per cent), chemistry, wood and paper production industries (4.5 per cent each).

Hard currency receipts from exports of domestic licences accounted for 23.1 per cent of their total value in 1989. The ratio of hard currency receipts to payments for the purchase of licences was some 0.93 (Figure 3.16). Most of the receipts were related to free licences, which were less profitable from the commercial point of view, whereas the share of patent licences in total exports decreased to less than 10 per cent by the late 1980s. In general, hard currency receipts from trade in licences of the former Soviet Union were less than 2 per cent of those of Japan and some 0.4 per cent of those of the United States.

Prototypes of new technologies and renovation of machinery products

Since the beginning of 1971, the annual number of prototypes of new technologies and new types of machinery products has decreased in the former USSR and now in Russia. In 1991, the number of new prototypes of machines, equipment, instruments and means of automation was inferior to that of 1990 by 23.4 per cent. The distribution of such prototypes by type is presented in Table A1.31.

In 1992 innovative activities revived to some extent, largely in connection with the implementation of the results of earlier R&D projects with a view to receiving some additional financing from industry. In 1992, 11.6 per cent more prototypes were developed than in 1990, but the number was still 14.5 per cent below the 1989 figure.

Products accepted for series production accounted for 80.4 per cent of the total number of prototypes created. However, only 11.3 per cent of the new machinery products developed in 1991, or 6.4 per cent of those presented for the first time in the country, were put into production the same year. The share of products manufactured according to "obsolete techniques" was some 52.1 per cent of the total value of machinery production, including products developed six to nine years earlier (22.8 per cent of the total) and those ten years of age and over (29.3 per cent). These trends seem to confirm the technological backwardness of the country.

The share of new prototypes containing inventions is decreasing: during 1981-89 it fell from 42 per cent to 27 per cent. Only 20.7 per cent of a total of 997 prototypes created in 1992 involved patent applications or patents, and 30 per cent of the total number were marked by "patent purity".

As a result, the technologies developed do not meet modern requirements. In 1991, only 3.8 per cent of new prototypes of machines, equipment, instruments and means of

Figure 3.15. **Geographical distribution of exports of licences***

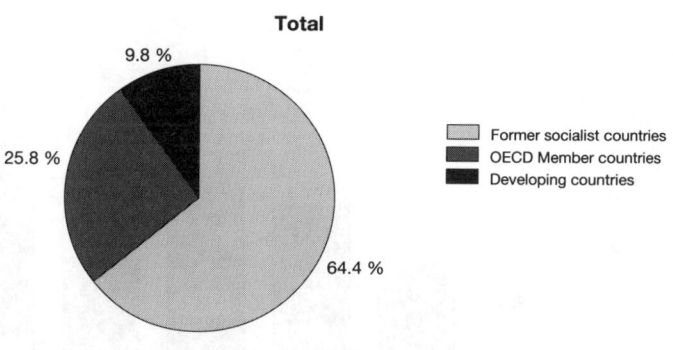

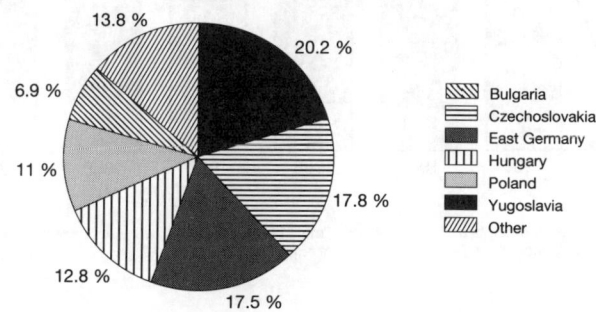

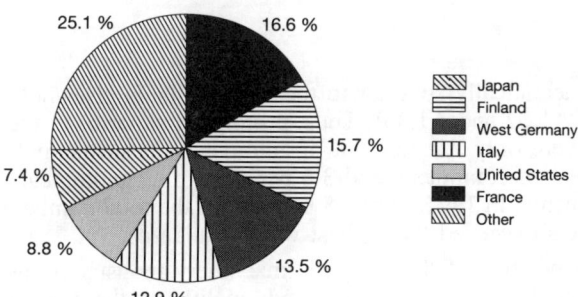

* Cumulative data for the whole period of trade in licences up to 1989.
Source: The Russian Patent Office, CSRS.

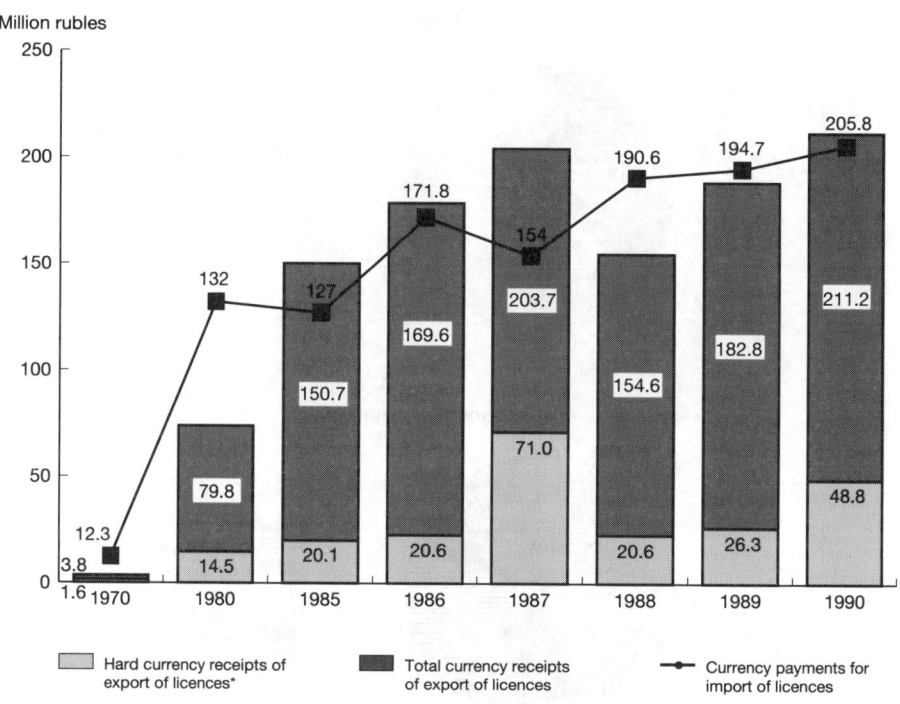

Figure 3.16. **Payments for and receipts from trade in licences**
(data for the former USSR)

* Estimated in rubles using the official exchange rates of the USSR State Bank.

Source: Research and Development in the USSR, Data Book: 1990. CSRS, 1992, p. 51; RF Ministry of Science and Technological Policy.

automation were technically superior to the best available elsewhere even for high-tech products (Tables A1.32 and A1.33). Thus, prototypes superior to the international state-of-the-art level, were only 7.7 per cent of automated lines, manipulators, and industrial robots, 3.8 per cent of computers, and 3.6 per cent of technological process control and regulation instruments. In 1991, only 1.8 per cent of the total number of the new types of machinery products exceeded the highest world standards.

The difficult position of the domestic machinery industry in international competition is due to the low technical level and quality of the machines and equipment produced. The share of machinery products intended for export was 19.3 per cent in 1991 (14.7 per cent in 1992), but only 1.8 per cent were sold for hard currency (see Table A1.34).

Notes

1. There are two levels of post-university researcher degrees in Russia: candidates and doctors of science. In the West, the equivalent is the PhD.
2. Including higher education teaching staff working as part-time researchers.
3. The Laboratory for the Economics of the Social and Cultural Sectors, Moscow State University.
4. Statistical data on resource distribution by field of science are available only for 1989, but proportions of fixed assets do not appear to have changed significantly. The survey data cover both Academy and industrial R&D institutes. The higher education institutes were not included, because the variety of types of equipment used for R&D and educational purposes made it difficult to obtain reliable estimates.
5. National Science Foundation, *National Patterns of R&D Resources – 1992*, Washington, D.C., 1992, p. 68.
6. The value of R&D includes current expenditure on R&D and profits obtained by R&D institutions from R&D activities during the year.
7. National Science Board, *Science and Engineering Indicators – 1991*, Washington, 1991, p. 344.
8. *Analiz vozmozhnostei vyzhyvanija akademicheskoj nauki v krizishych uslovijakh.* CSRS, Institute of Sociology, 1992, p. 50.
9. The data on applications presented include those for the period after the break-up of the USSR (297 of the total 1 203 applications assigned to Russia from 25-31 December 1991 belonged to authors from the CIS countries), because applications were made in accordance with still valid USSR legislation and were included in the total number of domestic applications.
10. The analysis presented in this chapter is based on the data for the former USSR to the end of 1990. The reorganisation of the state patent services following the break-up of the USSR led to the loss of new statistical data.
11. The total number of protective documents granted abroad, besides patents, included author certificates and some other protective documents used in Bulgaria, Czechoslovakia, Mongolia, Cuba, East Germany.
12. To 1990, enterprises in the former USSR annually reported data on exports of licences, including numbers of licences exported, country of destination, receipts in hard currency. This reporting has been discontinued since 1991 due to the reorganisation of the statistical system.

Chapter IV
The organisation of science and technology

1. The principal sectors

In Russia, scientific research is conducted in research institutes, institutions of higher education (higher school and universities), design organisations and bureaus, R&D departments of state industrial (branch) enterprises, and scientific/industrial and industrial associations. These are traditionally grouped into three sectors: industry (branch), academy, and universities and technical institutes (see Chapter 3). Scientific research saw a period of rapid growth beginning in 1950, and the network of scientific organisations expanded at an annual rate of more than 3 per cent for some two decades. After 1980, growth slowed markedly to an average of only 0.4 per cent annually from 1980 to 1988.

A particularity of Russian science inherited from the USSR is that most institutions are state organisations which receive their financing directly or indirectly from the state budget. Science institutions were formed within the framework of the administrative command system, and this gave rise to organisational forms and mechanisms of operation and management that tended to favour the isolation of the various ministries or agencies. The structure imposed on scientific activities thus did not promote, and indeed often hindered, the dissemination of scientific results. Research was duplicated, and the use of R&D results was restricted. When the science network ceased growing in the mid-1980s, dependence on parent departments continued, with the result that scientific organisations became even more isolated, and mobility of scientific personnel was low.

The correspondence between the scientific organisations and the interests of their government departments and the position of the latter within the hierarchy of economic activity also reflect the priorities of the USSR in 1970-80: defence, space, some areas of basic science, and heavy industry. As a result, there developed, within the formal sectoral structure, an informal hierarchy that determined the financial position, the manner of conducting R&D, and the research directions of scientific organisations. By order of importance, there were:

- the scientific organisations of the defence sector (mainly machine-building industries) and some institutions of higher education that trained highly skilled personnel for these organisations [in Moscow, the Aviation Institute, the Institute of Engineering and Physics, the Technical University (formerly Bauman's Institute), the Energy Institute];

- the scientific organisations of the Russian Academy of Sciences (RAS) and the largest research institutes and universities (the universities of Moscow, St. Petersburg, Tomsk and Novosibirsk, the Physical Technical Institute in Moscow, etc.), which undertake basic and some applied research;
- the priority part of the civil industrial (branch) scientific establishment (mainly large research institutes);
- other scientific organisations (most outlying institutions of higher education and the scientific organisations of non-priority civil branches).

In 1991, shares of R&D for the Academy, higher school, branch and sectors were: by number of organisations engaged in R&D, 12.8 per cent, 9.9 per cent, 68.5 per cent, and 8.8 per cent, respectively; by volume of expenditure for R&D, 11.8 per cent, 5.5 per cent, 78.5 per cent, and 4.2 per cent, respectively; and by number of R&D personnel, 11.4 per cent, 6.1 per cent, 75.6 per cent and 6.9 per cent, respectively.[1] According to preliminary estimates for 1992, the Academy's share of R&D personnel increases to 12.3 per cent and that of institutions of higher education to 7.5 per cent, while the share of the industrial (branch) sector drops to 73.4 per cent. Other changes during the period 1990-92 are of the order of 1 to 3 per cent and do not affect the basic organisation of science.

The departmental organisation of science no longer seems appropriate to the new conditions, and Russia must now create a new model of scientific research. Increasing numbers of the giant research institutes (the Physics Institute of the Russian Academy of Sciences, the Kurchatov Institute, etc.) are being divided up, and new means of implementing R&D, including commercial and non-commercial structures, research conducted on the basis of contracts and grants, and the broader possibilities open to research groups all indicate that the process has begun. These new forms are linked to manufacturing, higher education and state structures in reality, not only administratively.

However, these changes in the organisation of scientific research take place against the background of destructive processes occurring in the economy and in policy, and still only concern a small part of R&D.

The industrial (branch) sector

Industrial R&D includes some 3 574 scientific organisations (including scientific subdivisions of industrial enterprises), about 1.4 million employees (including 889 000 R&D personnel), with total expenditures of 19.2 billion roubles. Some 81 per cent of the specialists with university degrees engaged in R&D [37 per cent of doctors and 55 per cent of candidates of sciences (PhDs)] are employed in the industrial sector.

The scientific organisations in this sector are responsible to industrial ministries and departments and mainly conduct applied research and development of technology, although some also do basic research. Applied industrial research obtains the largest share of the financial and material resources allocated to science. At present, the organisational and economic environment for industrial (branch) research organisations has the following characteristics:

- isolation from consumers of S&T production and reduced demand from solvent customers;
- new regulations for taxation, creation of funds, and systems of payments, which do not take account of the differences between R&D organisations and industrial enterprises;
- decreased amounts of centralised R&D financing;
- increasing prices for energy and services;
- a situation of "mutual non-payments";[2]
- dismantling of the structures of material-technical supply;
- increased market competition for S&T products, due to conversion in the defence industry and the emergence of innovation in the commercial sector.

Reorganisation of scientific institutions began in the late 1980s, when R&D was declared to be a commodity to which contract prices could be applied. However, laws enacted at that time made industrial scientific organisations independent industrial enterprises but did not take their specific activities into account.[3] Price liberalisation and new economic conditions caused short-term improvement in the financial position of research organisations.[4] However, in 1991, a weakening of the economy, the lack of a market structure for S&T, and the high taxes on profits in industrial research organisations made it difficult for them to undertake high-level R&D. In 1991, profits in industrial research organisations decreased by half in comparison with 1990, while for machine building the decline was even greater. Thus, if in 1990 the financial position of industrial scientific institutes was two to three times better than that of organisations in other sectors, in 1991 the situation changed for the worse for many organisations.

The crisis of non-payments in 1992 made the situation worse. In the first quarter of 1992, almost all industrial research institutes were placed under the control of financial organisations.[5] The elimination of vertical links in the organisational structure left industrial science without direction; ex-USSR ministries were broken up and were massively transformed into Russian ministries and agencies against a background of considerable confusion. Changes in ministry functions had adverse effects on departmental research institutes, and, as the economic crisis deepened, the position of research and design organisations worsened.

Scientific divisions of industrial firms directly connected with manufacturing have a special position. These organisations (about 700 in the former USSR and 400 in Russia) represented about 9 per cent of all R&D organisations, and they had, overall, 7 per cent of scientists (of which 0.5 per cent of doctors and 1.3 per cent of candidates of sciences) and accounted for 4.2 per cent of total R&D volume. The machine-building and metal-treatment industries have 89 per cent of the labour, the chemical and petrochemical industry 4 per cent, and electric power 2 per cent.

Despite the small number of employees and small volume of work as compared with other scientific institutions, the conditions in these organisations are relatively favourable:
- Industrial R&D is directly linked to industrial or commercial structures, so that their results can be introduced to create the basis for solid industrial R&D.

- These organisations are mainly oriented towards development (about 86 per cent of all research) and react directly to the technological environment and to government regulations.
- In 1990-91, the scientific divisions of industrial enterprises demonstrated some ability to survive. Despite the elimination of many departments, due to closure of firms or a change of activity, and the decrease in the number of personnel, enterprises are financing their "own" research. Monopoly pricing and the possibility of including R&D costs in their products play a role.

As centralised financing of scientific activities has lessened, trends are developing that reflect a response to reduction of demand for S&T production. As the volume of R&D and its profitability decrease, structural changes (reduction of basic research and increase of applied research and design) negatively affect the scientific capacity (reduced personnel and material resources).

The clearest evidence of the crisis in industrial R&D can be seen at the level of personnel. In 1991, the number of R&D personnel fell by 13 per cent and in 1992 by 30 per cent. In 1992, the industrial sector accounted for 21 per cent of the overall reduction in the personnel employed in scientific organisations in Russia. About half were young specialists,[6] who left for the better salaries available in the commercial sector. The practice of working at two jobs is spreading (for example, a scientist may work in a state research organisation and in a small business). As a result, the average age of personnel engaged in industrial research has risen sharply.

At the same time, the R&D material and technical base has deteriorated. Obsolete equipment is no longer replaced, due to rising prices;[7] the net profits of scientific organisations are insufficient for financing the improvement of their technical infrastructure. The re-evaluation of capital assets in manufacturing, due to the extremely sharp rises in prices, and the related increase in the amounts of amortisation payments (to 20 times their original level) have put industrial science on the brink of bankruptcy. The possibility that fixed capital will be sold as R&D is reorganised also has a negative influence, as has the enormous escalation of overhead costs (transport, power), especially for large enterprises, which are unable to respond quickly to new conditions.

The new economic conditions have given rise to notable changes in the structure of research. From 1990, the volume of advanced and applied research has fallen, while the share of R&D services has increased. Today's manufacturing applies research results obtained in the past, but there are neither the material nor the financial resources necessary to implement progressive technologies. The development of new research methods has practically ceased.

Before "perestroika", the main sources of funding in the industrial science sector were: the target-oriented budget funds (state programmes and cross-sectoral science and technology complexes), the centralised funds of ministries, and the profits of industrial enterprises. In 1991-92, centralised funding (ministry sources) ceased, owing to the reorganisation of ministry structures and the transformation of the economic system. The opportunities for enterprises to use their profits worsened as well. In this situation, the programme approach and the competitive contract approach are used in an attempt to improve the organisation and financing of applied research. However, these forms of financing lack the stability that (basic) financing gave the Academy institutes. Furthermore, given the decreasing demand for R&D from industry, this form of organisation of R&D does not assure the survival of even the most useful applied research.

The industrial sector is now obliged to finance applied research and cross-sectoral and general industry developments through non-budget funding. The Russian Fund for Technological Development (RFTD) has been created; it consists of 150 branch funds and one federal fund, to which firms must contribute, from their profits, a sum equal to 1.5 per cent of their total production costs. Funds from the branch industry structures are collected by the ministries and major concerns;[8] the federal fund, which is controlled by the Ministry of Science, receives 25 per cent of these funds; the branch funds, which receive 75 per cent of the sum, are used to finance cross-sectoral R&D projects and programmes. The Ministry of Science selects the ministries and concerns (generally the most powerful ones) to collect the funds from the branches.

However, these non-budget funds are not presently used efficiently. When regulations for non-budget financing were being prepared, these funds were also given responsibility for financing cross-sectoral and general industry R&D, which lie outside the more specifically economic interests of production factories. In practice, the funds were used to compensate partly for the reduction of the R&D resources within firms, and, due to poor discipline in 1992, the Russian Fund for Technological Development received only some 10 per cent of the expected sum.

This use of non-budget resources recalls the way in which centralised industrial funds were used in the former USSR: they tended to support scientific organisations in a difficult financial position and to compensate them for additional costs relating to new products. Thus, under current conditions, the substitution of non-budget funds for the eliminated central industrial funds indicates that the problem of support for applied research as an important part of the innovation process remains open. A Presidential Decree "On urgent measures to preserve the scientific/technical potential of the Russian Federation", which bans changes of activity (*e.g.* from scientific to commercial or production) and separating pilot (experimental) plants from research institutes, has not affected this trend.

The above-mentioned Presidential Decree does not ban the creation of enterprises, but it bans their association, so that the parts of scientific organisations most able to survive in the market economy have preferred to enter the market alone. As a result, moving from R&D to production prototypes remains difficult, and scientific/industrial associations are breaking up.

The situation is especially alarming, because it is accompanied by privatisation of R&D (see Chapters VI and VII),[9] which is likely to destroy scientific research bodies and teams that worked informally and effectively on given problems. Their re-establishment will require much time and resources. Economic and organisational isolation may allow some bodies to survive but will result in the ruin of applied science within a few years.

In light of the shortage of state resources for supporting all industrial scientific research, the best solution is to seek to preserve the best components as a basis for further scientific development. One way to reach this goal is to create, using leading research institutes with good facilities, state science centres which can also support state research priorities. While this may preserve industrial scientific research during the transition period, it can also lead to the formation of new monopoly structures.

Another possibility would be to transform some industrial and branch institutes into contract research centres, with state financing of the S&T programmes. Co-operation between the centres and the research institutes of the Academy could take the form of joint projects, exchange of experts, and leasing of scientific equipment for research and training. Once the economic turmoil is over, the centres will mostly undertake contract research with manufacturing concerns, but some will have the opportunity to become industrial consortiums or research ventures financed by the firms of one or several industries (*e.g.* Stroyprogress, or R&D in the construction industries).

However, to a great extent, saving industrial research capability in the near future will obviously depend on enterprise demand for S&T, which will vary markedly among industries and types of activity. Stable demand is expected in the oil industry, for example, where price liberalisation has created new financial opportunities, and outmoded equipment will have to be replaced to conform to changing technical and economic requirements.

New technologies will be needed in many areas. The demands of commercial banks, insurance companies, various exchanges (stock, commodity, labour, etc.), of an increasing number of small consumer businesses, of construction and agriculture in areas that Russian science essentially never entered will have to be addressed. New technologies will be required for diminishing consumption in energy-intensive industries, for implementing new standards for consumer goods as incomes become differentiated, and for addressing environmental problems.

At the same time, scientific organisations should be significantly reduced and adapted to meet market demand, and some should be reoriented towards commercial activity. A state agency for technology transfer is to be created in order to increase the efficient use of R&D in industry, and organisations of this kind will play an important role in economic growth. Principal tasks of the agency are to develop a juridical and organisational framework, to market scientific products, to create demand for scientific products, to organise co-operation among research organisations and manufacturing, to transfer licences to manufacturing, and to assist in the application of inventions.

The academy sector and the role of the Russian Academy of Sciences

The scientific institutes of the Academy were founded as centralised hierarchical organisms which mainly conducted basic research (see Table 4.1 for the allocations for R&D by types of research in the RAS in 1990-91). Unlike academies in the West, Soviet and Russian academies were never an elite club; they were composed not only of individuals but also of scientific organisations. Until the USSR was split up, the USSR Academy of Sciences and its governing bodies (Praesidium, divisions) played the leading role in the Academy hierarchy, along with the national academies in the Soviet republics. More than 60 per cent of the Academy institutes were located in Russia, and there was a highly developed Academy structure in Ukraine and Belarus. Today, the Academy sector

Table 4.1. **Structure of costs for R&D in the Russian Academy of Sciences by type of research**

Per cent

	Total	Basic research	Applied research	Development
RAS (without regional divisions)				
1990	100	62.2	25.0	12.8
1991	100	64.6	29.8	5.6
Ural division				
1990	100	62.6	20.7	16.7
1991	100	60.8	24.7	14.5
Far Eastern division				
1990	100	71.6	22.5	5.9
1991	100	74.0	21.7	4.3
Siberian division				
1990	100	47.8	31.4	20.8
1991	100	45.1	37.1	17.8

Source: Analytical Centre, Russian Academy of Sciences.

includes the 600 organisations of the Russian Academy of Sciences (RAS), the Russian Agricultural Academy, the Russian Medical Academy, and branch academies.[10]

The Russian academies employ more than 190 000 persons (65 per cent are R&D personnel, 7 per cent are doctors and 31 per cent are candidates of sciences). Overall, some 35 per cent of all highly skilled scientific personnel work in Academy institutes. Academy R&D received approximately 2.8 billion roubles in 1991. The Academy of Sciences, formerly of the USSR and now of Russia, has played a leading role in basic research.[11] The Russian Academy of Sciences is an all-Russian, self-governing body under the laws of the Russian Federation and the Charter of the Academy. In 1991, financing of the Russian Academy of Sciences cost 2.7 billion roubles (2.5 billion in 1990). In 1991, Russian Academy of Sciences' organisations received 63 per cent of their financing directly from the budget as basic financing, 24 per cent came from state programmes, and 13 per cent from contracts with external organisations.

The Academy of Sciences still has one of the largest bodies of R&D personnel in the world, famous scientific schools and institutes, and outstanding scientists. It has 18 divisions run by its scientific administrations, three regional divisions (Ural, Far Eastern, Siberian), and more than 15 regional science centres. In 1992, the Russian Academy of Sciences, together with its regional divisions, had a membership of 442 academicians and 620 corresponding members. At the beginning of 1992, there were more than 65 000 research workers employed by the RAS, among them 7 300 doctors and about 30 000 candidates of sciences. On 1 January 1993, there were some 123 000 persons employed in 416 academic units, of which more than 96 000 work in 313 scientific institutes.

The Academy publishes 193 scientific journals, and 143 of these are translated and republished abroad. The Russian Academy of Sciences has 127 foreign members. It has concluded about 80 agreements on scientific co-operation with foreign countries and participates in 236 international scientific organisations. Institutes and individual scientists of the Academy maintain independent professional relations with 800 international and national scientific organisations.

The break-up of the USSR led to serious problems with regard to property of the USSR Academy of Sciences located on the territory of former Soviet republics. This property includes 29 assets valued at 59 million roubles in 1990 prices. The Russian Academy of Sciences, which is the legal successor of the USSR Academy, is concluding co-operative agreements with academies in the former Union republics in order to solve this problem. The Russian Academy of Sciences is unfavourably affected by the process of "sovereignisation" of the former autonomous units of Russia.

Large institutes remain the principal structural unit of the Academy. The Academy also includes scientific and engineering centres, testing areas, and large installations, as well as its own auxiliary branch, with self-supporting industrial, construction, and design organisations, as well as laboratories, experimental production units, construction and transport enterprises.

Academy science fully reflects the "departmental" character of Russian science as a whole. It was developed by the administrative command system to act as a monopoly for fundamental knowledge. Economic and political reforms in Russia will inevitably lead to changes in the organisational forms of the RAS. However, owing to its status and its particular role in organising and conducting basic research, change is slow and rather painful. The Academy structures have proved to be very conservative and often reluctant to enter the market economy.

The process of transforming the RAS while preserving its administrative structure is being carried out primarily on the initiative of research collectives. Scientific activities and scientific institutions are being diversified by: dividing research institutes into lesser units;[12] integrating the Academy and the universities;[13] and establishing business enterprises, such as joint-stock companies, associations, and limited liability companies.

By the beginning of 1992, more than 300 venture companies and business enterprises originating in institutes of the Academy were established as independent legal entities. The largest enterprises have about 100 employees, but on average they employ from ten to 20 persons.[14] This spontaneous process only serves to create temporary social protection for a part of the scientific community, and relations between parent institutes and their "subordinate" business enterprises are very often restricted to the allocation of budgetary resources by the former to the latter.

The following areas of business activity are being developed within the RAS system: research and services that provide Academy support to large projects; professional evaluation of products, projects, and services; vocational and advanced training facilities for personnel;[15] participation of scientists in consulting activities and the paid education system;[16] the use of information resources of academic institutes.[17]

Changes presently occurring in the organisational structure and activities of Academy institutes make it impossible to discuss the reorganisation of the Academy system and Academy science at this time.

In the wake of the continuing economic crisis, state financing of science has decreased sharply. Basic state budget financing of the Russian Academy of Sciences and its regional divisions was 12.7 billion roubles in 1992. Academy institutions received 4.5 billion roubles for their participation in state S&T programmes from reserve funds of the Ministry of Science and other budgetary sources. Taking increasing prices into account, total financing in 1992 was only about 40 per cent of the 1990 figure. The budget deficit of the Russian Academy of Sciences was over 1 billion roubles in the last quarter of 1992.

The funds allocated were insufficient to meet the basic needs of the institutes, *i.e.* salaries (which comprise, together with additional payments, about 60 per cent of all expenditures), grants for postgraduates, payments for heat and electricity, rent and security.

In many RAS institutes, especially those that conducted energy-intensive research requiring large quantities of equipment and materials, research is practically paralysed; equipment is no longer being bought, shipments are cancelled, reserves of materials and chemicals are not replenished when exhausted, and no scientific literature is being acquired owing to lack of funds. The research and technological facilities of the Academy are essentially inactive.

The professional research personnel of the RAS has suffered serious losses. The impossibility of continuing normal scientific research, low salaries, and psychological and social distress have caused increasing numbers of the most qualified scientists and researchers to flee the Academy for other fields of activity, to engage in a non-scientific secondary activity, or to emigrate to other countries.[18]

The average age of Academy scientists has decreased, primarily due to the change in the average age of "young" scientists. Thus, the average age of academicians decreased from 70 years in 1981 to 68.1 in 1992. The average age of corresponding members remained almost stationary, rising from 62.1 to 62.8 years over the same period. The average age of doctors of science increased from 54.8 to 55.3, but the difference for candidates is more striking, with an increase from 43.2 to 45.5. The average age of research workers without degrees increased from 36.2 to 38.4 years. As a result, the 40-year old age group will become the "young" generation in Academy science.

There will be a 25-30 per cent reduction of Russian Academy of Sciences research workers in the very near future. In 1992, the decrease was 10 per cent. The number of dissertations accepted and the number and quality of postgraduates have also dropped. The number of university graduates hired by Russian Academy of Sciences institutes dropped by 43 per cent from 3 555 in 1989 to 2 043 in 1991 and by more than 50 per cent, from 2 043 in 1991 to 1 000 in 1992.

The decreasing trend is unevenly distributed over different departments of the Russian Academy of Sciences. The Department of Problems of World Economy and International Relations lost 12 out of 84 divisions and sections, and 39 changed their specialisation. Personnel decreased by 350 persons (11.5 percent), and 132 (6.3 per cent) more were transferred to contract jobs. Regional divisions and centres have suffered the greatest reductions. If this process is not arrested in the very near future, the Academy system will be forced to undergo substantial changes.

Reorganisation of the Russian Academy of Sciences requires, first, a clear view of the kind of basic science needed by Russia today and in the future. This is not solely an internal Academy matter; on the contrary, it must concern the highest state authorities, because Russia's basic science capability is a strategic resource, and without state support, it will not survive. In 1993, the key problems are to preserve the state-supported status of basic science as a whole, to adopt a law on the status of Academy institutes, and to provide sufficient resources, rationally distributed among the research sectors.

If reforms fail or are inconsistent, the reduction in budget allocations will increase the speed at which the large institutes are transformed, since smaller units can more easily survive, as they react more quickly to changing economic conditions. Some laboratories and departments of scientific and research institutes will break away from the institutes and form small venture concerns and scientific and research centres. In addition, large institutes will form associations for the joint use of equipment and buildings, so as to reduce duplication.

The lack of financial resources will necessitate a search for new sources of financing, in industry and the commercial sector for example, and can lead to the development of various forms of co-operation. At first, it is likely that large industrial firms or associations will finance research programmes and that joint research will be undertaken by Russian Academy of Sciences' scientists and industry institutes. This would help alleviate the crisis in the Academy and could improve the situation of firms, which do not have the financial resources to undertake research internally, which do not have a sufficiently skilled research staff for science-intensive civil industries, and which are seeking ways of entering or strengthening a position in the global market or competing on the domestic market. Such co-operation might eventually lead to the creation of co-operative research centres or research/training/production consortia with appropriate state support within the framework of science and innovation policy. At the outset, however, such forms of co-operation will evolve in relatively narrow areas, particularly at the development stage and, to a lesser extent, at the applied research stage.

The creation of associations of Academy institutes and university training institutions offers another way to improve the Academy's financial situation. For a fee, these associations could train professionals (economists, lawyers, managers, sociologists, political scientists) who could upgrade their skills through lectures given by distinguished scientists. They could also implement courses for upgrading skills and retraining personnel.[19]

Research in universities and technical institutes (higher schools)

Research in universities and technical institutes is undertaken by independent science and research institutes, by project organisations, by individual professors, by laboratories and research groups. There are also training and pilot and experimental units, clinics, observatories, botanical gardens, and computer centres. Specific to this sector is the fact that its research bodies are an integral part of the system of higher education, provide the basis of modern education, and depend on the situation and trends in this sphere of activity.

The strong Russian higher school system trains specialists for all sectors of the economy and for a wide range of professions. At the end of 1991, it encompassed 539 university-type institutions (including 155 in the field of industry and construction, 157 pedagogical institutes, and 60 in agriculture), and 182 subsidiaries of the main institutes in various locations or formed by the large enterprises, with nearly three million students. Russia also has 48 universities with more than 382 000 students and 224 100 teaching staff, of which 14 300 are doctors and 115 000 are candidates of sciences, *i.e.* approximately 45 per cent of the scientific personnel with scientific degrees. Finally, there are 2 685 technical schools, with 2.3 million students.

There are 1 051 educational institutions involved in upgrading of skills and retraining of personnel. More than two million persons are enrolled annually, but, according to expert estimates, only 25 per cent of Russia's requirements for basic professions are satisfied and only 1 per cent for modern ones.

In higher schools, the most important trends affecting the performance of its research organisations are:
- The transformation of Russian higher schools from a regional subsystem into an independent national system, following the disintegration of the USSR and its integrated educational system.
- The reduction of budget allocations for educational needs.[20] In 1993, 65 to 70 per cent of higher school requirements are expected to be covered from the state budget (mainly from the educational sector), and this will mean that spending for the development of educational institutions will be at least halved (in constant prices of the previous year).
- Reduction in the prestige of the profession of education, coupled with low salary levels, will result in a substantial outflow of young and middle-aged educational staff.[21] At the same time, the low level of social security and the threat of unemployment may increase the attractiveness of teaching jobs for older employees with academic degrees and titles. A continuation of this process would mean the gradual elimination of the main reserve of scientific and educational potential.
- A drop in the number of students engaging in postgraduate studies (in 1991, the number of postgraduate students in university-type educational institutions declined by 4 per cent from to 1990, and the number of graduates and enrolments declined to the same extent). According to estimates by top administrators of educational institutions, the number of candidate and doctoral dissertations defended in the higher school dropped by 50 per cent in 1992, compared to 1991. Annual rates of decline in the number of doctors of sciences in the higher school are estimated at 2 to 5 per cent.
- In 1985-91, the growth rates in student enrolment (except for universities) diminished, on average, by 7 per cent a year, and in 1991 the number of students

enrolled was 89.5 per cent of the number enrolled in 1985, while the corresponding number of graduate students was 85.4 per cent.
- Lack of equipment: in 1992, there was practically no budget financing for equipment and computer hardware purchases.[22]
- The employment situation for graduates has deteriorated. Even prestigious educational institutions were unable to find jobs for 15 to 20 per cent of their graduates, and the figure might soon rise to 60 per cent.[23] In 1992, demand for young graduates by the Academy of Sciences institutes was less than one-third the 1989 level; in 1988, they refused to accept 110 graduates, and in 1991 they refused 536.

At the beginning of 1992, 450 educational institutions with more than 90 000 employees (a 20 per cent reduction compared with 1990) were engaged in R&D. Of this number, 66 000 were specialists (a 15 per cent reduction compared with 1990), including 1 400 doctors and 15 100 candidates of sciences. Sources of funding for R&D are indicated in Table 4.2.

Three periods can be defined in the R&D activities of universities and technical institutes. Up to 1985, there was little change, and growth occurred with the increase in the number of technical institutes. Scientific activity in universities and technical institutes increased in 1985-89.[24] Institutes of higher education always received relatively less financing but had greater numbers of personnel and organisations; they received 10 per cent of financing and had one-third of the specialists and more than 50 per cent of the highly skilled personnel. For this reason, they engaged in contract work with enterprises and industrial and academic institutes in order to supplement their financial resources, a practice that ensured their viability.

At the end of the 1980s, technical institutes began to market their scientific activity. State budget financing of science in technical institutes has almost tripled, and contract work has increased by more than 60 per cent. Special funding for persons engaged in scientific research has also increased.

In 1991-92, scientific organisations in the higher schools gained an unexpected advantage due to additional support from various state and regional structures. During the same period, the first experiments with paid education began; however, paid education cannot yet be considered an alternative to financing the technical institutes, although it is planned that its share will reach 15 per cent.[25] Nonetheless, as a whole, the situation of higher school science in Russia was as disastrous as in other sectors, because of the lack of all kinds of resources and the negative effects of commercialisation, since, in the absence of serious state support, commercial work entailed a reduction of basic research and of scientific work in general.[26]

Today, the technical institutes themselves must mobilise in order to maintain the priority of basic over applied science and prevent the danger of the collapse of scientific schools. Even such a leading educational and scientific centre as Moscow University has been forced to compensate for the lack of orders for basic research (in physics, chemistry, etc.) by undertaking applied work and has in fact had to cease all scientific activities in some faculties. Under such conditions, efforts to incite scientists "to transform their

Table 4.2. **R&D funding in some Russian colleges in 1991**

Millions of roubles and per cent

Name of college	Total budget R&D	State budget	Contracts[1]	R&D performance		
				Basic research	Applied research	Development
Volgorad Polytechnic	14.4	6.5	8.0	2.8	94.4	2.8
State Academy of Oil and Gas	46.4	5.2	41.2	10.0	80.0	10.0
Ekaterinburg National Economy Institute	5.45	0.45	0.50	–	5.4	–
Kazan Aviation Institute	39.6	9.6	30.0	1.0	96.5	2.5
Moscow Institute	196.0	166.0	30.0	80.0	20.0	–
Moscow Institute of Physics and Technology	13.3	11.8	1.5	20.0	70.0	10.0
Moscow Institute of Electronic Equipment	32.2	6.5	25.7	25.0	52.0	23.0
Moscow Institute of Energy	74.2	32.2	42.0	25.0	65.0	10.0
St. Petersbourg University	59.6	50.6	9.0	80.0	20.0	–
St. Petersbourg Electric Technology Institute	35.9	30.6	5.3	10.0	80.0	10.0
Tomsk Polytechnic University	50.2	25.2	25.0	2.0	94.0	4.0
Tyumen Industrial Institute	1.5	0.5	1.0	–	87.0	13.0
Cheliabinsk State Polytechnic University	40.0	10.0	30.0	2.5	92.5	5.0
Total in colleges under Higher School Committee	5 841	1 669	4 172	21.9	54.3	23.8

1. Funds allocated on contracts include some state budget organisations' funds.

Source: Analytical Centre, Russian Academy of Sciences.

knowledge into capital'' lead the most skilled personnel to leave the higher school and, consequently, basic science.[27] Up to 60 per cent of educators and scientists are compelled to take second jobs in various commercial activities to compensate for their low wages, thus reducing their basic research activity.

The situation is even more difficult in other Russian technical institutes. The Russian Union of Rectors estimates that, at the end of 1992, science allocations from the state budget to the technical institutes had been reduced by two-thirds in real prices and that industry orders were only a tenth of their level at the end of 1991. The Committee on Higher School estimates a drop of over 50 per cent in the number of educational and scientific personnel engaged in R&D. In Moscow technical institutes, the number has decreased by 24.4 per cent, and the number of candidates of sciences is falling on average by 12 per cent annually. Most student scientific research has stopped, and student scientific and technological centres have largely been transformed into commercial operations.

The technical institutes of economics are enjoying a boom. Their scientific activity attracts the attention of educational institutions, major commercial firms, and foreign organisations, and an extensive network of commercial scientific and educational structures has been created around them. Most non-state educational institutions licensed to train personnel (more than 20 in all) are in this field.

The exodus of young people from technical institutes and centrifugal tendencies within the higher schools themselves will have a very serious effect on the scientific disciplines and faculties and will lead to a rise in narrowly specialised training, especially in those areas that previously offered broad general training, *e.g.* physics and chemistry in preparation for engineering. There will be a gradual, but large-scale, reduction of technical institute science in its traditional form, and personnel will move to new forms of science (industrial, corporate) outside the state sphere of higher education, while traditional forms will persist in some prestigious state schools, such as Moscow University, that are able to obtain large state subsidies.

The system of higher education is unlikely to be able to surmount the crisis in scientific research without state support to preserve the overall structure for scientific research and professional education. Survival of higher school science will depend on several factors.

First, scientific research and education must be integrated so as to overcome the existing gap between training scientific personnel and research activity. Scientific and educational centres have been created, through the integration of related departments of Moscow University, the Moscow Institute of Physics and Technology, the Moscow Institute of Electronic Technology, the State Academy of Oil and Gas, and the Moscow Mining Institute, as well as other technical institutes, with the institutes of the Russian Academy of Sciences. Technical institutes that apply non-traditional methods of learning are being created (the Higher School of Economics in Moscow, the State University in Puschino, the Educational Centre in Dubna), in which, as a rule, corresponding divisions of technical institutes and scientific organisations provide the personnel and share the basic and applied research work.

Second, the technical institutes are actively engaged in mastering the principles of modern innovative activity. Science and technology parks are beginning to play a significant part in the co-operation between the higher school and industry. The technical institutes of Siberia have been the most successful. The first such park was opened at Tomsk Polytechnic University and includes the research and production base of other technical institutes and the industrial R&D institutes of the region.[28] Technoparks have been created in Moscow, St. Petersburg, Mytyishi, Zelenograd, Zarechny (Sverdlovsk region), and Perm.

Third, because they have been neglected by the state structures, the heads of technical institutes have joined together to attract both foreign and domestic investment, and associations of technical institutes have been formed, on a corporate basis, by the universities, the engineering and medical schools, the scientific and technological parks of the higher school, and the Union of Rectors. The International Academy of Sciences of the Higher School, which brings together the leading scientists of the technical institutes of Russia and other CIS states, has begun its work.

Fourth, the university and technical institute sector is more evenly distributed throughout the territory of Russia (in comparison with industrial and, especially, Academy science), so that under conditions of increasing regional social and economic independence, institutions of higher education will have greater opportunity to obtain funding support on the regional as well as the federal level. Local budgets (aided by regional industrial and commercial structures) will probably finance regional technical institutes, which may reorient the direction of their scientific research. They might conduct research into regional problems or carry out minor applied research of interest to local industry. Any serious integration with industrial and Academy science is out of the question, and it is more likely that a certain number of technical institute/factory laboratories will emerge to form the basis for renewing industry science.

Fifth, a trend towards establishing new elite higher schools and universities, including international ones, emerged over 1990-92 in the former USSR and then in Russia. The trend is likely to continue, as these institutions can maintain high wages for scientists and educators, as well as material and technical security, thanks to paid education and Western financial aid.

Other aspects of the reform include the concentration of budget funds, allocated on a competitive basis, on the most important programmes in basic science (81 intercollege scientific and technical programmes) and on involving the technical institutes in the solution of regional problems. The following programmes have a special role: "Russian universities" (development of the regional scientific centres), "The higher school in Russia", "The peoples of Russia: revival and development", and "Wider education in humanities and broader use of informatics".

Development of new forms of R&D organisations

Although the traditional organisational structure of science in Russia seems stable on the surface, it is, nevertheless, undergoing deep changes. New trends can be most vividly seen in the formation of a new research sector that is mainly oriented towards market relations and non-state property. It will consist entirely of small organisations with less than 100 employees. In 1992 the scientific institutions considered as small enterprises were divided among state, collective and private ownership, with approximately 25 per cent each; the remaining 25 per cent was attributed to public and municipal associations.

Co-operatives are one of the first new forms of industrial science organisation in Russia. S&T co-operatives began to spread as early as 1987, and 1991 was a turning point for the co-operative movement. Under the crisis conditions, the number of scientific co-operatives in operation (7 870) and the number of persons employed by them (200 000) essentially remained at the 1990 level, as many enterprises changed their status to joint stock companies or limited societies.

Among co-operatives involved in R&D, one-third conducted research for development, one-third were engaged in designing and introducing new developments, and one-third wrote the relevant software. The co-operatives operating in the innovation sphere are, as a rule, small enterprises employing on average from 20 to 30 persons. Around 40 per cent of those employed are on the regular staff, 30 per cent hold part-time jobs, and about 30 per cent work on the basis of temporary contracts.

Proceeds from the realisation of scientific and technical products fell by 3.4 per cent (or from 3.1 to 3.0 billion roubles) from 1990 to 1991. In fact, scientific and technical production dropped further, as the enterprises registered as scientific and technical organisations are working for commerce and on commission or are making products that are not science-intensive.

In the developed countries small enterprises are a key element in innovation, but there is practically no Russian equivalent. It is estimated that the Russian economy needs 10 to 12 million small enterprises; it now has only 300 000 to 400 000. Goskomstat (the Bureau of Statistics) of the Russian Federation surveyed 67 000 small enterprises in 1991. Only 7 000 are involved in science and science services (about 36 per cent were involved in R&D and 54 per cent in design and introduction). Their revenue was 4.3 billion roubles.

From January to May 1992, joint ventures on Russian territory produced goods and services worth 33 billion roubles. Exports amounted to $548 million and imports to $300 million. Goods and services brought in $157 million and 16.9 billion roubles. Foreign investors invested $7.4 billion in joint ventures, including $2.3 billion in industry and $303 million in science and science services. Joint ventures in the computer business play a special role, as they account for 40 to 50 per cent of the total proceeds of joint ventures operating in the country, although they only represent 13 per cent of the number of enterprises and 8 per cent of investment in 1991.

The main problems for developing small innovative enterprises in the domestic economy are: the lack of a mechanism for creating initial capital; the difficulties involved in creating the infrastructure for developing new products; the lack of regulations concerning property rights for intellectual products; and the effect of the generally unfavourable background on external investment in the innovation process. Yet, in spite of these difficulties new scientific organisations are developing and becoming widespread.

Scientific and technological exchanges were designed to play a part in overcoming barriers between product designers and potential investors. However, the lack of legal protection for intellectual property has negatively affected their operation. According to the Law of the Russian Federation "On Commodity Exchanges", trade in intellectual property is illegitimate, yet it continues. Special divisions for trading scientific and technical products have been opened at many commodity exchanges, and ten are specialised in this area (patents, licences, know-how, technical designs, technologies, finished science-intensive products) and provide scientific and technical services. Among the exchanges operating in Moscow are Intellect-Capital, Ideas and Technologies Exchange, Russian Scientific and Technical Exchange, Technologies Exchange, International Exchange of TV Video Industry, Moscow Biotechnological Exchange, Software Exchange (created by the joint venture Transelectro), TIM which operates in microelectronics, the intellectual property exchange called House of Scientists, the Siberian Scientific Exchange, etc.

Commercial organisations seek information on export-oriented technologies and are keenly interested in the developments and technologies competitive on the world market that are to be found in enterprises in the formerly classified areas of the military-industrial complex and Academy institutes. As a result, one of the largest commercial concerns, Binitech (involved in international exchange of science-intensive and information technologies, an all-Russian technology centre, three technoparks and other structures), is seeking out and introducing new laser technologies in microelectronics and instruments production and in the field of high energy physics.[29]

Some innovative "subsidiaries" are forming a "business sphere" near scientific centres. Examples of successful activities include the promotion of Russian technologies and innovations in Western markets, the conversion of military industry, and promoting foreign technologies in the Russian market.

Special structures for applied science have been created, and in mid-1992, the Engineering Council was set up to promote multilateral co-operation on projects for new machines, equipment and other types of science-intensive production, to improve export policy for high technologies, and to seek sources willing to finance scientific research. In order to implement its programme more quickly and efficiently, the Council is going to set up a series of holding companies oriented to specific markets and to create a data bank of promising developments.

There are also organisations that collect and make available scientific and technical information, such as central libraries, state information centres, industrial information and analytical centres, and regional centres of scientific and technical information.

The creation of new organisational forms of scientific work is a slow and uncertain process. However, the wide spectrum shows the sector's vitality and its ability to adapt. Nonetheless, changes in economic conditions since 1991 have led to the collapse or change of activity of many small organisations.

2. The regional structure of science

The spatial organisation of R&D is considered particularly critical for countries with broad scientific activity and vast territory. This is the case for Russia, and this is why it is necessary to analyse the dissemination of scientific activity and to define the "image" of science in various regions and clarify their prospects for development in light of the present economic, social and political limitations of Russia.

R&D in the regions: structure and dynamics[30]

At present, organisations engaged in R&D are very unevenly distributed. On 1 January 1992, one-third of the country's 4 564 organisations engaged in R&D were located in the Moscow and St. Petersburg area, and 17 per cent were in Moscow itself. Next in line were the Novosibirsk, Sverdlovsk, Rostov, and Nizhni Novgorod districts and the Republic of Bashkhortostan (with, on average, 3 per cent each). Thus, more than 45 per cent of the Russian organisations engaged in R&D are in these nine regions.

This distribution obviously determines the regional allocation of R&D personnel, R&D capital assets and expenditures for R&D, and the degree of their concentration. In terms of size, the most important locations are, in order, Moscow, Moscow district, St. Petersburg and the districts of Nizhni Novgorod, Novosibirsk and Sverdlovsk (see Table 4.3). Moscow stands in first place; the concentration of capital assets in Moscow is substantially greater than the concentration of R&D personnel (doctors of science excluded), an indirect indicator of the quality of its science.

The territorial organisation of R&D in Russia is distinguished not only by substantial differences in the magnitude of science in various regions, but also by the specific type practised. Three indicators have been used to estimate science in the regions: R&D personnel, R&D expenditures and R&D capital assets. On this basis, the 73 Russian regions, each with its distinctive characteristics, may be reduced to four principal models:

- First, *"science of the centre"*, in Moscow and St. Petersburg and in the Moscow, Novosibirsk and Nizhni Novgorod districts. These regions differ from the others by the magnitude of their science sector and differ substantially from each other as well (see Table 4.3). All except the Novosibirsk district are located in the European territory of Russia. Regions in this group are much more advanced than others, not only in terms of the extent of R&D but also for a range of other parameters (in particular, their share of R&D personnel of higher qualification).

- Second, *the major provincial centres of industrial science*. These include a few regions close to Moscow, as well as the Samara, Penza, Omsk, Perm, and Cheliabinsk districts and the Krasnoyarsk territory). These regions all lie in the second tenth of Russian regions, by numbers of R&D personnel. However, the qualification of R&D personnel (or, more precisely, the share of doctors and candidates of science) is lower than in the first model. Some general features of the major centres of industrial science are:
  • They are not located only in the European part of Russia; some are in the Ural region (Sverdlovsk and Perm districts and Bashkhortostan) and some

Table 4.3. **The R&D share of some regions in Russia in 1991**
Per cent

Indicators	Russia	Total six regions	Moscow	Moscow region	St. Petersbourg	Novosibirsk region	Nizhni Novgorod	Sverdlovsk region
Science and technology personnel (1 January 1992)	100	57.8	26.5	5.9	15.8	3.2	3.4	3.1
R&D personnel	100	59.8	29.0	5.4	15.9	3.0	3.3	3.2
Doctors of science	100	84.2	53.1	6.8	15.2	5.3	1.1	2.0
Candidates of science	100	74.8	43.5	6.9	15.9	3.9	1.4	2.4
R&D expenditures	100	71.4	39.6	7.3	14.9	4.9	2.3	2.5
Basic research	100	75.3	44.4	6.5	10.6	7.7	3.7	2.3
Applied research	100	70.4	38.2	7.5	16.1	4.1	2.0	2.6
Development	100	55.2	23.8	5.9	15.3	2.9	3.9	3.4
Average annual capital assets (total)	100	65.7	32.0	9.0	14.7	4.1	3.1	2.8
Machines and equipment	100	66.6	32.9	7.8	15.3	4.5	3.3	2.6

Source: On the Activities of the Scientific Organisations in RF in 1991, State Statistics Committee, Moscow, 1992.

regions are far from the main science centres (Samara, Saratov and Rostov districts and Tatarstan).
- The high level of industrial development in the regions, substantially differentiated by economic specialisation. Bashkhortostan and Tatarstan are the regions of raw materials; Rostov, Sverdlovsk and Perm districts are characterised by their defence industry, etc.
- The historically stable and high concentration of science in regions such as the Republic of Tatarstan and the Sverdlovsk and Saratov districts.

– *Third, the principal provincial centres of Academy science*, including some regions with a high proportion of university and technical institute science. The regions of this group are characterised by the comparatively average amount of their science, but the R&D personnel includes a considerable share of highly qualified personnel (doctors and candidates of science). This model is largely found in regions very remote from the principal science centres (Primorsky region, Irkutsk and Tomsk districts, and neighbouring regions).

– *Fourth, some 40 regions with comparatively little science*. Geographically, all are situated in the European territory of the country, a fact which suggests that the small amount may be due to their proximity to the major centres of Russian science. It should be noted that, despite the similarity of the amount of R&D in this group, it is a heterogeneous group with quite different "science images". The group includes the St. Petersburg district, which occupies the 48th place by the number of R&D personnel, but the 13th place by the quantity of its doctors of science. The Chuvash Republic is also included in this group; it occupies the 37th place in Russia by its R&D personnel, but on 1 January 1992 no doctor of science was registered in organisations engaged in R&D in the Republic.

Against the background of the significant overall decrease in Russian science over the last few years, there are important differences among regions for the years analysed, and with respect to the various indicators. Thus, while the number of R&D personnel decreased overall, it increased in 13 regions in 1989-90, most of them located in the North-West and the Centre and with a low level of scientific research (*i.e.* they fall into the fourth category mentioned above). In contrast, the greatest decrease in the number of R&D personnel occurred in Moscow, in the districts of Nizhni Novgorod, Sverdlovsk and Rostov and in the Republic of Tatarstan. Thus, the reduction of R&D personnel in Russia in 1989-91 was to some extent related to the magnitude of the region's science, as the greatest changes occurred in the regions with the most and the least scientific research.

In 1989-92, the most significant regional variation concerns changes in the number of doctors of science. The number grew most in regions with a relatively high concentration of Academy science (Republic of Karelia, Komi SSR, Irkutsk district) and in the regions where universities and technical institutes predominate but have an extremely low share of doctors of sciences among their R&D personnel (Arkhangelsk, Murmansk, Briansk, Tver, Ivanovo, Riazan, Smolensk and Kursk districts). In some cases, the movement of highly qualified personnel from certain Russian peripheral regions was affected by the migration of scientists within the territory of the former USSR.

The interregional differences in the growth of R&D expenditures in 1989-91 depend primarily on the magnitude of science in the regions: during this period, the greatest percentage increase was registered in the European area of the country characterised by comparatively little science and traditionally low R&D expenditures, although growth was low in absolute terms. In addition, growth in R&D expenditures in regions with concentrations of raw materials (Kemerovo and Tumen districts, Komi SSR, Krasnoyarsk territory) outran average national growth. There are reasons to believe that the fuel and energy branches will continue to be strong for 1992-93.

Finally, the indicators of capital assets of scientific institutions in the Russian regions in 1989-92 were affected by the reduction of R&D personnel and inflation.

Variations over the past few years in the dynamics of the development of science of different regions have been negligible and no clear tendencies have emerged. In the past, the R&D sector developed almost independently of the social and economic features of the regions where they were located: for example, growth in R&D in the principal regions for conversion (the Urals, Moscow, St. Petersburg, the districts of Nizhni Novgorod, Kemerovo and Rosto differed substantially, and depended on the size of the science sector.

Science in the large cities

The following discussion concerns 34 cities with a population of over 500 000 as of 1 January 1991.

In 1985, 43.7 per cent of the scientists and scientific-pedagogical personnel in scientific organisations (and 65 per cent of doctors and 54.2 per cent of candidates of science) were located in the 34 largest cities of Russia. These cities accounted for 27 per cent of the total population and 38 per cent of the urban population. In 1991, the share of total population in these cities remained unchanged; the figures for R&D personnel (36.2 per cent, including 81.1 per cent of doctors of science and 66.5 per cent of candidates of science) are incompatible with those of 1985 due to a 1989 revision of the content and structure of science statistics. While there is as yet no index that allows comparison of the two systems, it is clear that the differences for "numbers of doctors of science" are less than the differences for other science indicators. Given the nature of the statistical changes, it can be assumed that the concentration of doctors of science in the largest cities of Russia has increased, although the trend is less clear for candidates of science. As the concentration of material scientific resources in the largest scientific centres traditionally exceeded by a substantial margin the concentration of R&D personnel (in 1989, for example, over 60 per cent of the scientific and technical information from abroad (scientific journals, etc.) remained in Moscow, it is certain that scientific activity was further concentrated in the largest cities during the period 1985-90.

The tendency to concentrate R&D in the large cities has been estimated by taking the ratio of the amount of their science to that of the surrounding region.[31] In 1990, about 40 per cent of the population of their districts, territories and republics were in the cities, as were 38 per cent of the R&D personnel (including 86 per cent of doctors and 73 per cent of candidates of science). Despite the differences in indicators already mentioned, it is clear that the share of doctors and candidates of science in the large cities has increased.

Overall, the highest science concentrations in the capitals in 1990 are in some of the eastern regions, in Astrakhan, Volgograd, Orenburg and Sverdlovsk districts, and in Bashkhortostan. Examples of highly dispersed science can be found in the districts of Nechernozemnie and Povolgye, where the share of R&D personnel in the capitals does not exceed 30 per cent.

In 1990, 13.2 per cent of the R&D personnel (11 per cent of doctors and over 18 per cent of candidates of science) of the 34 largest Russian cities were in the university and technical institute science sector, 14.6 per cent (46.6 per cent of doctors and 26.1 per cent of candidates of science) were in the Academy sector, and the remaining 70 per cent were in the industrial sector. The Academy sector dominated in the large cities, where the university and technical institute sector was smallest. This is due not only to changes in science statistics, but also to the emergence of new higher education institutes outside the large cities during the period 1985-90.

New trends have emerged in the structure of R&D in the large cities of Russia, particularly in the non-state sector (private bodies, but also those founded by state organisations). Novosibirsk may serve as an example, as its situation is similar to that of other large Russian cities with respect to non-state science.

Advantageous economic and political conditions in 1988-91 promoted relatively intensive growth of small businesses in Novosibirsk. These firms aimed for quick turn-over of invested funds, high efficiency and adaptation to variable regional market conditions, and they had a variety of specialisations. Uneven growth in the different areas of specialisation led to structural changes in small businesses (particularly high growth was registered in intermediate trade activities).

Structural changes in small businesses in Novosibirsk were also caused by changes in previously established enterprises: the relatively stable activity in manufacturing, construction and transport firms contrasted strongly with the considerable reduction, by 1991, of organisations specialised in scientific research, development, and software development for computerised production (Table 4.4). Nearly 60 per cent of these enterprises changed activity by 1991, mostly to the service sector and to production that could quickly improve the enterprise's financial status.

When commercial science organisations begin their activities they have to deal primarily in minor scientific and technical problems: realisation of individual projects, consulting services, know-how, and development of technical documentation for specific technological processes and products. Because volume is small and activities tend to be varied, considerable amounts of labour are involved in meeting contracts. In addition, customers have no motivation to innovate, given their meagre financial resources. Thus, the small business innovation sector is relatively unprofitable (profit margins of 10 to 16 per cent) and likely to shrink. Federal administrative institutions and local authorities will have to act together, if the non-state science sector is to be developed.

In conclusion, research on Russian regional science in 1989-91 indicates substantial regional variations concerning the prospects for developing the science sphere in the

Table 4.4. **Change of specialisation of small business enterprises in Novosibirsk in 1991**

Per cent of the entire number of enterprises of given specialisation, 1 January 1992

Specialisation of the small business	Initially stated specialisation of enterprise	Change of specialisation
Scientific innovations	15.6	31.2
Scientific production	11.5	30.8
Software development	28	25
Commercial	31	4.4
Production	8	2.5
Construction	–	–
Transport	33	–
Services	25	35
Medicine	–	–
Education	20	–

Source: Analytical Centre, Russian Academy of Sciences.

Russian regions. Factors involved include the size of regional R&D and its distribution among the sectors of science, the social and political situation, its geographical position (distance or position in terms of the "centre-periphery" opposition), etc. The circumstances make it unlikely that the regions can develop their science sector alone in the near future. Thus, science development in the regions is likely to be defined by the main trends of R&D in Russia as a whole.

3. Science cities: problems and perspectives

Naukograds, or science cities, were founded between 1930 and 1970 by special decisions of the highest government authorities in order to solve problems relating to production for defence and to provide world pre-eminence in strategically important areas of science and technology. Among them are Zhukovsky, Kaliningrad, Pushino, Obninsk, Obolensk, Protvino, Dubna, Dolgoprudny, Troitsk, Klimovsk, Chernogolovka, and Friazino. Several naukograds were closed and required special permits for entering their territory, *e.g.* Arzamas-16, Cheliabinsk-70, Golitsino-2, and Krasnoyarsk-26. In all, there are more than 50 naukograds in the Russian Federation (see Table 4.5), and their specialisations cover most fields of science and technology: nuclear physics, biotechnologies, precise mechanical engineering, aerospace, materials, microelectronics and instrument-making, among others.

The mission of naukograds determined their characteristics. All were built around several enterprises, essentially specialised in a single scientific and technological area. Generally, there were no other industrial enterprises. The only source of financing was the state budget, and financing was provided through trade ministries and the Academy of

Table 4.5. **Russian science cities**

1	Academgorodok of Novosibirsk scientific centre
2	Academgorodok of Tomsk scientific centre
3	Academgorodok of Krasnoyarsk scientific centre
4	Academgorodok of Irkutsk scientific centre
5	Aleksin (Hula region)
6	Arzamas-16 (Nizhni Novgorod region)
7	Beloiarsky (Ekaterinburg region)
8	Bolshevo-2 (Moscow region)
9	Borok (Yaroslavl region)
10	Golitsino-2 (Moscow region)
11	Dzerginsk (Moscow region)
12	Dzerginsk (Vladimir region)
13	Dimitrovgrad (Ulianovsk region)
14	Dmitrov-7 (Moscow region)
15	Dolgoprudny (Moscow region)
16	Dubna (Moscow region)
17	Zheleznorogny (Moscow region)
18	Zhukovsky (Moscow region)
19	Zelenodolsk (Tatarstan)
20	Zelenograd (Moscow region)
21	Zlatoust-36
22	Kaliningrad (Moscow region)
23	Kazan-75
24	Klimovsk (Moscow region)
25	Klimovsk-3 (Moscow region)
26	Koltsovo (Novosibirsk region)
27	Krasnodar-59
28	Krasnoiarsk-26
29	Krasnoarmeisk (Moscow region)
30	Mendeleevo (Moscow region)
31	Melenky (Vladimir region)
32	Miass-16 (Cheliabinsk region)
33	Niznaia Salda (Ekaterinburg region)
34	Novosibirsk-49
35	Obolensk (Moscow region)
36	Obninsk (Kaluga region)
37	Omsk-5
38	Penza-19
39	Perm-6
40	Primorsk (St. Petersburg region)
41	Pravdinsk (Nizhni Novgorod region)
42	Protvino (Moscow region)
43	Pushino (Moscow region)
44	Redkino (Tver region)
45	Reutov (Moscow region)
46	Sosnovy Bor (St. Petersburg region)
47	Troitsk (Moscow region)
48	Turaevo (Lytkarino-1, Moscow region)
49	Friazino (Moscow region)
50	Chernogolovka (Moscow region)
51	Cheliabinsk-40
52	Cheliabinsk-65
53	Cheliabinsk-70

Note: In Russian alphabetical order.

Sciences. The naukograds not only engaged in scientific developments but also met all the social needs of their community. The whole territory, its housing resources, municipal economy and social sphere, belonged to one enterprise or was divided among several. There was generally no town budget, and decisions about development of the town were taken by directors of enterprises and ministries. The settlements were offshoots of departmental organisations, and their existence, and their fate, was tied to the changing importance of the branch on which they depended.

These characteristics caused the difficult problems that arose following the disintegration of the USSR and the ensuing economic crisis. At present, the naukograds have less than half the sum required to ensure the municipal economy. Improved housing is needed for some 40 per cent of the population in several towns, and some residents have lived in hostels for ten years. The population does not have the means to build, nor can the city budget fund the building of houses.

In connection with conversion, funding from the state budget was suspended, and the science cities therefore lost their livelihood. Expensive experimental equipment unique in Russia or even in the world is deteriorating. The termination of scientific work in these cities will mean the loss of a leading role in a number of fields. Lack of funds for guarding dangerous technologies and materials creates a real threat to the population. The best specialists are going abroad or moving to other spheres of activity. There is a sharp increase in unemployment, especially among women over 40 years of age. If these trends continue, there will be an irretrievable loss of unique scientific and technical capacity, not only for Russia but for the whole world.

In March 1993, the Ministry of Science and Technological Policy of the Russian Federation presented to the Parliament of the Supreme Soviet of the Russian Federation, which backed it, a programme for preserving and developing the science cities. The main points are as follows:

- The present role of naukograds is radically changed. Instead of single-purpose cities oriented to S&T for defence, naukograds should become centres for developing new knowledge, technologies and modern education, for directing innovative technologies to all spheres of the national economy, and for improving the ability of territories to become centres for large-scale international projects in ecology, health protection, and nuclear research. They should serve as the basis for state science centres, and they should make an essential contribution to the conversion of industrial firms by providing them with advanced civil technologies and aiding in the structural reorganisation of industry and agriculture.
- The administrative management of the science cities and their production must be replaced by mechanisms of self-development and self-organisation with a variety of forms of property and business activity.
- The case of every naukograd must be treated individually, on the basis of an analysis of its present capacity and its potential role in the development of Russia and the region. Decisions should be made jointly at the level of the Federation, the region and the naukograd itself on the basis of the specialisation of the naukograd, the S&T needs it is capable of satisfying, the forms of property and sources of financing available, etc.

Given the new role to be played by naukograds, the main strategic task is to create the conditions for transforming them and to find the means of compensating for the consequences of recent events and avoiding their collapse. The state will have to help construct mechanisms that will allow the naukograds to function effectively in the new economic conditions. They will need to:
- rebuild organisational and economic mechanisms so that the naukograds can function effectively in complex economic conditions;
- attract domestic and foreign investors to undertake innovative scientific, technical and social projects;
- intensify scientific and technical innovative activity in existing enterprises in naukograds and establish new ones that are not state property;
- maintain a high level of S&T personnel by attracting talented young people and leading specialists on a contract basis;
- increase the use of technologies produced in naukograds by industrial and agricultural firms situated outside their territories;
- accelerate scientific output for the world market.

It is assumed that the preservation and reconfiguration of naukograds will require a special state programme. State policy with respect to each naukograd will be determined on the basis of an inventory of its science capacity and the results of a study of its future possibilities. It will then decide on one of four basic directions:
- provision of minimum support;
- preservation of the science capacity;
- elimination of redundancy;
- active development.

Realisation of the state programme will require the formulation and introduction of normative and legal regulations concerning, in particular, the budget of the naukograd, tax policy and privileges, government guarantees for the rights of domestic and foreign investors, regimes for privatisation, and social policy.

For the Moscow region, the elaboration and realisation of this policy is especially important, as its S&T complex is one of the largest in Russia, with one-third of the naukograds working with advanced technologies. Almost half of the working population is employed in the scientific and technical sphere, and the main part of Russia's scientific elite is located there. Its unique features suggest that it can take on the leading role in innovation and become the centre of innovative activity in Russia.

In May 1993 a special agreement was signed by the Soviet of People's Deputies, the Administration of the Moscow region and the Ministry of Science and Technological Policy, by which the Moscow region will be used to test federal and regional mechanisms for managing innovative activity and state policy with respect to science cities.

Notes

1. Data in this chapter are from Goskomstat (Russian Federation) and the Analytical Centre of the Russian Academy of Sciences.
2. With the elimination of existing economic and financial mechanisms, manufacturing establishments can no longer pay their suppliers for raw materials, semi-finished products, etc. The inability to pay spread through the economy in 1992, creating a domino effect, and the ensuing financial crisis was called a "crisis of mutual non-payments".
3. The relevant laws of the USSR and the Russian Federation are "Concerning state enterprise" (1987) and "Concerning taxation of the profits of firms" and "Concerning firms and business activity" (1990-91). In 1987, there were more than 1 200 industrial research organisations in the areas of machine building, timber, metallurgy, power, transport, light industries, trade, fishing, etc.
4. In 1987-89, the average salary in R&D increased 1.4 times and outstripped salaries in industry. Profits increased in some industrial research institutes (Central Research Institute for Heavy Industry, Central Research Institute for Metallurgy, All-Union Research Institute for Metallurgical Machine Building); as sales quadrupled in 1990-91, profits increased by a factor of six, and the payroll fund by a factor of 3.5. However, figures for 1990-91 show decreasing technical level and quality of production in manufacturing; a drop in the share of machine building, as total production fell from 23.6 per cent to 21.4 per cent over the last three years; a decrease in the share of products sold for hard currency from 4.4 per cent to 1.0 per cent; and a decline in the share of really new products among newly manufactured products from 43.4 per cent to 32.6 per cent.
5. The "crisis of non-payments" gave birth in 1992 to a system whereby enterprises are put "on file" with their financial organisation [according to Russian law, enterprises must have their account (or accounts) with a single bank]. Thus, when a firm needs to make a payment, it gives an order to its bank to transfer funds to the relevant organisation. In the crisis of mutual non-payments, enterprises often were unable to settle accounts because of a lack of payment from other firms. In this case, the bank puts the enterprise on file, and when funds are received they are used to pay accounts due. In 1992, many enterprises were both creditors and debitors, but whatever the balance, an enterprises with an unpaid account is placed on file.
6. In some institutes, the share of employees under age 35 fell 30 per cent in 1991-93; among employees discharged, 40 per cent were from the this age group, and the number of post-graduates decreased by a factor of ten.
7. In the institutes investigated, the share of equipment more than ten years old increased 25 per cent in 1990-92. Most equipment in the institutes is five to ten years old. In the Institute of Metallurgical Machine Building, only one new major piece of equipment was introduced in 1991.

8. Concerns were formed in the process of restructuring the economy. They are a new form of enterprise association and function in many respects like the ministries they replace, but they play more a co-ordination than a management role.

9. As a result of a presidential statement of 1 July 1992, "On measures for transforming state enterprises, free associations of state enterprises and joint-stock companies", industrial bodies with over 1 000 employees (or with capital assets of more than 50 million roubles at 1 January 1992) must be privatised in 1992. However, at the end of 1992, only 16 large industrial scientific units had been privatised.

10. Also included in this sector are the institutions of the Academy of Fine Arts (1), of the Academy of Pedagogical Sciences (7) and of the Academy of Municipal Services (5). The number of personnel and the volume of output are not significant (in total, about 1 800 persons and 21 million roubles).

11. Before the disintegration of the USSR, 24.5 per cent of academy organisations were under the Academy of Sciences, with 12.8 per cent for the Ukrainian Academy, 3.5 per cent each for the Belarus and Kasakhstan academies, and 36 per cent for the branch academies.

12. For example, the largest research institution, the P.N. Lebedev Physical Institute, became a federation of five research units.

13. Over ten joint research centres, and about 50 temporary research collectives have been set up in Russia. Plans for establishing scientific training centres and science and technology parks are being developed. The interaction between Academy and university science in the Ural and Siberian Divisions of the RAS has been encouraging.

14. An "average" institute has one or two such organisations, but some institutes had set up more than ten commercial enterprises by the end of 1992.

15. There are some scientific and technological centres for research and testing in the field of construction materials in the Institute of Physical Chemistry in Moscow. Business enterprises can contact these centres and quickly receive, for example, information, evaluation of quality of construction materials, and the procedure to be followed for acquiring very large amounts.

16. The Institute of Organic Chemistry takes an active part in the work of the Chemical Lyceum in Moscow, which provides unique training. The Institute provides the Lyceum not only with lecturers but also with equipment and facilities for training in a very wide range of disciplines.

17. The Moscow Information Centre RAS-STN was established by the Institute of Organic Chemistry. It makes available the databases of the International Scientific and Technological Information Net, which include chemistry, the biological sciences, geology and related sciences, energy engineering, engineering, mathematics, physics, and thermodynamics. There are also databases with information on institutions, sources of financing, programmes and proceedings of conferences, etc. The Institute of Space Research is establishing a Telecommunications Centre to improve Russian communication networks, using the technology of its own integrated digital network.

18. The issue of part-time (secondary) employment has particular significance for RAS scientists. First, many economists and information scientists can very often add to their professional qualifications and apply their knowledge in practical work. Second, the knowledge gained from such work can often be applied to their principal job, and this makes the transition back to normal scientific work very smooth. For the most part, those engaged in such activities are relatively young.

19. The Committee for University Education estimates that as many as 200 000 managers and specialists with university education require retraining, while nearly a million people need

skills upgrading. In 1992, universities were able to meet only 9 per cent of the need for upgrading of skills and retraining.

20. In the 1988-89 budget, allocations for higher school development constituted 1.6 to 1.8 per cent of expenditure. More than three-quarters of these funds were used for current expenditures and approximately 9 per cent for purchases of equipment and for fixed capital investment. In 1990-91 the amount allocated to university-type educational institutions under the auspices of the Committee for University Education was increased from 1.5 to 4.4 billion roubles, but given the high rate of inflation, real allocations were more than halved. In 1992 spending for higher school was 2.7 per cent of the state budget and allowed educational institutions to cover 30 to 40 per cent of essential costs.

21. In 1992, salaries of the very large numbers of teaching staff in educational institutions was less than half and sometimes only a third of that of their colleagues in other CIS countries.

22. According to the Committee on University Education of the Ministry of Education, more than 8 billion roubles were needed to repair unsafe buildings and to finish construction that had been started previously; in 1992, 2.2 billion roubles were planned (26 per cent of the 1991 level) and some 1.7 billion were actually allocated.

23. Even today, half of the officially registered unemployed are specialists with technical school or university-type education; the young are particularly threatened.

24. Owing to Government Decree N 326 of 13 March 1987, "On increasing the role of technical institute science in order to accelerate scientific and technical progress and to improve the quality of specialists' training".

25. In 1992, 10 to 15 per cent of total admissions (3 000 persons) at Moscow State University were involved in an experiment with paid education. There is also an interesting experiment to set up higher schools with advanced learning programmes; for example, a higher school of management was opened at the Moscow Institute of Electronic Equipment. In 1992 alone the latter received revenues of 940 000 roubles, a sum close to what was received by the Institute from all other paid education for principal specialties (1.1 million roubles).

26. Russia's Goskomstat data show that in 1992 more than 4 billion roubles' worth of unrealised R&D were lost in technical institutes. The sum almost equals the total of all higher school spending in the 1991 state budget.

27. In the period 1987-91, more than 20 per cent of doctors and candidates of sciences left Moscow University's physical and chemical faculties.

28. In 1992, 18 scientific and technological parks were operating on the territory of the CIS, 13 of which are located at Russian technical institutes, *e.g.* Moscow University, the Moscow Institute of Energy, the Moscow Institute of Electronic Equipment, as well as technical institutes in St. Petersburg, Tver, Saratov, and other Russian cities.

29. Binitech has already financed the powerful lasers department of the General Physics Institute of the Russian Academy of Sciences for the development of technologies of interest to American companies. It is planned to unite all the design departments of the Academy under a holding company.

30. The spatial distribution of Russian science is examined in the light of the 73 regions (in accordance with the political and administrative division of the territory as of 1 January 1992) and 34 big cities.

31. The surrounding territories are in this case the regions, territories and republics, whose capitals (centres) are the investigated cities.

Chapter V

State science and technology policy: formation and implementation

1. Management of science and technology

The previous science and technology management system was based on rigid plans and decisions of the Communist Party Central Committee and the Council of Ministers. In the transition to the market economy, the former system is being abolished and greater independence is being granted to enterprises and organisations. The role of the state, in the field of science and technology as elsewhere, is being drastically reduced; at the same time, it is acquiring new features, as the command administrative system is replaced by economic and programme-oriented management methods.

Present policies are aimed at creating the necessary economic and political conditions for the active involvement of science and technology in the reorganisation of the national economy. These include:
- increasing the role of legislative bodies in R&D management;
- a fundamentally new role for administrative bodies, which will formulate and conduct state policy within the framework of, and in accordance with, economic and legislative regulations;
- active use of the market as a regulator of economic development and efficiency, which is only possible by exploiting the achievements of science and technology.

Under these conditions, it is possible to create a new management system for science and technology. Key to its successful functioning are the rejection of rigid planning and management mandates and of all-encompassing government orders, along with the adoption of comprehensive legislative, political, economic and social principles as the basis of regulation.

A brief outline of the present management system is presented in Figure 5.1. *The Supreme Soviet of the Russian Federation* is the highest legislative, managerial and supervisory body. Its functions include:
- identifying the main principles, orientations and objectives of state S&T policy;
- elaborating legislation to regulate R&D and its interaction with other spheres;

Figure 5.1. **State-Public regulation in the science and technology sphere in Russia**

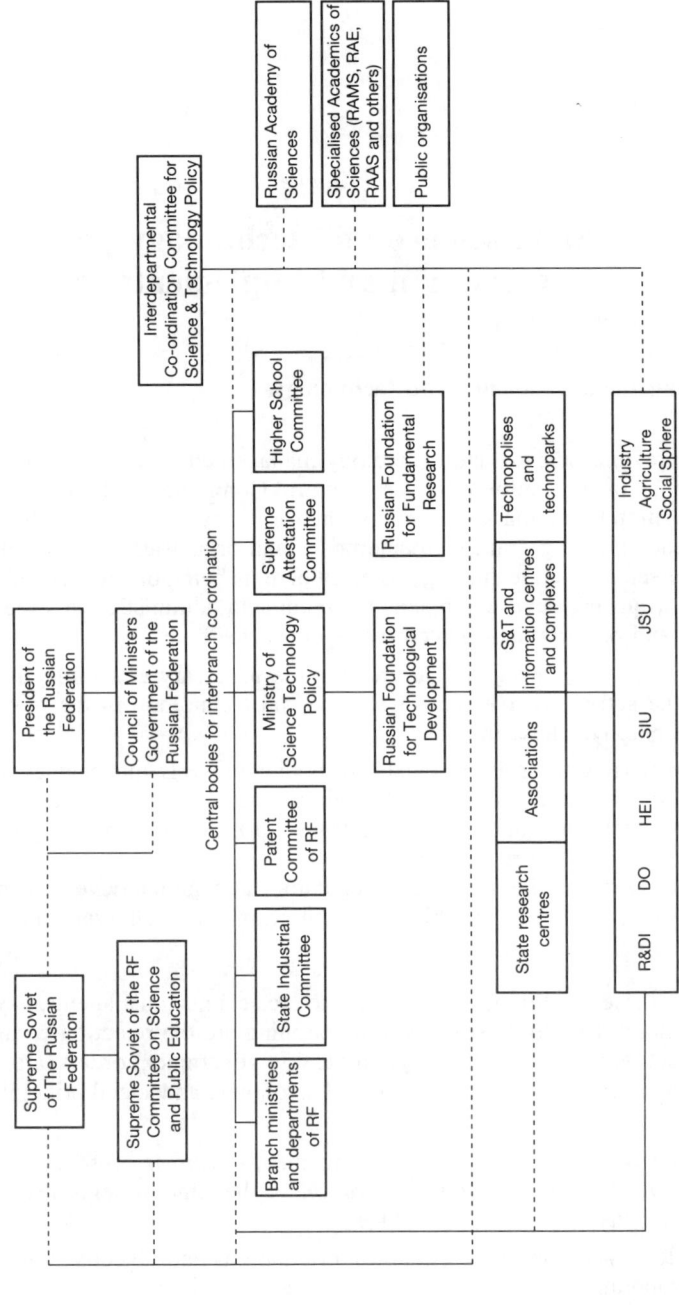

- approving science and technology priorities and state S&T programmes, along with the amount and terms of their financing, and appointing the state bodies responsible for their implementation;
- determining the size of the Russian Federation's R&D budget, including allocations for basic research and for implementing S&T development priorities;
- establishing a system of credit, financial, tax, customs and other privileges in the S&T sphere;
- supervising the implementation of state S&T policy and the spending of appropriations.

The Supreme Soviet's Committee for Science and Public Education examines materials on the aforementioned questions (enlisting experts when necessary), drafts resolutions on these questions, and submits them to its parent body. The Committee also oversees adopted resolutions from the point of view of their efficiency and controls the implementation of state S&T programmes and budget.

The new system for managing S&T should include annual review, by the Supreme Soviet, of a special government report on S&T policy, so that it can specify the basic orientations of the latter, draw up a list of federal programmes, determine their annual budget allocations, the size of direct federal budget funding of research organisations and the financial resources to be channelled to state funds for S&T, as well as determine the economic preferences that encourage S&T activities.

The *President of the Russian Federation*, who embodies the supreme executive power, directs the work of the Council of Ministers of the Russian Federation. Advisory bodies can also be set up under the direction of the President for preliminary consideration of national problems and the preparation of proposals for solving them.

In compliance with legislation, the *Council of Ministers* (the government) of the Russian Federation adopts practical measures for science and technology, that is:
- It implements state S&T policy on the basis of, and in order to execute, the laws of the Russian Federation, the resolutions of the Congress of People's Deputies of the Russian Federation and the Supreme Soviet, the President's decrees and orders; and it elaborates and carries out measures to maintain and develop S&T resources.
- It approves the distribution of budget appropriations for R&D among ministries, departments, scientific organisations, state S&T funds and customers of federal S&T programmes.
- It prepares, for submission to the Supreme Soviet, proposals concerning S&T priorities and federal S&T programmes; it chooses which state management bodies are to be entrusted with elaborating these programmes, also for submission to the Supreme Soviet; and it oversees their implementation.
- It provides for the creation and development of advanced organisational structures needed to implement the S&T priorities.
- It establishes and controls funds for basic research and technological development financed through the budget and other sources.

- It elaborates and manages the economic, legal and organisational mechanisms for encouraging S&T activities in individual enterprises, associations and other organisations by means of direct and indirect support.
- It develops international S&T co-operation.

The Secretariat of the Council of Ministers has a special department responsible for S&T development.

The recently created Interdepartmental Co-ordination Committee for Science and Technology Policy co-ordinates the efforts of various state bodies in order to identify and implement state S&T policy with respect to issues of national importance and generates proposals concerning S&T priorities. The Council of Ministers has approved the statute of the Committee and its composition, which includes representatives of federal and regional executive bodies of the Russian Federation and representatives of various scientific communities (eminent scientists and experts). The Committee is administered by the Ministry of Science and Technological Policy.

In the management of science and technology, the Council of Ministers relies on state administrative bodies and interacts with non-government S&T organisations. State administrative bodies participate in the implementation of S&T policy as provided for by existing legislation.

The *Ministry of Science and Technological Policy* is the central federal body responsible for developing and implementing state S&T policy. The Ministry:
- organises jointly – with the Russian Academy of Sciences, sectoral academies of sciences, the Ministry of Economy, and other central federal bodies – national S&T prospective planning, and prepares proposals for S&T priorities and a list of programmes for implementing them;
- provides for the management and co-ordination of state S&T programmes, for the competitive selection of promising research projects, and for the subsequent development of relevant advanced technologies and demonstration prototypes; it also acts as a state customer for these programmes and oversees their implementation; and it takes part in the elaboration of federal, international and regional programmes;
- submits proposals to the government for the state funding of basic research and the science infrastructure;
- works to improve economic mechanisms for promoting research and innovation;
- elaborates proposals for improved legislation in the field of science and technology;
- organises international S&T co-operation;
- develops the S&T information network, and the training of scientific and educational personnel.

In its work the Ministry of Science and Technological Policy interacts with appropriate central legislative and executive bodies of the republics incorporated into the Russian Federation.

The *Ministry of Economy*, as the main body for carrying out state economic policy:

- provides for the co-ordination of structural, investment and S&T policy, national economic and S&T programmes, for concentration of state financial, material and technical resources in order to ensure broad diffusion of basically new equipment and technology as well as the manufacture of science-intensive products;
- jointly with the Ministry of Science and Technological Policy and other ministries, makes proposals and drafts the programme for restructuring the national economy on the basis of S&T achievements, in order to submit those materials to the President and the Supreme Soviet of Russia; it also makes proposals for the funding of the aforementioned programme.

The sectoral ministries and other federal bodies concentrate their activities on implementing state S&T policy and on supporting individual enterprises, associations and organisations that carry out S&T programmes in corresponding areas.

The Russian Academy of Sciences, the Russian Agricultural Academy, the Russian Academy of Medical Sciences and the Russian Academy of Education play an important role in the implementation of state S&T policy, particularly in basic research. These *academies* were established on the basis of the corresponding academies of the former USSR. Unlike federal ministries, they are high-level, self-administered scientific organisations guided in their activities by the legislation of the Russian Federation and by statutes adopted at general meetings of their members.

The main tasks of the academies can be exemplified by the Russian Academy of Sciences whose objectives consist in providing for:
- conducting basic research that promotes the economic, social and cultural development of Russian society;
- promoting Russian science and integrating academic, higher school and sectoral science;
- training highly skilled personnel;
- conducting applied research and forming and developing science-intensive branches of the economy;
- participating in the drafting of state resolutions on S&T development and in the elaboration and evaluation of major scientific, technical, economic and social programmes for the development of Russia.

In 1992, the Academy of Technological Sciences of the Russian Federation was established. The aim of this new scientific association is to ensure applied research in the fields of nanotechnology, nanoelectronics and other technological sciences, as well as to provide for the progress of conversion in science-intensive branches and the practical application of S&T results.

In addition to these high-level, government-funded scientific institutions, there are also public (non-government-funded) academies, in particular the Engineering Academy of the Russian Federation. The latter unites engineers, scientists and work collectives on a voluntary basis. The Academy's role, according to its regulations, is to carry out promising R&D, to create new types of equipment, technologies and materials, to forecast S&T

development, to evaluate independent public (non-government) programmes and projects, and to assist in the implementation of promising inventions and applications.

In the formulation and implementation of S&T policy, state administrative bodies interact with the Russian Union of Industrialists and Businessmen, the All-Russian Society of Inventors and Innovators, the Union of Scientific and Engineering Associations and other public S&T organisations that include hundreds of thousands of people. Such *public scientific and technical organisations* are widely enlisted for preparing and overseeing draft resolutions in the S&T field, and for performing evaluations.

The status and tasks of such organisations can be exemplified by the Russian Union of Industrialists and Businessmen. According to its charter, the Union is a public organisation established by individuals and work collectives of enterprises and public organisations in order to unite their efforts to speed up radical economic reform. The Union promotes market structures and mechanisms, free enterprise, and the process of privatisation. It also supports the increased business activity displayed by the heads of enterprises and encourages economic and S&T co-operation.

The new system of S&T management will require: time; the elaboration and adoption of a package of laws and regulations; close co-operation between state administrative bodies, various state and non-state structures, scientists and experts; and the continuous monitoring of the effectiveness of administrative decisions and the timely introduction of improvements, when necessary. What is more important, extensive organisational work will be needed, so that the system will not only assure the preservation of national S&T resources, but will also create the conditions for further S&T development, thus allowing Russia to regain its leadership in key sectors.

2. Contents and objectives of state science and technology policy

State S&T policy, as an integral part of national social and economic policy, aims to create a favourable environment for science and technology by furnishing the legal, economic and organisational conditions that foster the growth of scientific knowledge and enhance the application of S&T results.

In May 1992 and in January 1993 the Government of Russia examined the problem of state S&T policy. It stated that economic stabilisation measures based on traditional market mechanisms (liberalisation of prices, privatisation, breaking up of monopolies, etc.) must be supplemented by effective S&T policy both for solving the most urgent social and economic problems and for more long-term restructuring of the Russian economy on the basis of the most advanced technologies.

The main elements of state S&T policy developed in 1992-93 include:
- the democratisation and decentralisation of S&T management;
- a legal basis for intellectual property rights;
- the concentration of resources on priority S&T directions and the selective support of particular research projects and organisations on the basis of the chosen priorities;

- the development of a competitive entrepreneurial environment in applied science and technology, *i.e.* the transition from departmental to intra-firm science;
- state support for military R&D conversion;
- provisions for multiple financing sources, the encouragement of foreign investments in R&D, and the integration of domestic S&T resources into the world innovation system;
- the upgrading of the quality and level of education and co-ordination of education with S&T activities;
- ensuring the development of basic research;
- restructuring of R&D, partially removed from state control;
- the regulation of R&D with regard to regional aspects;
- the social protection of S&T personnel.

3. Selection of S&T development priorities

The most important prerequisite for effective state S&T policy is the concentration of financial, material and technical resources on priority directions of S&T development.

At the present time, Russia has no legally established mechanism for identifying and implementing S&T priorities. Selection is performed, mainly, by the Ministry of Science and Technological Policy, which organises the collection and evaluation of research applications in various fields of science. For the year 1993, the Ministry presented to the Government a working list of state S&T programmes in the following fields:

- industrial technologies;
- information and communications;
- new materials;
- energy;
- transportation;
- life sciences and biotechnologies;
- health care;
- environment;
- aerospace technologies (including aviation);
- fundamental problems of social and cultural development;
- research on basic properties of matter.

The main drawback of the present practice for defining priorities is its predominantly sectoral approach. Forecasts concerning social, economic and S&T development, including those for results of the chosen priorities, are usually underestimated. The co-ordination of goals and means for reaching them have not been well worked out.

The Ministry of Science and Technological Policy has begun work on an integrated set of mechanisms for identifying priorities and relevant projects and programmes, including the development of the necessary infrastructure and information support. Given the ongoing crisis in the Russian economy, priorities should only concern the most immediate goals. These are:

- providing appropriate standards and quality of living based on the level of economic development;
- stabilising the ecological situation: first and foremost, the prevention of ecological disasters;
- saving resources and energy;
- preserving production and S&T resources in some of the key branches;
- strengthening the export potential.

The strategic social and economic goals, when choosing priority directions, include:
- ensuring national security;
- supporting market structures and relations;
- integrating the world community (with a long-term view to occupying an appropriate place in the world division of labour and attaining a new standard of living);
- supporting breakthrough (or critical) technologies, primarily, dual-use technologies, based largely on the use of the country's S&T resources, which make it possible to take leading positions on global markets;
- supporting technologies that foster either the development of other technologies or the production of goods and/or their marketing.

Taking into account these goals, forecasts of overall development and the projected results of the chosen priorities, experts should identify and prioritise key S&T orientations according to their economic importance. Priority directions should also be subject to legislative approval and should provide the basis for state support of relevant programmes and projects.

Priorities for restructuring the national economy appear to offer the most important basis for identifying S&T priorities. The draft government programme for restructuring the economy identifies the following federal economic priorities:
- fuel and energy;
- foodstuffs;
- housing;
- conversion of defence industry;
- transport and communications;
- preservation of Russia's S&T resources.

State S&T programmes are assumed to play a strategic role in implementing S&T priorities.

4. State S&T programmes

By the beginning of 1993, 38 state S&T programmes were being implemented in Russia. The list is provided in Table 5.1, which also shows the amount of federal budget funding (at current prices; for 1993, the projected financing is calculated at prices in early 1993).

Table 5.1. **Russian S&T programmes**

Programme	Budget funding, million roubles		
	1991	1992	1993 (planned at February 1993 prices)
1. Promising technologies in agricultural production	158.0	449.6	1 275.0
2. Promising technologies in agricultural products processing	36.0	362.0	1 026.0
3. Promising information technologies	60.0	210.4	601.0
4. Promising telecommunication technologies and integrated communication system	30.0	104.9	451.0
5. Informatisation of Russia	60.0	210.0	520.0
6. Promising technologies and devices of micro- and nanoelectronics	–	120.5	575.0
7. The human genome	32.0	130.5	375.0
8. Priorities for genetics	–	119.8	375.0
9. Advanced methods of bio-engineering	40.0	207.8	590.0
10. Research support means in biophysics/biochemistry and biotechnology	–	56.2	175.0
11. New materials	58.0	535.4	1 568.0
12. Environment-saving energy	66.6	400.6	1 136.0
13. Resource saving and ecologically safe technologies in mining and metallurgy	–	142.5	383.5
14. Promising technologies in the development of fuel and energy resources	8.3	70.4	455.0
15. Peoples of Russia: revival and development	9.8	79.2	224.5
16. Development of education	21.9	98.2	278.5
17. Ecologically safe and resource saving technologies in chemistry	43.4	347.4	986.0
18. New principles and methods for creating chemical substances and materials	–	140.8	399.0
19. High-energy physics	100.0	422.6	1 198.5
20. Basic nuclear physics	–	158.6	450.0
21. Synchrotron radiation, beam applications	–	125.2	320.0
22. High-temperature superconductivity	130.0	455.4	1 163.0
23. Controlled fusion and plasma processes	30.0	120.0	306.5
24. National priorities in medicine and health care	71.0	306.4	819.0
25. Health of the population of Russia	15.2	66.5	434.0
26. Creation of new pharmaceuticals using methods of chemical and biological synthesis	–	75.0	439.0
27. Global environmental and climatic changes	50.0	220.7	667.0
28. Safety of the population and economic installations with allowance for risk of natural and technological disasters	40.0	180.0	508.0
29. Integrated research on oceans and seas, on the Arctic and Antarctica	80.0	381.2	1 150.0
30. Stroyprogress	50.0	295.0	837.0
31. Wood production and forestry management	10.0	143.1	598.0
32. Advanced technologies and machinery	75.0	375.9	1 083.0
33. Science-intensive technologies	–	39.9	113.5
34. High-speed environmentally safe transport	50.0	200.4	568.0
35. Highly effective technologies in the development of the social sphere	16.1	55.2	350.0
36. Federal S&T data bank	–	–	250.0
37. Development and use of space vehicles for science and economy	40.0	8 720.0	39 000.0
38. Civil aviation development	–	10 641.0	30 220.0
Total	1 381.9	26 768.8	91 868.0

Within the framework of the above-mentioned programmes, 4 000 projects selected on a competitive basis from more than 30 000 applications are being carried out in 1993. The largest programmes in terms of financing are:
- Development and Use of Space Vehicles for Science and the Economy (1993: 39 billion roubles);
- Civil Aviation Development (1993: 30.2 billion roubles);
- New Materials (1993: 1.6 billion roubles);
- Promising Technologies for Agricultural Production (1993: 1.3 billion roubles).

To speed up scientific research and put results on the market, foreign partners are being actively invited to participate in state S&T programmes. In 1993, R&D is expected to be undertaken on more than 300 international projects involving partners from over 30 countries of Europe, Asia and the Americas.

From the point of view of their status, the state S&T programmes of Russia are high-level, federal, target-oriented S&T programmes and are intended to perform a wide range of promising basic research and hence to stimulate the development of science-intensive industries.

The government procurement agency for state S&T programmes is the Ministry of Science, except for the programmes for developing and using space vehicles and for developing civil aviation, for which the government procurement agencies are the Russian Space Agency and the Ministry of Transport, respectively.

Special scientific councils are set up for organising the implementation of the state S&T programmes.

Programmes are evaluated on a open competitive basis by the scientific councils, which, on the basis of the results, present to the Ministry of Science their recommendations on particular projects (together with relevant contractors). The programmes are financed through the federal budget and also through the budgets of various ministries, agencies, associations, individual enterprises and customer organisations (on a cost-sharing basis, among others).

In 1992, in the course of implementing the state S&T programmes, hundreds of types of new equipment, technologies and materials in all S&T fields were developed and advanced to the pre-production stage as blueprints and experimental prototypes that either meet or surpass world standards or conform to the most advanced domestic achievements. All these new S&T products were intended to help in restructuring the national economy, solving important social problems, saving resources, substantially increasing labour productivity, improving the quality of products, achieving successful import substitution, and creating a competitive export potential.

The programmes implemented by intersectoral S&T complexes are another means of focusing the efforts of R&D, S&T, engineering and production institutions on intersectoral research priorities. Since 1986-87, 24 such complexes have been established: three in the Ukraine and 21 in Russia. Of the Russian ones, 16 are located in the Moscow region, three in St. Petersburg, one in Novosibirsk and one in Vladimir. They include about 600 organisations, of which 346 are research institutes, 96 are research and production associations, 39 are design bureaus and 104 are production associations. Since

1986, these complexes have developed over 750 types of new equipment, technologies and materials.

The state S&T programmes, as well as other S&T programmes (basic, sectoral, regional, etc.) including the main intersectoral and international R&D projects, remain the key instrument for implementing state S&T policy. Recently, new draft regulations concerning state S&T programmes have been drawn up for submission to the Council of Ministers. They have already undergone an independent international study.

5. S&T policy in key industries

Production and S&T resources of key industries

The dynamism of S&T development and the technological level in key industries (metallurgy, energy, chemicals, wood, machine building, construction materials) largely determine the general technological level of the national economy. In Russia, these industries form the largest share of national industry and determine many aspects of other industries' development. In 1991, they accounted for 87 per cent of all capital assets, 78 per cent of employment, 78 per cent of total production.

State S&T policy for the key industries envisages:
- direct state support for research areas in which Russia has achieved world-class results and its leadership is acknowledged by the world community (aerospace equipment and technologies, new materials, biotechnologies, etc.);
- support for research areas that address the priorities for restructuring the key industries.

As the orientation towards raw materials has increased, demand for the S&T output is less and less in demand.

Analysis shows that resource-saving technologies have disseminated very slowly, and replacement of obsolete technologies may take decades, thus resulting in resource-intensive production, an excessively large raw materials sector, and a chronic technological lag (developed during the 1970s and 1980s).

In the key industries, the percentage of dilapidated capital assets is very high. With worn-out, outmoded, and obsolete equipment accounting for 43.3 (and up to 43.8 per cent in heavy industry) of all industrial equipment, the key industries display the following trend: power industry, 43.8 per cent (against 41 per cent in 1985); metallurgy, 44.3 per cent (against 43 per cent in 1985); machine building, 42.7 per cent (against 41.1 per cent); and chemicals, 52.1 per cent (against 44.8 per cent in 1985).

The metallurgical industry is now witnessing a decline in the production of some promising types of products. The machine-building industry has seen a decline in the production of programmed control devices for all types of technological equipment. The chemical and wood industries have reduced the output of synthetic fibres and filaments. Domestic refineries are able to process only 70 per cent of the oil that is extracted, and, of that amount, the technology used can only extract 65 per cent of the products contained in it. According to our calculations, science-intensive production has dropped both overall and in the key industries.

In recent years, the efficiency of S&T in key industries has been declining, as data showing a steady decrease in the number of new types of equipment demonstrate. In 1991, the number had decreased by more than half from 1985; the number of new automated devices dropped by 66 per cent over the same period. The same was true for all types of technological equipment: numbers of new electrotechnical prototypes dropped by 54 per cent, of chemical and compressor equipment, by 40 per cent, of transportation and parts handling equipment, by 62 per cent, etc.

This trend is likely to continue in the near future, due to the decline of technical demand and the lack of R&D innovations and/or highly skilled personnel, unless appropriate measures are taken to preserve and develop national science. More refined state regulation of R&D is needed to ensure continued production and adequate utilisation of S&T resources for innovation.

Main orientations of S&T policy in key industries

With respect to the key industries, S&T policy must work to transform the technological structure of production and use advanced technologies to solve social and economic problems. The first concern is to develop new technologies in order to build up the national capacity for export of high-technology products; the second is to assure the broad introduction of technologies that can ensure high quality products, ecological safety and resource saving. State S&T policy must also recognise that in order to avoid the destruction of the domestic technological complex, it is necessary to support its most viable part and provide for its competitiveness and ability to export.

Support should be provided for the production of machinery that is likely to be in great demand on the domestic market, *i.e.* machine tools and welding equipment, heavy – especially metallurgical – equipment for machine building, energy, electrical engineering, the automotive industry, and agriculture.

Some custom-designed machines (*e.g.* very powerful presses and machine tools for the manufacture of extremely large components) also seem to be highly competitive on foreign markets.

In order to help integrate key industries into world markets the state will need to ensure:

- the creation of the infrastructure for marketing industrial products and technologies (patent and licensing activities, information banks);
- regulation of external trade in intellectual products;
- means of attracting foreign capital, perhaps most effectively by creating S&T centres and technological parks.

The State will have to make all possible additional efforts to solve the problem of financing sectoral science, because any further decline in production may lead to a substantial reduction of financial support for sectoral S&T. Enterprise spending on R&D is likely to be reduced in the near future by at least 50 per cent.

In the key industries, special funds for developing new science-intensive equipment, obtained by a levy of 1.5 per cent on production costs, may provide a significant source of R&D finance. However, in the near future, the state is likely to remain the only sponsor of science. When the economic crisis is over, new sources of comprehensive financing may arise.

If applied R&D is to be possible, it will be necessary to break down departmental barriers, so that science and industry can be integrated in newly established economic and organisational institutions (research centres, technological parks, technopolises). Technological parks may be especially suitable in large cities and centres of the defence industry. Unlike technoparks in other countries, which are mainly associated with university research centres, technoparks in Russia may be based on military R&D centres.

6. The evaluation of R&D

Evaluation is one of the most important elements of state S&T policy. Present Russian laws and regulations distinguish between state, departmental, independent and judicial evaluation. For instance, the bill "On state science and technology policy" contains a special article which states that independent evaluation is an integral part of R&D and is to be conducted at all stages: in formulating priorities, setting up and supervising S&T programmes and projects, as well as for competitive awards.

Foreign organisations, scientists and experts may be enlisted in this work. Evaluation procedures and the responsibilities of examiners are regulated by a special federal law. For example, the Ministry of Environment and Natural Resources organises and ensures the evaluation of various environmental approaches, programmes and foresight planning. Some other state institutions have the same functions, among them the State Committee for Sanitary and Epidemiological Control, the Russian services of the Federal Control of Nuclear and Radiological Safety and the Federal Mining and Industrial Control, and the Russian Scientific Commission on Radiological Protection.

According to some estimates, there are more than 43 000 expert organisations in the S&T sphere. At the grass-roots level, these are the nearly 38 000 scientific councils of various types that act as consulting bodies for the top management of R&D, engineering and other organisations (enterprises, firms, institutions). At the top of the administrative hierarchy – in government, parliamentary and presidential structures – some 500 units, located either within the parent body or acting as a permanent or *ad hoc* commission or working group, play nearly the same role.

The grass-roots level generally evaluates scientific work for its innovative and practical value or its technological and economic importance, usually via peer review. As the administrative hierarchy grows, organisational, legal, social and political aspects are being added to the purely S&T and economic ones. Analysis and evaluation of programmes are being included as well. Specialised expert councils are also being established within the framework of state structures. These councils are entitled to evaluate qualifications and their conclusions may provide a basis for the decision of other competent bodies (including judicial). For example, the Supreme Attestation Committee prepares recommendations jointly with relevant organisations, using the results of evaluations of S&T programmes and projects. To provide for the scientific evaluation of dissertations and for granting scientific degrees, the Supreme Attestation Committee establishes expert councils consisting of leading scientists and experts in technology, education and culture.

It should be noted that the mechanisms and rules of expert work are still rather vague and that each decision-making body prefers to use its own structures and rules for evaluation.

An ever-increasing influence on decision making is being exerted by public opinion and by independent studies. State authorities tend to make ever greater use of the latter to determines what types of scientific, economic and technological activities are most likely to be criticised. For example, on this basis, the government ordered that three federal ministries should revise the terms and deadlines for the construction/reconstruction of nuclear power stations in the Saratov, Voronezh, Cheliabinsk and Sverdlovsk regions, and the Ministry of Environment was ordered to make an ecological evaluation of projects for constructing nuclear power stations.

At the present time, the number of independent experts is rising rapidly, as new consulting firms, associations, and interest groups emerge. For instance, four large firms with foreign capital participation (JV Vneshconsult, Continental-invest, Expertec, and Ernst and Young Vneshaudit) have formed a powerful Association of Consultants on Economy and Management with over 70 member companies in Russia and other CIS countries.

Overall, the problem of the effective evaluation of R&D appears to be a social infrastructure problem. In today's Russia, the most important features of R&D evaluation are its independence, objectivity and precision. In terms of organisation, there are two interacting systems, one defined by strictly scientific evaluation by scientists, the second by scientific evaluation in the context of decision making that directly or indirectly influences the management of R&D. At the same time, an independent evaluation system is being established. The independence of the evaluation is subject to verification and confirmation by a state body.

7. Regional S&T policy and development prospects for regional R&D

The growing independence of the Russian Federation's territorial constituents is having a powerful influence on the formation and implementation of state S&T policy at the regional level. The former distribution of industrial and S&T resources, with its intrinsic disproportions, is proving inappropriate for the market economy, as it reflected centralised management and financing rather than the logic of economic development. Therefore, for the regions, the main S&T policy priority is the creation of favourable conditions for the smooth transformation of regional S&T resources, as part of the overall restructuring of economy, and for the solution of social and economic problems of the regions and of the Federation as a whole. The implementation of such policy presupposes an active role for federal administrative bodies and their close interaction with regional bodies.

In accordance with the Federative Treaty, general issues of education and science are the joint responsibility of federal administrative bodies and the administrative bodies of the republics of the Russian Federation. The previous administrative system had no mechanism to provide for interaction among federal and regional bodies for implementing S&T policy, and such a mechanism has yet to be created.

Work on regional S&T policy formation and implementation is assured:
- At the federal level, by the Ministry of Science and Technological Policy, which has established a joint Interdepartmental Council on Regional S&T Policy with the Russian Academy of Sciences. The Ministry plans to appoint its representatives in regions with a high level of science and education.
- At the regional level, by special administrative units (committees, departments, directorates) within regional administrations (republic governments). Local organisational structures (regional scientific and co-ordination centres and councils, regional centres of the Russian Academy of Sciences, etc.) are to be used and given appropriate powers.

The financial mechanism to be used to implement state S&T policy at the regional level includes partial decentralisation and regional differentiation of the use of R&D budget funds, as well as the creation of non-budget regional funds for R&D.

The Federal Fund for Regional Science and Innovation, created in 1993 under the auspices of the Ministry of Science and Technological Policy, should become a catalyst for co-operation between the Ministry and regional administrative bodies. It will receive 1 per cent of the total R&D budget. In co-operation with the Councils of Ministers (governments) of the republics, the heads of territorial administrations, regions, autonomous regions, autonomous districts, and the cities of Moscow and St. Petersburg, the Ministry has begun to create a network of regional S&T development funds that are to collect revenues from various local sources as well as part of the resources (1 to 5 per cent) remitted by regional enterprises to federal non-budget funds.

With the emergence of independent actors in regional management, with the partial transfer of state property to regional owners, with incorporation and privatisation, the problem of regional R&D financing will become increasingly acute because, as a rule, the former local budgets had no separate provisions for R&D funding.

At the present time, it is difficult to assess the prospects for regional development of R&D, because of the need to reassess the whole question of state regulation of R&D. There are several important considerations.

First, while mining-oriented regions seem to have the possibility of maintaining at least the science that concerns the region directly, science was rather neglected among regional priorities in the past and little used by the relevant industries. Thus, in the short term, support for science from local sources is not likely to be greater than in Russia as a whole.

Second, regional R&D policy is of special importance in the main areas subject to conversion. Military R&D will remain under federal authority, and the role of local authorities will only be minor and occasional.

Third, the motivation for local support of R&D in regions with especially significant S&T resources (Moscow, Moscow region and St. Petersburg, in particular) is low, owing to the traditionally outward orientation of their R&D. Only 13 per cent of research performed in Moscow in 1989-90, for instance, met local needs. The R&D of these regions will have to be divided into federal and municipal property, since they cannot support the full R&D sphere and will naturally choose to support region-oriented R&D. The prospects for outward-oriented regional R&D will be determined not by the scale of state R&D support, which is likely to be quite modest in the next few years, but rather by the evolution of the market economy and by the penetration of market relations into different areas of activity, and in particular, into the R&D sphere.

8. Legal framework for S&T and innovation activities

The transition to a market economy revealed serious incompatibilities between existing legislation and the new terms of management for science and technology. In the past, S&T and innovation activities were subordinated to the requirements of an essentially administrative management system. There were no laws similar to those that regulate R&D in "Western" countries. However, there were many regulatory acts, which impeded the development of initiative, self-management and creativity in the areas of R&D.

As Russian legislation was rewritten following the collapse of the USSR, science and technology were influenced by new provisions, incorporated into the Constitution of the Russian Federation, concerning the protection of intellectual property, the freedom of scientific work, and the right to receive and disseminate information. The Law on the Council of Ministers (Government of the Russian Federation) stipulates that its core competence includes measures for developing science and technology.

In 1992, several laws were enacted that provide for the legal protection of a number of objects of intellectual property, namely: the Patent Law, the Law on Trademarks, the Law on Legal Protection of Software and Databases, and the Law on Legal Protection of Integrated Circuits Topology. In 1993, the Copyright Law was adopted.

Some provisions of the above laws are consistent with international legislation, in particular, the convention establishing the World Intellectual Property Organisation, the Bern Convention, the provisions of the Universal Declaration of Human Rights that specify the protection of authors' rights to research results. New legislation envisages lifting limitations on copyright provisions in R&D contracts and providing greater possibilities for an author's control over the use of R&D results. Legislation has also been envisaged to increase responsibility when copyright and other intellectual property rights are violated. Enactment of these laws will promote the introduction of better market relations into R&D and the development of international co-operation.

A number of tax and other privileges for organisations and enterprises engaged in R&D and/or in developing advanced equipment and technologies have been also stipulated by legislation.

Another area of legislation affecting R&D is represented, in particular, by the federal Law on Delivery of Products and Goods for State Needs and the Presidential Decree, "On measures for the establishment of the federal contract system". These laws, adopted in 1992, set the general legal and economic framework for solving federal problems and for implementing social, economic, S&T, environmental and other programmes. Further government regulations specified more precisely how they would be implemented.

The Law on Conversion of the Defence Industry in the Russian Federation helped settle a number of problems in the field of defence R&D, as it established the terms for exporting and re-exporting military hardware and technologies.

The most pressing S&T problems are addressed by presidential decrees and government decisions. Among them are the decrees "On urgent measures for the preservation of S&T resources of the Russian Federation" and "On the creation of the Russian Academy of Agricultural Sciences" (adopted in 1992) and the government decision "On the Russian Fund for Fundamental Research".

All the aforementioned Acts, although they address important issues, nonetheless have a fragmentary character and are weakly connected with each other and with legislation as a whole. Thus, at present, there is no legal definition of science, of the status of a scientist or of a scientific organisation, nor are there clear criteria for separating basic from applied science. Due to the legal imprecision of these notions, there can be no unequivocal interpretation of some provisions of tax legislation, in those cases where the right of this or that organisation to benefits is unclear. The most serious problem is the incompatibility of some decisions with the level of competence of the state bodies that have made them. It is further aggravated by the absence of a clear-cut legal separation of power among the different state bodies acting in the R&D sphere. As a result, the present legal basis for S&T and innovation activities essentially constitutes an obstacle to developing R&D.

The goals and main orientations in the restructuring of the legal basis for S&T and innovation activities are determined by the ongoing radical changes in social life. The leading factors are:
- the strengthening of the legal basis of the state, and the emergence of new political and organisational structures;
- the development of federative relations and the definition, in this connection, of the competencies of the federation and its subjects in the field of S&T management;
- the social orientation of S&T;
- the new economic environment and the economic independence of S&T and innovation organisations;
- the establishment of intellectual property and the emergence of a S&T products market;

- democratisation in the field of S&T management and innovation activities, the generalisation of self-management and democratic control over S&T;
- the breaking up of monopolies and the demilitarisation of R&D;
- the new feature of international and interstate co-operation in the field of S&T and innovation activities.

At present, it is most important to develop a legal basis for using economic methods for managing S&T and innovation activities and, in the first place, to develop contract law.

It is of the highest priority, in 1993-95, to implement a programme of immediate measures in preparation for new laws for regulating the R&D sphere and modifying those already in force.

The Law on State S&T Policy would be of very great importance for S&T. It should define the attitude of the State towards S&T activities, clarify the basic provisions of S&T policy and identify the administrative bodies in charge of implementing the latter, the responsibilities and powers assigned to these bodies, the order of their interaction with the public, and the forms of state support for S&T activities in the market economy.

The legal basis for the development of market relations in science and technology should take into account the fact that the marketing of scientific intellectual property must be an integral part of the national economy. Besides the laws already adopted in this field, laws are planned on copyright, know-how, and the protection of commercial secrets. The Civil Code of the Russian Federation will be supplemented as regards the right to own innovations, inventions and other products of S&T activities.

Present legislation on enterprises and entrepreneurship does not provide a solid legal basis for R&D institutes and design bureaus, nor for business S&T activities. For this reason, laws on scientific organisations and on the status of researchers are urgently needed. They would make it possible to start real privatisation of S&T intellectual property. A law on innovation activities to regulate the activities of different innovation structures (foundations, engineering and business centres, etc.) is planned.

The transition to predominantly economic methods of administration and management will be accompanied by the development of contract relations, which also requires relevant legislation.

Chapter VI

The economic environment of R&D

Changes in economic mechanisms for realising policy goals in the field of science, technology and innovation have occurred in three major stages.

The first stage, prior to 1987, may be described as a period of state monopoly over the introduction of technological innovations into manufacturing. There was an almost complete absence of economic incentives for creative scientific activity, and there was strict state control over sources of financing and stimulation of R&D.

The second stage (1987-90) saw scientific institutions switch to self-supporting management. Results of S&T research were declared a commodity that could be sold at negotiable prices. Profits became a principal source of funding for scientific institutions and their main financial incentive. Relatively stable budget financing and obligatory allotments of money to special funds for economic and S&T development were maintained.

The third stage began in 1991 with the gradual and, since 1992, rapid conversion of all industries to a market structure. It has been accompanied by the lifting of virtually all restrictions on the redistribution of profits within enterprises, by a certain decrease (due to the rise in prices) in the budget financing of R&D, and by a slight shift of emphasis in state R&D management to indirect methods, including fiscal regulation.

This transformation of the mechanism of the economic regulation of S&T development proceeded against the background of disinterest in innovation on the part of the manufacturing sector, of a non-competitive economy, and of regulatory measures inadequate to the actual economic situation.

1. Mechanisms for financing R&D

Under the command economy, R&D was financed from the following principal sources: state budget appropriations; centrally managed funds of ministries and agencies; funds of individual enterprises collected through imposed allocations to decentralised special-purpose funds, and expenditures for R&D provided in enterprises' estimates of costs. During the last five to seven years, sources of financing have undergone both quantitative and qualitative changes.

In 1992, of the overall budget R&D expenditure (over 100 billion roubles), 46 per cent were allocated to financing of priority areas for S&T development, 51 per cent to the programme for preserving the scientific resources of Russia, and 3 per cent to the Russian Fund for Fundamental Research.

In 1993, state budget support of R&D is distributed among federal purpose-oriented (and international) programmes, the Russian Fund for Fundamental Research, the programme for preserving the scientific resources of Russia, and regional scientific programmes.

Nominally, state budget support increased by several times in 1992 as compared to 1991. However, due to inflation, average wholesale prices grew in 1992 by 2 200 per cent, according to information from the Central Bank of Russia. As a result, budget support of science, as measured in comparable prices, has actually decreased. The same is true for 1993, and the amount of R&D financed through the budget continues to decrease.

In sectoral R&D institutions, this has meant a narrowing of the range of scientific research and a move towards design and engineering work. The spread of various highly profitable side-line services (mass production by pilot plants, rental of space) and the deterioration of scientific resources, aggravated by the lack of incentives to innovate, are also among the results.

Before 1991, state S&T was regulated on the basis of the so-called "voluntary-obligatory" nature of innovation. Enterprises, all formally independent as regards the rate and direction of their development, were influenced by the State in two ways. On the one hand, the disposal of their own assets was regulated through a system of allocations to the fund of economic stimulation and to the fund for the development of production, science, and technology. The latter was used, in particular, for carrying out R&D and for financing the development and dissemination of new machinery. On the other hand, state assignments to renew products, state orders for S&T development, and pricing mechanisms that stimulated (at least nominally) the manufacture of "new" equipment created conditions for an influx of industrial investments into R&D.

In 1990-91, measures were taken to reform this economic mechanism. Regulations concerning enterprises' allocations to the Fund for Economic Stimulation were revoked. Centralised sectoral funds were abolished, and the system of wages and salaries, as well as the system of price formation, were substantially liberalised. As a result, motivation to develop and master new equipment slackened. At the same time, factors that impeded the introduction of innovations strengthened rather than weakened. Inflation forced enterprises to allocate a good deal of their assets to consumption, and the disintegration of economic ties aggravated problems of materials and technology procurement for new production.

After the pre-1990 system of administrative-departmental financing of science collapsed, it became necessary to improve the system of multi-source funding by creating non-budget R&D funds and by providing favourable conditions for involving private capital and commercial banks in the funding of R&D and innovation projects.

Government regulations provide for the establishment of non-budget funds for R&D in order to ensure funding for sectoral and intersectoral R&D. Enterprises and organisations can include R&D expenses in production costs (not to exceed 1.5 per cent of the cost of production), subject to the reallocation of these expenses to special funds established in relevant ministries, agencies, concerns, corporations, and associations. Governments of the republics incorporated into the Russian Federation are advised to establish similar funds; they already exist in Udmurtia, Yakutia and some other republics. However, cities with large concentrations of scientific institutions, such as Moscow and Novosibirsk, do not yet enjoy this right.

The Russian Fund for Technological Development has been established to provide special-purpose financing for S&T programmes and projects aimed at application of key S&T results of special importance to the State or to industry groups. It receives resources from ministries, agencies, concerns, etc., 25 per cent of the special funds mentioned above, and voluntary contributions from legal and natural persons.

The Chairman of the Board, who is the first Vice-Minister of Science and Technological Policy of Russia, supervises the Fund. The Board's composition is approved by the Minister of Science and Technological Policy on the basis of the Chairman's recommendations.

Initially, resources were transferred irregularly to the Russian Fund for Technological Development; by the end of 1992, it had received 1.3 billion roubles, but by mid-1993 the amount had risen to 3.9 billion roubles. By 1 July 1993, 102 R&D contracts for a total of 2 billion roubles had been concluded. The contracts cover a wide variety of research areas, ranging from metallurgy to machine-building, electronics, agriculture, medicine and ecology, and all are intersectoral in nature.

In compliance with the Presidential Decree, "On urgent measures for preserving the S&T resources of the Russian Federation," the Russian Fund for Fundamental Research was established. Its Charter was approved by the government in November 1992. The Fund's mandate includes: supporting challenging basic research projects carried out by small research teams and individual scientists; providing assistance to research organisations and higher education institutions in developing their material and technical base; awarding grants and scholarships to the most gifted young scientists for postgraduate studies, training in research centres, and participation in scientific meetings (conferences, symposiums, etc.) in the Russian Federation and abroad; giving special grants for the publication and purchase of scientific literature and for the establishment and maintenance of scientific contacts.

Resources of the Russian Fund for Fundamental Research derive from state appropriations (3 per cent of budget expenditure for science) and voluntary contributions from enterprises, institutions, organisations and citizens, including foreign legal and natural persons.

The Fund's financial support is not subject to reimbursement. Resources for R&D projects are awarded on a competitive basis, regardless of the applicant's legal status, sector of work, age, scientific degree and administrative position. Candidates are obliged to publish the results of studies financed by the Fund, thereby making them available to all.

Grants and subsidies from international organisations are of the greatest financial and psychological importance to the Russian scientific community. For example, the International Foundation "Cultural Initiative" allocated more than $2 million in 1992 to research projects performed by Russian researchers in physics, biology, mathematics, economics, etc. However, until recently, assistance and investments from abroad have been hindered by the instability and the weakness of Russian legislation, in particular as regards taxation, customs duties, and intellectual property.

The state should ensure adequate support for the most advanced sectors of science and concentrate funds on the most valuable and vulnerable aspects of R&D, thereby promoting a limited range of key S&T programmes aimed at reaching both current and long-term objectives of national development. The mobilisation of multiple sources of financing and the creation of a favourable climate for the development and operation of such programmes would contribute much to this end. In the following section emphasis is placed on indirect, "climate-forming" methods of financial stimulation in the S&T sphere; methods of direct regulation are reviewed in Chapters III and IV.

2. Indirect stimulation mechanisms

The system of taxation is the most important instrument of indirect stimulation. In Russia, it includes 15 federal taxes, four republic taxes, and more than 20 local taxes. The most significant, from the viewpoint of their impact on the economic conditions for the activities of R&D organisations, are the value added tax (VAT), tax on profits, property tax, and land tax (land rent).

The VAT is a federal tax, and all receipts from it, according to the Law on Principles of the Taxation System in the Russian Federation, are to be transferred to the federal budget. However, in 1992, from 20 to 30 per cent of the total sum of VAT proceeds were in fact transferred to local budgets, those of national republics within the Russian Federation, and those of territories, regions, etc.

In 1992, the turnover of goods (excluding imported ones), services, and finished products was liable to VAT throughout the entire territory of Russia. The rate was 28 per cent, or 21.88 per cent in the case of regulated prices. Late in 1992, a preferential 15 per cent rate was introduced for some foodstuffs.

The tax on profits of enterprises is also a federal tax, but the receipts are distributed between federal and local budgets. The rate in 1992 was 32 per cent (except for exchanges, brokerage firms, and enterprises' earnings from transactions by intermediaries, in which cases the rate was 45 per cent). The federal budget received 13 per cent, while the local budgets of republics, territories, and regions received 19 per cent.

The property tax is a republic tax. The receipts are distributed in equal shares between national (ethnic) and territorial administrative units according to the place of residence of the taxpayer. The tax rate is determined by the laws of the republics, territories, regions, etc., and in 1992 the maximum tax rate was limited by federal legislation to 0.5 per cent of the taxable property base (the value of the assets of an enterprise).

The land tax is a local tax levied separately for agricultural and non-agricultural land. The tax rate on urban land is determined federally on the basis of average rates, according to economic regions and categories of cities. At the local level, average rates are set according to the location and value of the land for urban development. The annual land tax rate ranges between 0.5 and 4.5 roubles per square metre depending on the economic region and the category of city. In 1992, the average legal land tax was doubled. Taxes were also raised by applying coefficients of 1.5 to 8.0 in health resort zones, are 2.0 to 20.0 in cities and regions of historical importance.

According to Russian legislation, tax exemptions approved at the federal level are binding over the entire territory. In addition, local authorities may introduce exemptions for selected categories of taxpayers within the tax revenues allocated to their budgets. Thus, it is only for VAT that exemptions are made exclusively at the federal level. As for property tax, land tax and the greater part of tax on profits, incentives given by means of tax exemptions lie mainly in hands of local authorities.

As an instrument of state regulation, the taxation system is constantly being transformed, in line with the dynamic changes in Russia's economy. By the beginning of 1992, the use of tax policy as an incentive for R&D and innovation activities had not been activated, and R&D institutions continued to be treated like other categories of taxpayers. Sums allotted for R&D, technological design and experimental models, as well as earnings obtained through innovation services, were liable to the value added tax at the non-preferential rate of 28 per cent. Exemptions from VAT were only applied to state-funded R&D and to contract R&D conducted by institutions of public education (including higher schools). Activities connected with granting, obtaining and transfer of patents, copyright, and licences were also exempted.

The impact of VAT on scientific activities is not confined to the obligation to pay tax on purchases of basic assets for which the R&D institutions are final consumers. There are further consequences. First, VAT artificially increases the price of R&D products and thus further reduces the present low demand for R&D, with the result that R&D institutions must sometimes lower prices and therefore lose profits. Second, there is a time lag between payment of VAT for purchase of materials and the receipt of the tax when the product is sold, a delay that is especially lengthy for scientific and innovative activities. This further complicates the financial situation of R&D institutions and forces them to seek loans, for which the interest rate is presently very high.

The system of taxes on profits of enterprises and organisations does not offer any benefits for either innovation or S&T activities. Profits from sales of S&T products are taxed at the standard 32 per cent rate, which is applicable to all categories of taxpayers regardless of type of activity.

The procedure, adopted by the government, of including production and marketing costs in the cost price of a product, makes it possible to recover the following S&T-related costs:

- non-capital costs related to improvement of technology and organisation of production and to improvement of product quality, longevity, reliability and functioning;
- expenses related to inventions, including testing and experimental work, manufacturing and testing of experimental models and prototypes;
- amortisation of intangible assets (patents, licences, software, know-how, etc.) at rates calculated on the basis of their initial costs and service life.

At the same time, enterprises' expenditures for developing new technologies and for improving those already in use, for improving the quality of products, for mastering new kinds of raw and processed materials, and for retrofitting equipment are not included in the cost of the product. However, R&D activities that are taken into account in the selling price of S&T products include the purchase and/or manufacture of special equipment necessary for conducting contract work. The issue of including in the sales price expenses incurred by R&D organisations for the support of postgraduate courses has yet to be resolved.

Tax exemptions designed to reduce taxable profits by the amount of the cost of assimilating new equipment and technologies have only been used to stimulate innovation in small enterprises (for science and science services, "small" means enterprises with a maximum staff of 100 employees). Relevant activities include conducting R&D developing new methods and documentation for introducing advanced management technologies. Given that the purchase of new equipment, components, materials and know-how are included in the cost of production, they also benefit from tax exemptions.

Tax privileges for investments in fixed production assets, widely used throughout the world, were also introduced for small enterprises and for some industries and branches (oil and coal mining industries, medical equipment, pharmaceuticals and foodstuffs, among others).

In addition to the tax on profits and the VAT, institutions that conduct S&T work, with the exception of state budget organisations, pay the property tax on an equal footing with other organisations and, except for forestry and agricultural research institutions, the land tax. This has particularly affected scientific organisations that possess unique and costly equipment or occupy a great deal of land due to the nature of their activities (testing grounds, experimental stations, etc.). For example, the All-Russian Research Institute of Railway Transport has to pay, for 1992, land rent of 158 million roubles, or 53 per cent of the total cost of its research work. Almost 70 per cent of the earnings of the Moscow Radio Engineering Institute went for property tax, and the situation is similar for many other R&D institutions.

In 1992, a number of direct and indirect measures were taken to mitigate the economic problems of R&D institutions. In particular, they were granted the following privileges:
- exemption from VAT for R&D financed by the Russian Fund for Fundamental Research, the Russian Fund for Technological Development, and by non-budget funds established under current legislation by ministries, agencies, and associations;

- exemption from property tax and land tax for research institutions, enterprises and organisations of the Russian Academy of Sciences, the Russian Academy of Medical Sciences, the Russian Academy of Agricultural Sciences, and the Russian Academy of Education;
- exemption from land tax and tax on profits for institutions of higher education for profits allocated for developing educational and scientific activities and improvement of their material, technical and social infrastructure;
- exemption from property tax for state (federal) scientific centres.

Tax privileges have clearly defined recipients, and they are largely granted on the basis of two criteria: the source of R&D funding and the organisational-administrative affiliation of the R&D institution. Other organisations, if included in a special list approved by the government, can also enjoy privileges with regard to property and land tax. In 1992, 759 R&D institutions were exempted from property tax and 586 from land tax on this basis. Tax privileges thus granted amounted to some 7.2 billion roubles (estimated). In May 1993, the government approved the list of R&D institutions exempted from property tax for the current year; it includes 843 organisations, and the amount of exemptions exceeds 4 billion roubles. In September 1993, the list of R&D institutions exempted from land rent is expected to be approved. Exemption from taxation has also been accorded for grants provided to Russian researchers by foreign bodies and individuals.

All organisations, enterprises and associations that import equipment, instruments and materials for R&D and production purposes paid from central hard currency funds have been exempted from payment of customs duties. A Procedure of Customs Clearance of Goods, which allows prompt notification of exemption of goods purchased through funds for the support of basic science from customs duty, has been adopted.

As an incentive to innovative activities, an allowance was introduced that reduced taxable earnings in the amount of dividends paid to physical persons when the dividends were reinvested in technological modernisation and redesign of production facilities, including R&D. However, these individual measures do not alter the overall situation, as most R&D institutions are currently liable to standard taxation, and their situation depends on changes in tax legislation that affect all taxpayer categories.

Changes that have taken place in 1993 have indirectly fostered the growth of demand for S&T products and contributed to the improvement of the economic position of R&D institutions. Among them, the following are worth mentioning:
- reducing the standard VAT rate from 28 per cent to 20 per cent;
- introducing the possibility of paying the VAT over two years when purchasing fixed and intangible assets;
- providing for the possibility of reducing taxable profits by expenditures for productive and non-productive capital investments (provided that the amounts of depreciation calculated are spent wholly for this purpose).

Given the low level of competition in the present economic environment, however, these allowances are unlikely to lead to substantial growth of innovative activities in enterprises. Rather, capital assets are likely to be renewed at the present technological level.

A doubling of the property tax rate should be listed among recent negative changes. In addition, in 1993, it is anticipated that the share of profits spent on salaries and wages, when it exceeds twice the regulated ratio of remuneration to cost of production, will be more heavily taxed. Given the persistent growth of R&D production costs and the limited ability of R&D institutions to increase profits through pricing, the gap between the average level of wages in R&D and in the production sphere may further increase, thus acting as an additional impetus for skilled personnel to abandon science. In general, the changes introduced in the taxation system in 1993 do not indicate purposeful strengthening of its incentive function as regards S&T and innovation activities.

Other potential instruments of indirect stimulation have also remained virtually inactive. Loans are not accessible to R&D institutions because of high interest rates and their short-term character, and because there are far more efficient commercial projects. Commercial banks that are supposed to finance R&D retreat under the burden of taxes and inflation and fund scarcely 1 per cent of R&D.

As to accelerated depreciation, it is reserved mostly for massive replacement of dilapidated and obsolete equipment and requires approval from the Ministry of Economy and the Ministry of Finance. The increase in the absolute figures for depreciation deductions, which is due to the re-evaluation of fixed assets and the establishment of adjustment coefficients, does not keep up with the current inflation rate.

In the transition period, the main objectives of state regulation of R&D development must be support for raising the technological level in various sectors of the national economy and the preservation of national R&D resources.

Budget restrictions (in terms of direct expenses and budget revenue cuts due to various indirect benefits) require the reduction of privileges and preferences for research projects that are not relevant to the solution of the tasks mentioned above and a concentration of resources that encourages efforts in high priority directions.

A system of measures oriented towards supporting technical upgrading of industries might include the following:
- The procedure for granting tax benefits for capital investment financed from profits (adopted in 1993) must be modified. For this purpose, the innovation and the investment constituents of re-equipment measures should be strictly separated. The first should embrace processes connected with the development of new technologies and the updating of existing ones and with raising the quality of products, and should be co-ordinated with R&D (performed by the enterprise either on its own or on a contract basis). The second should include the process of retrofitting and renewing fixed assets.
- Profits invested in production should be exempted from taxation only when the investment is for the introduction of equipment and technologies included in special lists. Such lists should be compiled by experts and include very promising advances that have proved their efficiency and are ready for industrial application.
- Budget revenues restored through reduction of tax-exempt areas should be accumulated, on a goal-oriented basis, in special sectoral investment funds to

provide resources for reduced interest loans that allow enterprises to master new equipment and technologies from the same lists.
- It may be appropriate to concentrate a part of enterprise resources allotted to non-budget funds to the above-mentioned investment funds for use in ensuring S&T assistance to investment projects.
- Indirect incentives to enterprises that are renovating their production "according to the lists" might include granting them the right to reduce, for a period of two or three years, their taxable profits by an amount equal to 30 per cent of the earnings obtained from the sale of products manufactured by means of new technologies.

Indirect incentives can be used both to create economic protection for, and to stimulate investment flow into, the R&D sphere. Economic protection can be ensured by releasing all R&D institutions (regardless of their administrative affiliation) from property tax and land tax payments; by maintaining the present tax exemptions for profits spent on capital investment; and by including the expenses of research in the cost of production. In addition, bonuses for high-level R&D achievements should not be paid out of the sum for salaries.

To encourage investment, enterprises should be granted the right to write off R&D expenses, regardless of their type, and to include them in current production costs. More substantial privileges can be envisaged for implementing radical innovations. In particular, the profit tax might be reduced for a period of two or three years by a sum equal to 30 per cent of the profit obtained from implementing developments based on discoveries, inventions and other approaches that satisfy patenting requirements.

It would be advisable to introduce:
- full tax exemption for the share of profits allocated by enterprises and commercial organisations for joint financing of priority R&D directions;
- three- to five-year "tax vacations" for profits obtained from implementing priority projects (beginning when profits are declared);
- a three-year tax exemption, beginning when profits are declared, for dividends received by investors in a given project.

A differentiated approach to indirect stimulation of R&D is conditioned by the nature of the present transition period. With the further growth of competition in the Russian economy, incentives appropriate to a mature market economy may be invoked.

3. Reorganisation and privatisation in the R&D sphere

Sectoral organisation was and still is the basic structural foundation of Russian science. Russian R&D is divided among a small number of extremely monopolistic branches, each with its closed reproduction cycle. The most typical entity is a large monopolistic R&D institution closely linked to its sectoral parent body and virtually independent from the rest of the scientific community. This system is based on "leading"

R&D institutions, and under the administrative system, technological monopoly is inevitably associated with sectoral management.

In the new economic environment, R&D institutions need more flexibility in order to respond rapidly to new challenges. But the restructuring of R&D management and funding will require some time. This is why a package of measures favouring adaptive processes in the R&D sphere must be adopted and an appropriate organisational-economic environment must be ensured for bodies that will function under market conditions.

Optimal reorganisation schemes can vary considerably from case to case. In particular, some R&D institutions may be transformed into associations of small venture enterprises; centres for the collective utilisation of scientific instruments and equipment may be created from several specialised R&D institutions; and R&D institutions may acquire additional production facilities in order to facilitate the commercialisation of their results. Specialised R&D institutions that conduct R&D mostly for one customer might be merged with the latter into one scientific and industrial firm.

Large R&D institutions with a monopoly in a given area of knowledge can become centres for contractual research. They should become "incubators" of new knowledge and technologies. Close co-operation between such centres and educational institutions should be fostered: joint projects, creation of technopoles, exchange of qualified personnel, allocation of educational and production facilities for training purposes, etc. Groups of sectoral R&D institutions might be transformed into R&D consortia as a rational way to carry out expensive, highly specialised R&D for a limited number of enterprises.

To ensure an uninterrupted innovation cycle, it would be advisable to create corporate and association-like structures for integrating several enterprises and organisations that develop and manufacture related products.

Major institutions that possess unique research capabilities, unique experimental facilities and highly skilled personnel should be transformed into the state (or federal) research centres (SRC) that are being established in compliance with the Presidential Decree of 22 June 1993. SRCs are a special type of state research institution, which will co-ordinate strategic long-term state priorities for the development of the most important S&T goals, on the one hand, and attend to the economic and social interests of S&T performers, *i.e.* research teams and individual scholars, on the other.

Among the priorities that should be considered as nation-wide goals of the SRC system are:
- maintaining and developing scientific, technological, and intellectual resources in the main S&T fields, including support and development of renowned research schools;
- performing integrated basic research, development, and engineering in the most important S&T areas for maintaining world-class R&D levels in the Russian Federation;
- providing for possibilities of exerting state influence on the development of selected S&T areas, with due regard for the strategic and tactical targets of state S&T policy.

The restructuring of the R&D sphere has only begun in 1993 and is likely to last for two or three years. The issue of privatisation takes on special importance for the process of reorganisation. At present, privatisation in S&T proceeds in accordance with the rules provided by the State Programme of Privatisation of State and Municipal Enterprises of the Russian Federation and the Presidential Decree "On organisational measures for reorganising state enterprises and voluntary associations of state enterprises as joint stock companies". These regulations give close attention to various types of auctions and commercial competitions involving enterprises and shares. Both auctions and competitions are supposed to contribute to the process of political and financial stabilisation by maximising the revenue (including privatisation vouchers) obtained from the sale of different enterprises.

According to the above-mentioned documents, the institutions that are not liable to privatisation include: budgetary scientific institutions and those rendering science-related services; R&D institutions of the patent, standardisation, metrology, cartography, geodesy and hydrometeorology services and environmental control and protection agencies; R&D institutions carrying out work in the area of fusion and radioactive materials, nuclear weapons, and space vehicles; and unique assets stored in archives and libraries.

Considerations of national security currently require a prohibition against, or control over, privatisation of some types of R&D institutions. Their future privatisation, however, is not altogether excluded, as the State may waive its ownership rights and move to a system of licensing in those areas.

R&D institutions dealing in weapons systems and components, munitions, explosives and pyrotechnics can only be privatised through special governmental decision. By 1 May 1993, 37 R&D institutions were privatised by a government decision, including the Soyuz S&T complex, the Tupolev aviation complex, the All-Russian Institute of Light Alloys, and the Moscow Research Institute of Radio Communications.

The State Committee for Property of the Russian Federation has delegated a considerable part of its authority to its territorial agencies, and for the majority of R&D institutions, it is the territorial agency that actually decides on privatisation. This makes the privatisation process in science uncontrollable. Taking into account the general trend of selling property at auctions (including property voucher auctions), serious losses of R&D resources seem inevitable.

The present methods of privatising large industrial R&D institutions may lead to the collapse of well-established and potentially viable scientific complexes. To take a concrete example, the fixing of the charter capital size for transformation into joint stock companies depends not only on the value of the enterprise's property (at 1991 prices) but also on its current financial position. As a result, a large research and production association with 6.5 hectares of territory and ten laboratory buildings was recently evaluated at the trifling price of 20 million roubles.

The well-known error, which consists in non-critical application to R&D of forms and methods of regulation originally elaborated for material production, is being repeated. Privatisation in science must be regulated by a special programme based on principles which take into account the specifics of this area of activity and contain the prerequisites for the effective reorganisation of the R&D sphere.

The main distinctive feature of the S&T sphere is the existence of intellectual property that is closely tied to the bodies to be privatised, a factor that is not taken into account in fixing the book value of the property involved. Yet this is extremely important for the privatisation of a specific institution and for determining the appropriate forms and methods of privatisation.

The main goals of privatisation in the S&T sphere should be:
– enhanced productivity of S&T activities through more efficient distribution of property rights;
– the preservation of real S&T resources;
– the creation of a competitive environment and the promotion of R&D "demonopolisation";
– the involvement of reliable investors.

In the present economic situation, there are usually two main reasons behind a buyer's interest in the privatisation of R&D institutions:
– the commercial attractiveness of premises occupied by R&D institutions and supplied with office equipment, communications facilities, computer hardware, etc., to be used for other activities;
– the availability, at pilot plants of R&D institutions, of modern multi-purpose equipment, which may be used to manufacture products of commercial interest (provided that the R&D institution's fixed assets are its most valuable feature).

Thus, the privatisation scheme must exclude such forms as auctions and commercial competition, which afford hidden opportunities for changing the profile of an R&D organisation after commercialisation. In general terms, the most appropriate privatisation scheme for R&D institutions is incorporation as part of the open sale of large packages of investment shares. In this case, an R&D institution that is privatised will receive additional financial resources of an exclusively investment character. On the one hand, this will contribute to the development of its research potential; on the other, the S&T sphere as a whole will receive much needed additional funds to support its most viable components.

Proposals of the Ministry of Science and Technological Policy have been partly taken into account in the 1993 state programme of privatisation. The programme also presupposes the elaboration of special provisions for privatisation in the S&T sphere. A draft has been prepared by the Ministry, but it has not yet been approved by the highest authorities.

Chapter VII

The climate for innovation

1. Innovation activities prior to reform

Prior to the current reform, the state financial regulatory mechanism, characterised by compulsory and mobilisation-type practices, acted as a natural regulator of innovation. Large-scale innovation was performed exclusively by the State. Rapid mobilisation of national effort was assured by concentrating and centralising huge resources. This type of innovation produced the illusion that R&D results were essentially low-cost, in that the State had good control over their implementation, and that the interests of individual economic actors were insignificant and negligible. This eventually resulted in poor innovation performance and a decline in R&D effectiveness.

In the pre-reform period, the main actors for innovation in the USSR were: research and production associations, intersectoral S&T complexes, and various state S&T information services. Research and production associations were established in the mid-1960s in order to introduce the newest accomplishments of both science and engineering. They brought together major scientific research institutes, laboratories, and design offices. There were about 70 in 1970, 105 in 1975, 200 in 1980, and 230 in 1991. Most were complete research, production and economic complexes. Although their member institutions had a certain amount of independence, were financed from different sources and offered different material incentives to their personnel, the unified system of management, financing and planning of both scientific research and production provided nevertheless for an integrated process. The associations had, as a rule, rather powerful and well-equipped pilot production facilities, which allowed them to manufacture and test prototypes quickly and, sometimes, to produce small batches of new equipment. In general, they were up to their innovation-oriented mission.

Intersectoral scientific and technical complexes were intended to integrate science with industry on a broader basis than the research associations. The incorporation of scientific research institutes, design offices and pilot/mass production plants into the scientific complexes was expected to shorten the time from scientific ideas to finished products. The complexes were established as problem-oriented economic units for solving large-scale innovation problems that exceeded the limits of departmental interests. As of January 1988, there were 23 of these complexes operating in the USSR. With the collapse of the state, the decrease in the number of military orders, and the many political and economic changes, the complexes broke up into independent enterprises and virtually ceased to develop new generations of equipment.

The state offices of scientific and technical information offered a developed communications network for disseminating documented innovations. They were structured hierarchically (All-Union, branch, regional, local levels) and sectorally (on an economic/ branch basis), and had the following chief functions: the dissemination of S&T accomplishments and know-how at the interbranch, branch and regional levels and in large organisational structures (such as national economic complexes); the accumulation, systematisation and analysis of effective methods of commercialising new equipment; the staging of public demonstrations and exhibitions of new technologies and equipment in the country and abroad (including permanent expositions at the Moscow Exhibition of Achievements of the National Economy).

On the whole, this offered a unique system whose effectiveness depended essentially on the State's ability to exert strict control over the R&D sphere. Russia has managed to retain a large part of the information banks and information centres that support innovation activities. However, the Russian government no longer maintains this costly system, and it is likely either to disappear as a monopolistic system for information on innovation or be transformed and become part of the information infrastructure of the innovation market.

2. The innovation environment in Russia in 1993

As regards the climate for innovation, Russia has a considerable amount of promising preliminary R&D results, highly qualified personnel, and a sometimes unique R&D base. However, all these national resources are very poorly oriented towards practical ends.

The main factors that have contributed to the present situation seem to be the collapse of the USSR, the move by enterprises to a cost-accounting (self-supporting) system, and awkward privatisation and conversion practices.

When the USSR collapsed, co-operative ties among enterprises were broken, thereby destroying many technological networks that cannot be recreated within Russia itself. Russian scientific institutions have practically no opportunity to sell their products to industrial enterprises in Ukraine, Belarus, and other republics.

The political and economic fragmentation has meant that legislation on intellectual property rights adopted in the former Soviet republics varies considerably. In 1990, over 16 000 Soviet patents were valid in 50 foreign countries. By the beginning of 1993, more than 12 000 had lapsed owing to the lack of hard currency resources for paying annual fees. Thus, many innovations lost patent protection despite the fact that many still retain their technical novelty and topicality. In some of the former Soviet republics, the patents are invalid, and this deprives the developers of their author's rights.

The switch of enterprises to a cost-accounting (self-supporting) system facilitated their self-determination as independent economic actors. However, because of the absence of essential structural changes in the national economy, the State remains the monopolistic owner and the major source of financing for R&D. Profit taxes imposed on R&D institutions have substantially reduced both their own financing of R&D and purchases of new equipment, and the low rate of depreciation accorded does not encourage the modernisation of the R&D experimental base.

When profitable (or readily transformable) enterprises were privatised they were separated from the design bureaus and research institutes with which they had previously been integrated, and research associations and scientific complexes rapidly broke up.

The lack of a constructive state conversion policy adds to the uncertainty of the overall situation. As mobilisation plans have not been cancelled, heads of enterprises consider it their fundamental role to maintain the country's defence potential and to preserve the scientific and engineering personnel and the social infrastructure of the enterprises. Conversion appears all the more difficult because of high bank credit rates, lack of adequate information about the needs of civil branches, and the lack of adequate state investments. Thus, conditions for innovation in large enterprises subject to conversion are not favourable. The only suitable solution is small-scale innovation based, as a rule, on previous R&D results transferred to civil technologies. However, in comparison to the available potential, these options for innovation are so insignificant that the development of high technologies in Russia is irreversibly dying off.

One positive note is that some conversion enterprises are going into the civil market, as the quality of their products is well above that of the civil branches. For example, the R&D resources of the research and production association for metrology allow the latter to enter the market for telemetry communication facilities, measuring devices and transducers, as well as alarm and protection systems. In the sectors that require these products (*i.e.* railways, aircraft and automobile transport, oil and gas industry, medicine and public health services) there are no plants with a comparable scientific and engineering level. This encourages civil innovation activities by the research and production associations but may be insufficient for generating scientific knowledge.

In the present transition period, innovation processes in industry have further slowed, mostly due to the lack of assets for renewing fixed capital. In the 1980s the rate of renewal fell behind the rate of removal from service by 32 percentage points, but in the 1990s, the gap between the two reached 47 points. In 1980 the degree of wear of fixed production assets in the Russian economy was 30.3 per cent, but in 1990 it reached 41.9 per cent in the economy as a whole and 49.8 per cent in industry, *i.e.* as much as half were actually worn out. An examination of 15 S&T organisations in the Moscow region (1992) showed that the degree of dilapidation of buildings and constructions also averaged 50 per cent. The state of the experimental base and the infrastructure of R&D is also unsatisfactory: over 40 per cent of research institutes and design bureaus in machine building have no pilot production plants.

3. Small businesses

A comprehensive analysis of small-business activities in the field of innovation is not possible, because innovative small businesses are not covered separately in the available statistical data.

Small ventures are launched mostly by scientists and other specialists whose previous experience helps them manage innovation activities. Due to lack of initial capital and to high rates of bank credit, small ventures are established mainly on the basis of the state-owned enterprises where their key personnel formerly worked (and often continues to work). As a result, they can use the production capacity and equipment of the "parent" enterprises, as well as their previous scientific and engineering results, without breaking well-established co-operative relations. The management of the state enterprises usually resists this development and allows it only under threat of losing highly qualified personnel. Virtually none adjust themselves to the changing situation; as a result, technoparks and R&D incubators are rarely set up.

There is a new tendency towards merging innovation and business enterprises, which seems to be attributable to a higher propensity to innovate on the part of business enterprises. This is especially true for business enterprises founded by graduates of technical institutes, who are also buying up privatised R&D enterprises.

Table 7.1 presents the main indicators of small-business activity. R&D employees in small businesses (Table 7.2) are mainly (over 66 per cent) part-time and contract employees.

Over the last five years, the organisational forms of small ventures has kept changing in line with changes in relevant legislation. Prior to 1991, they existed mainly in the form of co-operatives and youth centres for S&T activities. Since 1991, most small ventures have been registered as open and closed joint stock companies, limited liability companies or private enterprises.

Small-business innovation activities can be illustrated in more detail by the example of the St. Petersburg region (results of a sociological survey). In 1991, there were 240 small S&T ventures in St. Petersburg proper and 24 in the St. Petersburg region, with 2 700 and 200 employees, respectively; in 1992, there were 577 small ventures (77 in the region) (Table 7.3), which produced up to 10 per cent of the area's total S&T output.

Table 7.1. **Activities of small ventures in science and science services**

	Number of small ventures	Number employed[1]	Turnover (thousand roubles)
Total	7 071	478 450	4 344 472
Percentage	100	100	100
Of which:			
Scientific research	2 537	142 877	1 700 641
Percentage	35.87	29.86	39.14
Engineering and commercialisation	3 820	292 944	2 204 613
Percentage	54.02	61.22	50.74

1. Including those who work on contract.
Source: *Science in Russia*, 1991, Statsbornik/TsISN-Moscow, 1992.

Table 7.2. **Employment in R&D small ventures at the end of 1991**

	Total R&D	Of which:	
		Scientific research	Engineering and commercialisation
1. Total	478 450	142 877	292 944
2. Per venture	68	56	77
3. Employed:			
Staff workers	141 274	42 499	87 725
% of total	29.6	29.8	29.9
Part-time employed	42 776	16 040	21 854
% of total	8.9	11.2	7.5
Employed on contract	294 400	84 338	183 365
% of total	61.5	59.0	62.6

Source: Information issue 1, Moscow, TsISN, 1992, p. 24.

There are three general types of small ventures, engaged in:
- predominantly innovation activities (R&D, development and design of innovations, development and dissemination of software products): over 30 per cent of the total number of small ventures examined;
- services (such as agency, commerce, consulting, personnel training, servicing new equipment): around 40 per cent;
- manufacture of high-technology products: 10 per cent.

In 1991, 80 per cent of small ventures were state-owned (formed either by separating out divisions of research institutes, design bureaus and research and production associations, or by contributing state property to the registered fund); in 1992, only 74.8 per cent were state-owned. In 1991, of all the small ventures, 7 per cent undertook only R&D, and over 30 per cent combined innovation activities with manufacture and provision of services. In 1992, the figures were 9.8 per cent and 31.6 per cent, respectively. Of 172 small innovation ventures, 38 provide the full cycle from applied research to commercialisation of new products and provide personnel training.

The manufacture of high-technology products which require considerable investment is not attractive to entrepreneurs, due to the unstable conditions of taxation and the overall political and economic situation. Because of the low volume of sales and low revenues, small ventures are very prone to bankruptcy, and a special regional system of insurance against commercial risks is therefore necessary.

The goals and strategies of 30 small ventures surveyed in St. Petersburg are presented in Tables 7.4 and 7.5. Their priorities indicate that they are still in the process of formation, and they face relatively weak competition (Table 7.6). Nevertheless, 60 per cent of them plan measures to enhance the competitiveness of their products. The goals

Table 7.3. **Performance of small ventures in the St. Petersburg region at mid-1992**

Percentage of total number of small ventures

	All small ventures	Including those engaged in		
		Innovation	Innovation and services	Innovation and manufacturing
By amount of work (at 1990-91 prices):				
Below 100 000 rbl.	11.7	5.9	4.3	5.3
0.1 to 1 million rbl.	75.0	82.3	87.1	57.9
1 to 2 million rbl.	10.2	11.8	8.6	15.8
Above 2 million rbl.	3.1	–	–	21.0
Total	100.0	100.0	100.0	100.0
By type of property:				
State	74.8	75.6	73.7	71.2
Public	19.2	16.2	21.1	19.3
Joint stock	0.9	5.4	–	–
Co-operative	1.1	2.8	–	1.4
Joint with foreign partner	4.0	–	5.2	8.2
Total	100.0	100.0	100.0	100.0
By branch:				
Industry	37.4	55.3	46.0	66.2
Construction	16.6	2.6	4.0	9.9
Services	9.5	–	12.0	2.8
Science	9.8	31.6	24.0	16.9
Education	8.7	10.5	10.0	1.4
Other	18.0	–	4.0	2.8
Total	100.0	100.0	100.0	100.0

Source: Ministry of Science and Technological Policy, Innovation Department.

and competition strategies of small ventures are, in many respects, determined by their activities and the structure of their R&D.

A survey of heads of small ventures indicates that the problems that affect innovation are, in order:

- high rate of inflation;
- high credit rates;
- difficulties in obtaining raw materials and components;
- insolvency of customer organisations;
- lack of adequate information about products, suppliers, and the market situation;
- instability and imprecision, or even ambiguity, of many Russian laws, and hence, various interpretations of many legal provisions, along with the use by officials of regulations that are often inconsistent with the laws and mostly not known to employers.

Table 7.4. **Objectives of small ventures for the near future**

Percentage of total number of small ventures surveyed

Gaining prestige, increasing the level of competitiveness of products/services	60
Renewal of range of products, improving quality	56
Increase in the amount of manufacturing, search for reliable business partners	53
Finding extra financial resources, developing foreign economic links, covering new markets	47
Increasing hourly output, reduction of manufacturing costs	37
Technical improvement	33
Diversification of activities	23
Purchase of leased equipment, changing the form of property	17
Retaining the present volume of production	10

Source: Ministry of Science and Technological Policy, Innovation Department.

Table 7.5. **Competition strategies of small ventures**

Percentage of total number of small ventures surveyed

Search for new markets	77
Improving quality and competitiveness of products	70
Reduction of cost of products/services	53
Reduction of prices for products/services	43
Improvement of manufacturing processes	40
Using consulting, marketing, agency services; reduction of staff, improving the skills of personnel	23
Increase in volume of government orders; gaining subsidies and tax preferences	7

Source: Ministry of Science and Technological Policy, Innovation Department.

Table 7.6. **Level of competition in the main sphere of activities of small ventures**

Percentage of total number of small ventures surveyed

High	13
Medium	47
Negligible	35
No reliable data	5
Total	100

Source: Ministry of Science and Technological Policy, Innovation Department.

Flexible scientific and production structures of the technopark type are being actively established in Russia. Their present priorities are primarily information science, biotechnology, new materials, etc. A technopark was first established in Russia in 1990 in the city of Tomsk. It was set up by higher education and scientific institutions and industrial enterprises, including those subject to conversion. It has an incubator with some 50 small companies; they manufacture a wide range of products, from consumer goods, ointments and creams to complex diagnostic equipment for preventing accidents in chemical plants and monitoring systems for nuclear reactors.

Presently, there are 12 parks in operation in Moscow, Zelenograd, St. Petersburg, Tomsk, Saratov, Ivanovo, Vladivostok, Ufa, etc. Projects for new parks in Moscow, St. Petersburg, Krasnodar, Rostov, Barnaul, Ekaterinburg, Samara, Irkutsk, Mytishchi, etc., are under way. The Association of Scientific and Technological Parks has recently been formed, with representation from 11 out of the 15 former Soviet republics.

Science cities and technoparks cannot realise their full potential due to the lack of adequate legislation and financial support mechanisms. Even the role and place of science cities and technoparks within the state R&D framework have not yet been clearly identified, nor have measures for the comprehensive involvement of their intellectual and S&T resources in innovation activities. Finally, there are almost no specialists able to train businessmen and managers for working in technoparks and incubators.

4. Infrastructures

The present state of the infrastructure (*i.e.* means of transport, communications, information networks, etc.) is inseparable from the overall poor condition of the Russian economy, which is now in a transitional stage. In the new socio-economic environment, the old infrastructure does not promote innovation. Nevertheless, some innovation activity is still being carried out, and, as a result, a new infrastructure is gradually being put in place. In 1991-92, the old infrastructure became ownerless as the property of the former USSR was redistributed among the joint stock companies that were being formed, and between Russia and the former Soviet republics.

Means of transport and communication

A sharp reduction of state subsidies, along with price liberalisation, has resulted in exorbitant transport and communications costs. The situation is especially critical in the Russian North and Far East. Local airline fares have risen 100 to 200 times. The situation in automobile and railway transport, which accounts for as much as 80 per cent of transportation in Russia, is no less dramatic.

Prices for mail and phone communications have more than centupled and are still mounting, in some cases they exceed the rate of inflation. The quality of the services remains below European standards.

Information and telecommunications

Organisations of the former State Office of Scientific and Technical Information (including the central libraries and information distribution agencies) were not suited to market conditions. The system for distributing information collected in state information centres has become obsolete and alternative information centres are being formed. For instance, the commercial database Project, created at the Russian Institute for Intersectoral Information, furnishes information on new developments in non-standard processing equipment and provides users with technical documentation, drawings, catalogues and other materials.

Information services are also rendered by the mass media. One example is the Business World Information Bank, created in 1991 by the newspaper of the same name. It seeks to provide enterprises and organisations with data that allows them to interact without resorting to intermediaries.

The Information and Consulting Centre for Collaboration with the European Community and the Intersectoral S&T Consulting Centre Technikon are more purpose-oriented. There is also the Technology Exchange, a joint stock company established as an open commercial information system for integrating commercial and S&T information and preparing concrete project proposals.

There is a new tendency to develop data acquisition systems at the municipal level. Obninsk, for example, has set up an information system with a database network containing information on the town and its population; the municipal staff has computer workstations and computer communication with foreign partners is possible.

By the beginning of 1993, the situation in telecommunications gradually began to improve. In particular, different commercial networks are being established and operated. These are ISTOK-K, REMARK, SPRINT, SovAm Teleport, Interlink, Relcom, Glasnet, ADS, Mir and others. Defence conversion has offered new opportunities, and many satellite-based telecommunication systems that currently serve defence goals could be used (at little cost) to solve many problems in information services. The satellite systems Horizont, Molniya and others already satisfy a considerable part of the current demand for telecommunication services.

In early 1993, the Ministry of Communications invited tenders and on this basis chose the co-ordinators of a consortium for establishing a digital mobile radio-telephone communications network within Russia; the companies involved are US WEST International (USA), Intertelekom (Russia), and VART (Russia). Thus, Russia is the first East European country with a national radio-telephone network to be incorporated into the global mobile communication system (GSM) in the 900 Mhz band.

Techinfo, a joint stock company, has developed a project for a computer-assisted information system for managing Russian industry (the "Rossija" information retrieval system). A network of databases, using an integrated telecommunications and computer network, is to form the core of this system. It is realised by assembling a set of specialised fully functional subsystems. Although the network would draw on a large number of existing components (namely, state-owned and commercial data collection subsystems and databases), interconnecting them into a single system will require huge investments.

The state innovation programme "Argonaut" is intended to develop a national telecommunications network to provide the necessary database for the national financial system. Potential users of this network can be economic actors of all kinds, including enterprises, exchanges, insurance companies, banks, federal and local authorities, etc. The users are to be offered a wide range of services, through a rapid data transmission channel, via satellite, covering the entire territory of Russia and making communication with world markets possible.

However, the crisis in the telecommunications system still remains acute. Growing innovation in this field calls for an elaborate national policy and a new system of regulation. For example, state support is needed for the agreement on joint efforts by companies of different property types to create a single information clearing house.

Credit and finance

Commercial credit is presently not accessible to innovators, due to exorbitant interest rates and short repayment periods, generally of no more than six months. Under such conditions, financing of innovation activities will require special credit mechanisms. The key role here must be assumed by the innovation funds which have been set up since 1989. Among them are: the Government Innovation Fund, the Republic Innovation Fund, the Engineering Innovation Fund, the Fund for Promotion of Inventions and Innovations, and other non-budgetary funds, whose activities include financing innovation, such as the Federal Ecological Fund, the Federal Fund for Inventions, and the International Business Development Fund. However, there is a serious danger that the state funds destined for innovation processes may be used in commercial and banking operations, speculation on the securities market, etc. A significant share of funds' revenues is increasingly used by the funds' administrations for setting up private commercial enterprises that are very far from supporting innovative projects. It is hoped that this situation will be corrected in the near future. The recently formed Russian Bank for Reconstruction and Development (RBRD) is to elaborate a special mechanism for offering credit for innovation activities and to act as intermediary between international and Russian capital markets, on the one hand, and regional banks, on the other.

In 1990 and 1991, innovation projects were financed by specialised exchanges. After the adoption of the Law On Commodity Exchanges and Exchange Trade prohibiting exchanges from investment activities, the latter started to set up investment companies which, in turn, established joint stock and limited liability companies for particular innovation projects. Since the S&T resources lacked adequate state funding, the market demand for risky investment in R&D swiftly surpassed supply, thus allowing commercial enterprises more space to manœuvre when choosing innovation projects.

Inflation has significantly reduced investment in innovation (especially as regards two- and three-year programmes); only five to ten major investors, such as Binitech and Hermes, have survived. At the same time, more Russian innovations have reached external markets. However, due to lack of adequate packing and/or marketable condition, these products are usually offered at cost, and even below cost in some cases.

The stock market

In Russia, shares might offer an ideal instrument for bringing together innovators and potential investors. However, the stock market operates very poorly, due to lack of stable inflow of reliable securities. In Russia, nearly 90 per cent of shares have been emitted in flagrant violation of laws, rules of emission, and public accountability (a consequence of the careless State privatisation programme which admits of privatisation and incorporation of state enterprises that are actually or potentially bankrupt).

Furthermore, Russian investors tend to underestimate the intimate interrelation between liquidity and profitability of securities, and do not support prices and liquidity on the secondary market. In comparison with bank securities, market values of shares in investment companies appear to be very unstable. However, the situation seems to be gradually improving. As investors have gained confidence in shares of major commercial banks, trade in shares of privatised enterprises has revived, despite the peculiarities of share market behaviour under hyperinflation and the continued low price of privatisation vouchers (Table 7.7).

The Federation of Stock Exchanges of Russia plans to create a more favourable market structure, and to participate in the elaboration of laws concerning the securities market and the procedures for emitting and circulating securities, as well as in the adjustment of stock exchange mechanisms. The Federation will widely encourage the practice of public accountability and of issuers' liability for false or unreliable information, including punitive sanctions for transactions made by officials with access to confidential information, etc.

Rinaco, one of Russia's major investment companies, envisages establishing specialised investment funds to attract small investors. These would be venture funds fully adapted to investment activities, in the form of purchase of initial offerings of shares in innovation companies, allowing for failure of some projects. Rinaco was one of the first companies to conduct a large-scale subscription campaign for individuals and raised, by early 1992, a registered capital of 1.2 million roubles.

Table 7.7. **Volume of transactions on stock exchanges in Russia**
Million roubles

Month	Total	Including		
		Credit resources	Vouchers	Shares
March	3 327.5	2 107.7	752.0	175.3
April	4 180.0	2 522.0	629.0	933.9

Source: Ministry of Science and Technological Policy, Innovation Department.

Intermediaries

Agents specialised in establishing "horizontal" links among participants in innovation activities are an important element of the market infrastructure, even though the present market structures cannot fully serve the interests of companies concerned with innovation. Non-specialised commodity exchanges, for instance, cannot meet the needs of small and medium-sized innovation businesses, because they deal in a standard range of goods for average buyers. Brokers are generally unwilling to deal with small wholesale orders, which offer little profit. This reduces the role of commodity exchanges in establishing commercial relations with respect to innovation.

To some extent, this drawback is being compensated by the development of integrated agency services which cover almost all stages of the innovation cycle, from preliminary conception to commercialisation. A good example is the Centre for the Analysis of Science established in 1990. Experienced in the development and operation of continually updated databases, the Centre provides analyses of particular areas of science and engineering, conducts marketing studies prior to commercialisation, prepares business plans, examines projects, and evaluates the investment risk.

This sector of the market was initially formed by specialised S&T exchanges of which the most well-known are: Binitech, exchange of software for microelectronics; the joint venture Transelectro SPB, TIM exchange (technologies and informatisation of mechanical engineering); the intellectual property exchange House of Scientists; the Siberian scientific exchange; the Moscow Biotechnology Exchange, etc. The particularity of these exchanges is that they not only connect investors with innovators or manufacturers, they also participate in investment. It should be noted that the essence of their activities often does not correspond to their names. Thus, the International Exchange of Science-intensive and Information Technologies is a company that seeks interesting proposals at its clients' requests. Binitech, incorporating the All-Russian Technological Centre and three technoparks, uses the production facilities of the research associations Luch and Composite, leaders in the field of laser engineering and new materials. It is one of the largest commercial organisations operating on the Russian innovation market and a major venture fund.

Intermediaries oriented towards export operations constitute a special group. Formerly classified R&D institutions of the military-industrial complex and leading institutes of the Russian Academy of Sciences dispose of developments and technologies that are competitive on world markets. Business enterprises in relevant areas are seeking out these products. For instance, the joint stock company Dintsis promotes Russian products and industrial technologies on the markets of the Asia-Pacific region and offers services for patenting, evaluation and protection of intellectual property.

The joint venture Ingress acts as agent for the marketing of Russian products through US patent advisors. It selects proposals for which the American advisor obtains patent rights and negotiates for licensing or helps inventors organise joint production. The joint venture gets 10 to 20 per cent of the sum the inventor earns under the contract for the sale of know-how.

The Nort company (specialised in very new products and technologies) brings together enterprises having difficulties in finding manufacturers able to fill orders for sophisticated unique equipment and enterprises with idle manufacturing capacities. Nort's clients are offered an opportunity to choose among several potential partners. A considerable part of Nort's activities consists in placing profitable civil orders with enterprises under conversion.

The Innosoyuz company offers an example of a commercial agency. It seeks scientific organisations with new and effective R&D products and brings them together with business enterprises capable of investing in the implementation of the innovations. By now, promising projects on the manufacture of fibre optic communication facilities, technologies for reprocessing casing-head gases into high octane gasolines, etc., are under way.

Special services

Insurance of innovation activities and relevant economic actors is only beginning in Russia. The commercial insurance of small business is more developed, and the Novosist private insurance company is a case in point. It protects newly created companies against unlawful actions on the part of officials in the course of registering, licensing, and opening accounts of the companies and against unintentional non-payment of taxes. It also acts as a guarantor for bank credits on advantageous terms. Recently, companies that ensure owners, sellers and buyers of intellectual property have appeared: Rospotrebreserve, Megus, and others.

Private patent agents first appeared in 1992, but their status was only defined in early 1993. Under the new laws, only agents licensed by the Russian Patent Committee (Rospatent) can represent the interests of patent holders. They are few in number, and they cannot widen the range of their services. A private company, the Moscow Patent Office, attempts to take an integrated approach and is a pioneer in providing services for the entire duration of industrial property protection (including assessments of the effect of advertising and estimating trademark costs, etc.). (The average cost of TV commercials in January 1993 was 3.5 times the cost a year earlier, and increased an additional 2.6 times during the subsequent four months, to 620 000 roubles per minute. This means that only large commercial and financial companies can afford TV commercials.)

Public relations consulting is engaged in at present by some 20 companies, almost all of them located in Moscow. The range of their services is quite standard: organisation of advertising campaigns; creation of a "reliable company" image by means of indirect advertising; marketing studies; contacts with the press; and holding of briefings, press conferences and presentations. Few undertake the control of difficult situations, lobbying in state and commercial structures, or the adaptation of advertising techniques to local circumstances. The demand for these services has so far been minimal. The YA corporation, founded by graduates of the Moscow State Institute of Foreign Relations, the only Russian institute of higher education which provides training of specialists in public relations, is one of the leading companies in this area.

Large-scale financial consulting services are currently dominated by foreign firms attracted by an inexhaustible demand on the part of large economic actors and state authorities. The main clients are federal bodies, international financial organisations, regional and industrial associations, and large industrial enterprises which have enough hard currency resources. No small innovation enterprise can yet afford such services.

5. Standardisation and certification

The Soviet metrological base met world standards. After the collapse of the USSR, Russia found itself without a certain number of primary state measurement standards which now belong to the new independent states. The Gosstandart of the Russian Federation has developed and is currently carrying out a special programme to recover the metrological base in Russia. On 27 April 1993, the Law on Providing Unification of Measurements was adopted. It regulates the creation, adoption, preservation, use and regular monitoring of state standards. The Law on Standardisation was also adopted on 27 April 1993. The mechanism for standards that is being adopted is, in general, very similar to that of international standardisation organisations (ISO, etc.) and of industry in developed countries. (At the present time, the ISO 9000 international standards are being widely introduced in Russian industry.)

The principal elements of the above mechanism are:
- legitimacy of standardisation activities;
- participation of all interested parties in the preparation of a standard, including customers of relevant products/services;
- adoption of the standard on a consensus basis;
- publicity and availability of information about projects under development;
- combining in a standard the obligatory (human safety and environmental protection, replaceability and compatibility of products and services) and recommended requirements.

The Law on Standardisation determines: the functions and responsibilities of state bodies that exercise supervision over standards, norms and rules; the liability of state enterprises, heads of enterprises, and businessmen with respect to violation of requirements.

The certification of products was made mandatory from 1 January 1993 by the Law on Protection of Buyers' Rights. To administer the latter, a special Law on Certification of Products and Services was adopted on 27 April 1993. It sets forth the legal basis for mandatory certification, the liability of manufacturers and vendors, and the rules and responsibilities of the certification services.

The State has established and accredited 112 certification teams for different groups of products and 187 test laboratories (centres), including 43 for machine-building products, 48 for electronic and electrotechnical products, and 58 for raw and processed materials. By the beginning of 1993, certificates had been given to 320 types of products, including 97 domestic electrical appliances, 97 items of the electronics and electrotechnical industry, 51 types of raw and processed materials, and 26 mechanical engineering products. Quality control systems are being established and certified at individual enterprises; three certification teams for quality control systems have been accredited, and two quality control systems have been granted a certificate (at the Orel industrial consortium Nauchpribor and the Izhevsk machine-building plant).

According to the Law on Standardisation, the Law on Certification of Products and Services, and the Law on Providing for Unification of Measurements, the State Committee for Standards (Gosstandart) is entrusted with management of standardisation, certification and providing for traceability. It performs its functions through its regional branches and affiliated enterprises and institutions. The Gosstandart and its affiliates exercise official supervision over:
- observance of required standards in products/services not covered by mandatory certification;
- certified products/services, with a view to ensuring observance of the rules for mandatory certification;
- safety of imported products (at customs and in the course of their use or sale);
- export goods.

In addition, the Gosstandart exercises state metrological control.

The following activities of Gosstandart are financed through the federal budget:
- elaboration of national and international standards;
- establishment and management of the standards fund;
- manufacture, improvement and preservation of state primary standards;
- operation of the State Service on Time and Frequency;
- state control and supervisory activities.

The certification teams for products and the test laboratories (centres) operate at the expense of manufacturers and sellers of relevant products.

6. Actors involved in shaping innovation policy

Russia is a vivid example of the well-known management paradox: the more challenging a particular problem is for society, the more people wish to settle it to their advantage, and the further each one's effort is from a real solution to the problem. The lack of an accepted idea of how to develop innovation results in much exertion on the part of state and public structures to develop their own strategies and tactics, which they often claim represent national innovation policy. The only result so far is that many have declared their intention to formulate and implement "the only right" innovation policy, yet none has emerged that achieves consensus.

Especially noteworthy, in this respect, are the efforts of some former and present high officials in federal bodies (ministries, committees, agencies) to attempt to create a state managerial mechanism for controlling the implementation of scientific and technical achievements. The strategies set forth in official documents are not yet available to society at large but are widely circulated within the Russian establishment, which keenly feels the desire, in the present crisis situation, to return to mobilisation-type behaviour.

"Fully compulsory" S&T development would be replaced, in the transition period, by "partially compulsory" development within the state-owned sector of the economy. To this end, the commercialisation of advanced achievements obtained through state budget funding would be strictly separated from all other achievements, so that no business enterprises could profit from commercialisation of state intellectual capital. Second, "vertical" structures of R&D commercialisation would be restored in relevant ministries and departments, which should be made responsible to the State for the efficient and appropriate use of resources allocated from the state budget for R&D and for developing R&D results on an economically rational scale. Third, a state holding would be established to act in close co-operation with ministries and agencies and ensure the State's participation as a market agent for the purchase and sale of the most profitable S&T results, thus providing for the repayment of funds and the competitiveness of the state mechanism for commercialisation S&T results.

It should be mentioned that this strategy is greeted quite favourably by government officials and members of Parliament, since it gives them wide latitude for control and enforcement in the area of state innovation policy.

Public organisations such as associations of innovators are, to some extent, opponents of this "tough" policy scheme. Although such organisations are growing rapidly, few of them do really serious work. They fall roughly into two groups. In the first, industrial actors unite in order to settle common problems. In the second, diverse (heterogeneous) actors try to concentrate resources in order to solve a complex problem or reach a certain common goal.

The Union of Small Enterprises is an example of the first group. It renders all possible assistance to small businesses in Russia, protecting their legal, economic, social and other interests within official and public bodies and relevant international organisations. Examples of the second group are Technasib (based on the Academy R&D institutions of Novosibirsk), the Association for Business Co-operation (attached to the Moscow Energy Institute), Stroyprogress, the Association for S&T Co-operation in the Field of Superconductive Equipment, and the Advanced Materials Association.

In October 1990, the Russian Association for Projects Management (Sovnet) was set up as a union of working collectives of state and public organisations, co-operatives, small ventures and firms, as well as individual specialists who collaborate with each other on various projects. The association is a collective member of the International Association for Projects Management (Internet).

Besides these, the Association of Small Innovation Enterprises (Biznesinnovatsiya), the Association of Technoparks, the state association Trading House for Scientific and Technical Co-operation, the Union of Independent Engineering Organisations (Firms), the Union for Science Cities Development, etc., have recently been set up.

State authorities and self-governing public organisations have not yet formulated a legal concept of innovation management, so that their jurisdictions are defined pragmatically in the course of their work. Difficulties that arise may largely be attributed to the lack of appropriate legislation, in spite of the fact that numerous bodies within the Supreme Soviet are concerned with generating regulatory acts on the commercialisation of S&T results. For example, the legal basis of R&D commercialisation is dealt with by the Supreme Soviet committees on science and public education, on defence and security, and on industry and energy.

Given the important role played by foreign investment in innovation policy, the government is very interested in monitoring interaction with foreign investors. During 1991-92, attracting international investment (including investment in innovation projects) was the responsibility of the Committee for Foreign Investment, a small division within the Ministry of Finance, of insufficient status for potential foreign investors to take it seriously.

At the end of 1992, the Committee was transformed into the Russian Agency for International Co-operation and Development. It performs all functions concerned with Russian participation in international investment co-operation at both the government level and at the level of commercialisation, examination, co-ordination and insurance of particular projects. An information centre on privatisation-related issues is being set up. It is to inform foreign companies about concrete investment opportunities in enterprises subject to privatisation. A Tender Committee and a Technical Assistance Agency for Implementation of Joint Educational and Consulting Programmes is also to be established. The agency has arranged with the Ministry of Foreign Economic Relations to use Russian trade mission services abroad, and with the Russian Chamber of Commerce and Industry to use its regional infrastructure in major industrial centres of Russia. The Agency's Registration Office will become a centre for registering joint ventures, branch offices of foreign firms, and major investment projects.

Still, the lack of effective innovation activity is mainly attributable to the lack of appropriate legislation. The legislation of the USSR almost completely neglected this area. In 1992, the Russian Federation was wholly unprepared for regulating innovation-related activities in the newly emerged self-sufficient "horizontal" systems of dissemination and use of new knowledge and technologies. The lack of legislation for regulating certain stages and aspects of the innovation cycle is, in some cases, the only reason why the innovation cycle cannot be realised in full. In view of this, Russia will have to draft laws on innovation activities, protection of know-how and commercial secrets, recourse procedures, etc. As long as legislation is not enacted that specifically deals with innovation activities, there can be no broad development of innovation in the S&T sphere.

7. Ways of shaping national innovation policy

The central role in setting new innovation policy should be assigned to the federal government and its bodies. State policy should be implemented simultaneously in three areas:
- providing innovators with financial resources;
- establishing marketing, consulting, engineering and investment companies and banks and technology exchanges for promotion of innovation;
- elaborating legislative norms and mechanisms for co-ordination of activities of all actors in all stages of the innovation cycle.

The guiding principles of state innovation policy might be:

- Innovation policy should continuously adapt to the rapidly changing situation. The State should therefore monitor the overall state of innovation activities at all times and provide the feedback for correcting and redirecting policy efforts. Desirable results should be identified and specified so that the role of the State would eventually shift from an active to a passive one. At that point, the mechanisms of self-organisation of innovation actors are expected to be operative, so that the overall situation would then develop automatically. The active phase of state policy is planned to last two to three years, but it will depend on the difficulty of achieving the target results.

- An adaptive selective policy cannot be realised unless the general public is prepared for innovation efforts. This requires a national educational programme. The first phase of the programme should promote deeper public understanding of the key role of innovation activities in the national economic revival. Russian citizens may be unprepared for recovering from the crisis through the development of innovation, and this may cause social tension. National attitudes will ultimately determine the speed and direction of reform.

    The educational programme should concern all age groups, from children of pre-school age to elderly people. The following social groups are in pressing need of such an educational programme: employees of federal government bodies; employees of municipal bodies and deputies of local Soviets; employees of enterprises undergoing conversion; final-year students of institutes of higher education (technical, economic and sociological specialities).

    The chief educational task with regard to the above groups is to familiarise them with foreign management techniques, problems and practices, with innovation mechanisms characteristic of a decentralised economy, as well as with the principles of procedural behaviour of officials in the new economic environment.

    Special attention should be paid to the training of businessmen in the S&T sphere, primarily managers of innovation and venture funds, companies and technoparks. In parallel, specialists for planning new enterprises, integrated projects, design engineering, etc., should be trained.

    The educational activities would be concentrated at educational institutions, academic institutes, new educational institutions set up with the participation of foreign firms, etc. One of the main forms of instruction would be development seminars with psychological training aimed at eliminating stereotypes and directing students towards new knowledge and optimal solution of problems.

- Promoting innovation must be linked to cultivation of a taste for results of innovation among consumers. In this connection, it is necessary to create a channel for addressing consumers' wishes to innovators and investors. Mass innovation is currently feasible only where there is little capital expenditure, lack of risk in marketing the innovation products, and a short recoupment period. Such projects include: standard products using new technologies; new versions of standard products; new elements in standard products; new configurations of old components, etc.

- Support to innovators is urgent in order to maintain scientific and engineering groups. This aspect of innovation policy should concern "genuine" scientists and inventors who have valuable ideas or inventions. At the present stage, state support should be oriented to the following types of creators:
  - Basic researchers whose results have major scientific value. They are a strategic national resource and must be supported first and foremost. To this end, state-owned basic science centres must be established.
  - Creators of new paradigms, *i.e.* scientists whose ideas revolutionise scientific understanding. Whatever type of institution (organisation) they work in, they must be given "carte blanche" for access to a special fund set up by the State.
  - Authors of complex technological projects for whom the State should set up "author companies" to develop the project to a marketable form and carry it out in industry. State support should be provided primarily in the form of financial assistance to "business incubators" where the author can form a company for his/her project (project-oriented company).
  - Persons who are able to generate fruitful ideas but are unable to bring the latter up to marketable products.
- There is a need for a system for evaluating innovation projects to ensure that they are consumer-oriented and that the period of investment does not exceed a certain term. Specialised elements (subdivisions) of the innovation infrastructure should perform reliable evaluations of proposed projects and see to it that the project is carried out in accordance with its initial goal.
- With the increasing autonomy of regions and republics within the Russian Federation, it seems to be expedient to form regional innovation complexes that would include evaluation centres, financial centres, methodological centres, information centres, and audit centres. Such a complex would be a regional "metatechnopark"; unlike other technoparks, it would encourage innovation companies throughout the region. Successful regulation of innovation activities implies that a network of such complexes be set up throughout Russia.
- State assistance should be also directed at the inventory, evaluation and selection of technologies in open competition. Financial support should be given mainly for initiating manufacture based on these technologies. Support must be provided to R&D directed at upgrading and modernising technologies, but only on condition that it is coupled with a particular manufacture, so that funding would only be granted to a developer and manufacturer, as a pair, in the form of credits for design and start-up of manufacturing. The credits should be strictly purpose-oriented and subject to further control on the part of the creditor. In addition, state assistance may be offered in the form of tax exemptions and credits and of investment in the manufacture of a specific product, subject to receiving a share of the profits in proportion to the capital invested. Such assistance may be

rendered only if there is an order for the project from an enterprise or a guarantee that it will be introduced in the industry. State support might also be obtained if the product were judged, in an evaluation procedure, to be highly competitive on the world market. In addition to keeping the database on such technologies and performing evaluations, the State should select partners and form co-operation networks for the creation of complex technological systems.

- Close attention should be paid to state support for technoparks and science cities. The fundamental problem is launching innovation self-development. State assistance must be directed at rapid adoption of the relevant legal and procedural base, which would give state-owned and privatised S&T organisations freedom to innovate. Regional and municipal authorities must concentrate their efforts on technoparks as an effective means of regional development through innovation activities. The State must also create conditions for attracting investors to the development of technoparks. New mechanisms for indirect state financing should also be developed and introduced. The problem of the science cities (technopoles) must be settled within the framework set for maintaining and developing them (see Chapter IV).

- With the historical background of Russia in view, attention should be paid to the formation of a state mechanism for managing innovation within the Commonwealth of Independent States. Intergovernmental agreements in the field of innovation activities must provide for the restoration of broken innovation ties and contribute to their revival on a new legal and economic basis.

Chapter VIII

Conversion of defence S&T

1. Defence R&D in the science and technology of the USSR and Russia

The high level of militarisation of science in the former USSR was due to the general scale of development in the defence sector and the country's orientation towards self-sufficiency in the military sphere, especially in the field of new military technologies. This policy made it necessary to conduct research and development along all the lines of defence R&D conducted world-wide. According to official data, defence R&D spending in the USSR at the end of the 1980s amounted to some 20 per cent of the total defence budget and accounted for almost 70 per cent of the state funds appropriated to science. In 1989, the total defence budget was 77.3 billion roubles. Military R&D accounted for 15.3 billion roubles in the state budget, out of 23.6 billion for science as a whole. Industry and other sources accounted for 8.3 billion roubles spent for science (official statistics did not show defence industry data). In 1990, the defence budget fell to 71 billion roubles (in comparable 1989 prices; 96.5 billion roubles in current prices), and defence R&D expenditures dropped to 13.2 billion roubles (1989 prices). In 1991, further reductions in defence science expenditures were stipulated (more than 20 per cent in comparison with 1989, *i.e.* to 12.2 billion roubles), but the reduction was greater due to the collapse of the USSR.

A great part of the R&D connected with defence programmes was financed through numerous other channels, including the USSR Academy of Sciences and other ministries and government departments in the civil sector. This makes it difficult to estimate the total volume of expenditures on defence R&D. Basic research was conducted at research institutes of the defence ministries themselves (nuclear energy, air and space industry, electronics, new materials) and at the institutes of the Academy of Sciences, the Academy of Medical Sciences, etc. Applied research was also conducted at research institutes (RI) and design bureaus (DB) of both the defence and the civil sector. Defence orders provided opportunities for experimental development of the main share of scientific results.

Space programmes are an instance of S&T co-operation between the Academy of Sciences and the Ministry of Defence. Space units in the USSR Defence Ministry's organisations supported the construction of space centres, the preparation of flights and the launching of spacecraft and provided communication with vessels and satellites:

18 hours a day through ground stations and six hours a day through oceanic communication vessels. The unique equipment installed in the oceanic vessels (the equipment's cost considerably exceeds that of the hull) was maintained by specialists from the USSR Academy of Sciences. The equipment is now under the authority of the Space Exploration Service in the maritime expeditionary operations department of the Russian Academy of Sciences (the two largest ships, the Gagarin, which displaces 45 000 tonnes, and the Korolev, which displaces 21 000 tonnes, were passed to Ukraine).

The system of maintaining defence S&T programmes in the Academy and the civil branch institutes was reinforced by the institutes of higher education, which provided training of specialists and took an active part in conducting fundamental and applied research. Financing of the elite technical colleges was assured both by the Ministry of Higher and Secondary Education and by contracts with institutes and enterprises of the defence industry. A number of laboratories at such colleges were created with the participation of the defence ministries and were under their direct control.

The defence complex allocated financial and material resources for defence R&D in the civil sector, and, at the same time, undertook civil research. In 1988, before conversion, some 30 per cent, or around 6 billion roubles, of all R&D expenditure in the defence complex went to civil R&D. Research was overwhelmingly conducted not through orders from civil industries but according to plans of the defence ministries (up to 40 per cent of their production concerned civil equipment). However, most science-intensive civil products manufactured in the country were produced at defence enterprises. Representatives of the military-industrial complex always point out that a significant part of civil production was manufactured by the enterprises of the defence ministries, including civil aircraft, ships, telecommunication systems, electronics, and about half of all mechanical durable goods produced in the country: all televisions, radios, tape recorders, cameras and video cameras, and as much as 70 to 80 per cent of washing machines, refrigerators, etc. However, there was no full-fledged adaptation of military technologies to civil purposes.

Defence enterprises in the USSR were widely diversified, but there were no corporations, as in the United States. The manufacture of both military and civil goods is usually carried out in different plants of the same enterprise, so that civil goods often bear part of the costs of military expenditures and of maintaining the social infrastructure. Overhead is at the level of 700 to 800 per cent in many defence enterprises, and this sometimes causes great difficulties for selling their civil production. There is also often little connection between the civil goods manufactured and the main type of military production, but there are many problems, even in the case of dual-use technologies and the spin-off process.

In the centrally planned economy, relationships between military and civil production could allow even more rapid transfer of military technologies to the civil sector than in the West, because practically all high-technology civil production took place in the defence complex. However, technological spin-off was almost paralysed by the lack of incentives and mechanisms for adapting technologies to civil production, and even direct spin-off for civil-oriented final products had extremely low priority. Thus, although a large share of high-technology civil-oriented goods were produced by defence plants, defence technologies were never put to optimal use.

The diffusion of military technologies into the civil sector was of a "semi-military" character. Dual purpose products (made to military requirements and standards) were manufactured, and technologies were developed to produce goods that could be used for military purposes. To illustrate, the aircraft industry designed civil aircraft with the view to their applicability in war; aircraft engines were designed to satisfy military requirements, and consequently, the safe fatigue level and the service life of engines for civil aircraft were much below Western standards (the issue of making engines using normal resources for civil aircraft was never raised), and the composite materials used for military production were never used in the manufacture of civilian goods. Also, many military industries (*e.g.* radio-electronics) used parts and components that were of low quality or defective, by military standards, for civil-oriented mass production.

In addition to economic and technical obstacles to spin-off, there were also security-related information barriers. Access to all R&D in the defence sector was restricted. Considerable efforts were required to obtain clearance for technology transfer to the civil sector, while the lack of intellectual property legislation meant no benefit to development engineers.

Technology flow from military to civil industries was insufficient to create a normal civil technological base outside the military sector. It will be difficult in the short term to overcome the gap between the defence and the civil sectors, and the scale of science-intensive civil output will be determined largely by structural changes within the defence industries.

2. Industrial and regional features of defence R&D

Scientific research in military technologies and production of all types of weapons continued as the civil economy degenerated and resource shortages became more acute. This affected to some extent the choice of priorities and the allocation of funds among military programmes and various scientific and technical research areas, although, in the mid-1980s, military and technical programmes developed at a rapid pace despite evidence of a deepening economic crisis.

The scientific and design schools in the air/space and missile industry, in nuclear industry, and in many sub-divisions of the defence industry (small arms, armour, optics, etc.) encountered strong foreign and even internal competition (*e.g.* the Mig and SU fighters) and made a number of technological breakthroughs. At the same time, however, departmental disunity and competing interests in the defence industries, the gradual deterioration of some scientific and design schools which nonetheless retained their lobbying positions in the high echelons of power, the extremely high degree of secrecy in research (and, accordingly, the lack of co-ordination), led to increasingly negative effects:

- a choice of military and technical programmes and trends that proved ineffective with regard to defence, including extremely expensive and ambitious projects;
- duplication of research and waste of resources, *e.g.* the creation by almost every field of the defence complex of their own laser systems (defence industry, shipbuilding, nuclear industry, aviation, etc.) with a parallel development in the

civil machine building industries (automotive industry, electrical engineering, instruments) and at the USSR Academy of Sciences;
- technological deterioration, not only between the defence and civil sectors (discussed above) but also in individual branches and production facilities of the defence industry, with, as a result, a general reduction in the effectiveness of combat systems and increased risk of accidents in the defence industry and the armed forces.

An analysis of technological gaps within the defence complex also shows the generally unsatisfactory state of individual branches and their production (for example, in microelectronics and radio). The low level cannot be attributed to the level of scientific research, which in many sectors is equal to that elsewhere in the world, and the discrepancy between scientific and industrial sectors exists even in the military-industrial complex, despite infinitely higher innovative activity than in civil industry. Although there was strong scientific activity in all defence industries, industry rarely was able to use the results obtained by scientific and design organisations.

Industries engaged in limited production find it easier to compensate for inadequate technology (when a problem arises) because they have large numbers of highly skilled engineers and experienced, well-trained workers, unlike industries engaged in mass assembly-line production with equipment of a low technological level. In microelectronics, for example, close military supervision of the quality of final products did not extend to application of the technology for civil purposes. The electronics industry's isolation (both self-isolation and the blockade imposed by COCOM) inevitably led to catastrophic lagging behind leading world firms. In the case of sophisticated mass production, high quality of the total run could not be achieved for technological reasons; products were selected to meet the requirements of military customers. Even there, constantly rising requirements exceeded the ability to renew equipment. At first, pilot plants with relatively modern equipment could meet demand, but they gradually were converted from "experimental" to mass-production enterprises. This distanced them more and more from their founding institutes, as they less and less served the scientific base and undertook routine production tasks in order to increase gross output. As a result, they produced large quantities of useless 64K memory chips and, at best, 256K chips; there was little hope of producing 1M chips. The only possible technological breakthrough in mass microelectronics at present would come in the course of converting the nuclear industry's enterprises in close co-ordination with the research potential in the electronics industry.

The particular characteristics of the interaction between scientific, design and industrial elements of the military-industrial complex, in comparison with the United States and many other countries, are due to the principle of specialisation of enterprises in the unified state property framework. These features began to reveal themselves under conditions of transition to a market economy and with the disintegration of the industrial complexes. In general, military R&D in Russia is more isolated from industry than in other countries. In the United States, military R&D is largely conducted by research organisations in the major industrial companies, which later launch the production of military equipment, whereas in Russia, as a rule, defence R&D is carried out in institutes with no industrial base for production, although in most cases they have an experimental production plant. These organisations generally develop a package of engineering specifications and a prototype and pass it to industrial enterprises for production in series. When an experimental plant becomes a mass-production facility, it escapes the institute's control and determines its own production programme. As a result, its technological capacity is such, after several years, that it is no longer able to produce its founding institute's innovations.

The links of the innovation chain were supported by the very high concentration of production in comparison with other industries. There are almost no small enterprises (under 200 employees) in the defence sector, and the share of medium-sized enterprises (from 200 to 1 000 employees) accounts for less than 6 per cent. In the entire industrial sector, instead, the share of small and medium enterprises is 90 per cent (Table 8.1).

The organisational isolation of the scientific and design sectors is seriously narrowing the possibilities for shifting S&T resources during conversion, especially in view of the extremely uneven regional distribution. Defence science is mostly concentrated in Moscow and St. Petersburg. It is estimated that from 50 to 75 per cent of the science capacity of the Russian military-industrial complex is concentrated in these two cities and the Moscow region. Moscow and the Moscow region have:

- the leading scientific and research institutes (SRI) of the *nuclear industry's* civil sector: the Kurchatov Institute of Nuclear Energy, with a branch in Troitsk; the Institute of Theoretical and Experimental Physics; the United Institute of Nuclear Research (Dubna); the Scientific and Industrial Association (SIA) "Luch" (Podolsk); and a number of others;
- the main scientific and design organisations and part of the industrial capacity of the *missile and space industry*, with more than 20 scientific and research institutes and SIAs including the most prominent one, Energy, the central machine-building scientific and research institutes (CNIIMASH), the machine-building SIA (Reoutov), the space instruments scientific and research institutes, the heat processes scientific and research institutes, the Composites SIA, the Khrunichev plant, etc.;
- almost all the main scientific and research institutes and design departments of the *aviation industry*: the Central Aerohydrodynamic Institute (TsAGI); Test

Table 8.1. **Defence enterprises according to the number of industrial employees**
Percentage of the total number of enterprises

	Under 200	201-500	501-1 000	1 001-5 000	5 001-10 000	Over 10 000
Industry	66.2	16.2	8.2	7.7	1.1	0.6
Defence enterprises	0.3	1.6	3.9	49.8	28.3	16.1

Source: Rossija 1993: Ekonomicheskaja Konjunktura Vypusk, Vol. 1, Centre of Economic Conjuncture and Forecasting of the Ministry of Economy, Moscow, February.

Flying; the Institute of Aviation Materials; the Institute of Aviation Systems; the Institute of Aviation Engines; design bureaus, machine-building plants and SIAs named after Sukhoy, Ilyushin, Yakovlev, Mikoyan, Lyulka, Dementyev – in all about 30 major scientific, design and industrial firms;
- leading institutes and large SIAs of the *electronics industry* (Zelenograd is the centre of Russian electronics), the radio and telecommunications equipment industry;
- a number of institutes and SIAs of *other branches of the defence complex* (defence shipbuilding), with almost half of the research capacity of the former USSR in the field of shipbuilding concentrated in St. Petersburg, along with leading institutes and firms in the field of optics (Vavilov Institute of Optics and the optics and mechanics organisation, LOMO).

Outside the "two capitals", S&T capacity is concentrated in the defence complex technopolises, including those around Moscow. Such science towns as Arsamas-16, Zhukovsky, Kaliningrad (Podlipki), Krasnoyarsk-26, Friazino, Cheliabinsk-70, Chernogolovka and many others were developed as settlements or townships around the conglomerate of military scientific, design and experimental enterprises.

The location of defence science, its organisational separation from industry, and its regionalisation seriously complicate all stages of the conversion process, from the choice of new civil research trends to innovation and the adaptation of technology to civil production, including improvement of technologies and product modification.

In many regions of Russia where the concentration of defence enterprises is high (Southern Urals, the Volga region, Siberia), there are scientific and research institutes and design departments of the defence complex which carried out basic and applied research and provided the original engineering of military equipment and technologies. Yet the provincial S&T capacity (excluding defence technopolises and some leading institutes in big cities) was mainly reduced to launching industrial production and technological processes developed by "head" organisations.

In the regions with a high concentration of scientific and research institutes and design bureaus, problems have arisen for covering the cost of the conversion process and supporting the scientific and design organisations for which the sharp fall in military orders has not been compensated by an adequate growth of civil demand. Indeed, civil orders (in comparable prices) are falling, while current costs are rising fast. Under such conditions, it is becoming more difficult to support the energy and resource-intensive experimental production facilities that are largely located in the Moscow region (Kurchatov Institute, Central Aerohydrodynamic Institute (TsAGI), CNIIMASH, etc.).

The state conversion programme developed at the end of the 1980s has not used the clear advantages of the strong organisational structure of the defence industries to reorient the scientific and industrial sectors of the military-industrial complex in a co-ordinated manner. The loss in 1992 of state co-ordination, the intensification of centrifugal tendencies, and the collapse of co-operative ties among industrial enterprises and, what is more, between industrial and scientific sectors, raise questions about the future of Russia's most powerful science sector.

3. Conversion programmes for defence science: the USSR experience

In the field of defence R&D, the USSR programme stipulated:
- a transfer of technologies from defence industries to the civil sector;
- development of new types of machinery and equipment for civil production at defence institutes and design bureaus.

The first goal proved impossible to meet practically from the start: there were no enterprises in the civil sector with an adequate technological level for applying developments from defence science. For instance, specialists working at the "Energy-Buran" system invented 581 new materials. The names of the materials and the various technical units that were declassified fill three large volumes. However, by the end of 1992, not a single rouble had been obtained from the introduction of "Buran" technology into the national economy, even though it was available free of charge, due to:
- the conservatism of the economic system itself, and its inability to innovate;
- the lack, in the civil sector of equipment and materials used in the defence complex;
- the need to retrain personnel;
- the lack of a legal base for defining intellectual property rights.

At best, the technology "transfer" took the form of small venture enterprises attached to defence institutes and SIAs.

There was greater success in having technological equipment for civil industries developed by the defence scientific and research institutes and design bureaus. Tasks were set to conduct applied and design work in compliance with announced priorities (consumer goods, food-processing equipment, civil air and shipbuilding industries, electronics, telecommunications, civil space programmes, medical equipment, "green" equipment, etc.). State orders failed to stimulate serious basic research, but they made it possible to use part of the S&T capability of the defence complex to solve a number of economic and social problems, to shift defence firms towards large-scale technological spin-off, and to increase innovative activity oriented to the civil sector.

In many defence industries, serious programmes were worked out to reorient scientific and research institutes, design bureaus and industrial enterprises towards the production of close-to-civil goods, above all, in the industries engaged in dual purpose production and applied dual technologies (nuclear industry, avionics, shipbuilding, telecommunications, etc.). However, as these industries had previously been solely oriented towards solving military problems, conversion meant eliminating stereotypes and changing the thought patterns of scientists, designers and managers. This required serious investment, changes in co-operative networks, and completely new approaches to interaction with customers.

The conversion programme did not provide co-ordination of all three elements: science, industry, and final customers of conversion products. As a result, in spite of numerous successes achieved by both scientific and design organisations and industrial enterprises in entering various types of civil production, many aspects of the programme could not be realised.

This was true, in particular, for the manufacture of equipment for the agro-industrial complex and light industry. According to the programme, more than 3 000 new equipment prototypes for the agro-industry and almost 1 500 for light industry were scheduled to be created and produced. What was planned, in fact, was replacement of all imports and independent production of all the main types of equipment for these branches manufactured throughout the world. The lack of clear and well-grounded priorities, the inclusion of random or impossible points in the programme, when some key projects prepared by the enterprises themselves were dropped or largely ignored, led not only to the breakdown of many projects but was the first serious blow to defence science.

The programme's tasks for defence institutes and design bureaus had a number of weak points. The following concern the lack of co-ordination in the process of moving from science to production to the customer:

- New developments were not tied to the competencies and technological possibilities of defence institutes. In one extreme case, a design bureau that specialised in making small devices up to 800 mm in length was commissioned to develop equipment of more than 10 metres high. A prototype did not physically fit into the design bureaus' building.
- The technological resources of the enterprises selected to produce civil goods developed by related scientific and research institutes and design bureaus were not taken into consideration. For example, the air/space firm (Khrunichev plant) was charged with manufacturing stainless steel products, although the enterprise had always worked with "pure" aluminium and did not have "dirty" steel processing technologies.
- The technological situation of final customers were ignored. The technology used in a number of types of machinery developed and produced by industrial enterprises proved unsuitable for use (for example, separators and homogenisers for the milk-processing industry consumed more energy than collective farms sub-stations could produce).
- No market studies were carried out. Production prices proved to be too high, both because of the use of expensive special materials, and because of the desire to cover defence production costs from sales of new civil goods. As a result of the excessive prices, only 40 per cent of the cream maturation reservoirs and milk pasteurisation tanks manufactured at the Siberian chemical plant in Tomsk-7 (nuclear industry) in 1991 were sold.

All this combined had a demoralising effect upon the defence scientific and research institutes and design bureau collectives, deprived them of development prospects, and resulted in departure of skilled personnel.

Nevertheless, in the course of realising the conversion programmes, inefficient projects were gradually weeded out and the most effective and viable projects and programmes were further developed and given absolute priority: civil aircraft, shipbuilding, telecommunications equipment, medical equipment, etc. These were the areas in which it was possible to use to best advantage the S&T capacity of the defence complex. The problem of forming and maintaining civil demand for science-intensive production became extremely serious. It started to appear during the first stage of conversion in the former USSR and became much more acute in 1992 in Russia.

4. R&D priorities in the defence complex and problems of technology transfer to civil industry

The conversion of the S&T capacity of the defence complex is encountering serious difficulties. It is extremely difficult to estimate the process from an economic point of view, as statistical data on conversion in research organisations depend on the sources and methods of calculating different indices. A number of factors are involved, including:
- imprecise categorisation of research and design organisations and the difficulty of selecting data about such organisations when they are in the framework of scientific-industrial associations;
- imprecise criteria for placing organisations in the defence category (because of their role in the defence complex, the volume of earlier military orders, etc.);
- imprecise criteria for placing organisations in the conversion category (degree of conversion, the obtaining of conversion subsidies, etc.);
- fast-moving organisational changes, especially due to privatisation and share ownership, which statistics have not kept pace with;
- lack of unified procedures and a data collection centre.

Using data from the former Ministry of Industry, it appears that some 350 scientific and research institutes and design bureaus are included in conversion in Russia, around 300 of which are, in organisational terms, in the defence complex:
- aviation: 71 scientific and research institutes and design bureaus;
- defence: 26;
- machine building and ammunition: 30;
- general machine building (space rocket industry): 23;
- shipbuilding: 60;
- telecommunications: 24;
- radio: 51;
- electronics: 8;

for a total of 293.

Practically all state estimates concerning defence R&D bear witness to the difficult situation that arose in 1992 due to a drop in military orders and heightened problems regarding civil demand.

Military demand

In 1992, purchases of arms and military equipment in the Russian Federation fell by 64 per cent compared to the previous year. In current prices, defence expenditure in the Russian Federation in 1992 increased 7.4 times compared to the total USSR expenditure in 1990, and defence R&D expenditure increased 5.8 times (Table 8.2). The share of R&D in total defence expenditure decreased from 20 per cent in 1989 and 14 per cent in 1990 to less than 11 per cent in 1992.

According to the estimates, the inflation index for 1992/91 was 18.6 (December 1992/December 1991: 30.0), the wholesale price index was 20.5 (and 34.0), while the

Table 8.2. **Expenditure on defence R&D in the USSR (1990) and the Russian Federation (1992)**

In billion roubles at current prices

	1990	1992
Defence expenditure	96.5	716
Defence R&D expenditure	13.2	76

Source: Analytical Centre, Russian Academy of Sciences.

deflator index for GDP (which, unlike the price index, characterises inflation of wages, profits, and amortisation in material production and services, and changes in net taxes) was some 1 700 per cent.

Taking this deflator index into account for total defence expenditure, there was a 60 per cent reduction in R&D defence spending in Russia (which, according to various estimates was not less than 80 per cent of military-industrial and as much as 85 per cent of military-science capability of the USSR) in 1992 as compared to 1990, even ignoring inflation in 1991 (Table 8.3).

In the light of inflation of 7 000 to 10 000 per cent (by unofficial estimates) between October 1991 and October 1992 (still higher for most food products), defence R&D expenditure appears extremely low. If total defence spending in 1993 is 1.5 trillion roubles and the share of defence R&D is 12 to 15 per cent for a total of 200 billion roubles, it will be the equivalent of 2 billion roubles at 1991 prices. Even if total defence expenditure is raised to 2 trillion roubles or more, military research expenditures will not exceed 2.5 billion roubles or one-quarter of the USSR expenditure in 1990. Indexation, which is inadequate and incessantly lagged, as the 1992 experience showed, cannot change the situation, bringing the menace of the disintegration of the defence science-based complex, the most powerful science complex in Russia. As a point of comparison, defence spending in the USSR for Navy R&D in 1991 was 1.6 billion roubles (in absolute figures), and the corresponding figure in the United States was $7.2 billion. In 1992, the gap became several times greater.

Table 8.3. **Estimated defence expenditure in the Russian Federation**

In billion roubles

	1990[1]	1992[2]
Defence expenditure	77	42
Defence R&D expenditure	11	4.5

1. In current prices.
2. In 1991 prices with an estimated deflator of 1 700 per cent.

Source: Analytical Centre, Russian Academy of Sciences.

In the first half of 1992, long-term goals and tasks of military and technical policy were worked out, so that the S&T capabilities of the Russian armed forces would not fall critically behind those of the most advanced nations and would retain the ability to shift S&T resources. Priorities in defence R&D are connected with the general priorities of military and technical policy and the armaments programme to the year 2000, as established by the Defence Ministry. First among them are the maintaining of the strategic nuclear forces of restraint, the development of high-precision weapons, communications, intelligence, combat control, and radio-electronic warfare systems.

Civil demand

The sharp fall in military orders in 1992 was not accompanied by growth of civil demand for industrial goods, and even less for scientific goods from the defence enterprises that were being converted. In 1992, the share of civil production in the defence sector was 70 per cent, against 41 per cent in 1988 and 60 per cent in 1991. However, these changes are not due to conversion and the reorientation of production towards the civil sector; they are caused exclusively by the reduction of military production. In 1991, total military output was 74 per cent of that of 1990, and in 1992, it was 63 per cent of that of 1991 (1992 purchases of military equipment were only 46 per cent of the 1991 figure). Production of civilian goods in the military sector also decreased: output in 1991 was 96 per cent of that of 1990, and in 1992, it was 95 per cent of 1991. Total output fell by 18 per cent, and the labour force declined by 9 per cent; these figures show that latent unemployment increased in the defence sector.

As for R&D, the slump in military demand was not balanced by a growth in civil demand; on the contrary, in the context of a steep fall in investment activity, many defence research institutions lost in 1992 the small chance for reorientation that they had in the framework of the earlier state conversion programme. The 50 per cent drop in investment throughout the economy was primarily due to the rapid inflation rate and serious budget restrictions; it resulted in decreasing demand for science-intensive products, especially on the part of budget branches, such as health care. The negative aspects of the earlier programme for conversion of military R&D were intensified. Moreover, many projects that had shown promise during the previous three years of the conversion process were endangered.

From the start, the creation of effective demand for conversion in the field of civil (non-defence) space programmes, medical and ecological equipment, and a number of other priority conversion areas encountered difficulties that became acute in 1992. Thus, in 1992, the Ministry of Agriculture owed more than 600 million roubles (in 1991 prices) to defence organisations for the development of new equipment. A similar situation is developing for the scientific and design sector with the Health Ministry and other priority sectors. The consumer ministries, especially those financed from the budget such as public health, where the transition to new financing models (paid clinics, medical insurance) will inevitably last at least several years, are in no position to pay for work already done.

Some serious problems have arisen in the defence complex enterprises in the area of international co-operation. Financial difficulties and the extremely poor domestic demand for science-intensive non-defence products led managers of defence firms to search, from the start, for foreign customers, not only for military equipment but also for scientific and technical goods. But the process of technological co-operation with foreign firms also faces a number of problems. On the one hand, Western companies are trying to combat the penetration of final science-intensive products into world markets. At the same time, they are keenly interested in obtaining formerly classified technologies from the defence complex. The lack of clear policy on the part of Russia and the ambiguity surrounding intellectual property rights mean that, in many cases, the results of years of research are being sold to foreign firms for next to nothing. At the same time, the problem has arisen of attracting foreign investment for producing new types of science-intensive civil equipment on the basis of defence complex developments. As a rule, foreign firms are interested in exporting their own equipment (for example, the machinery for the fuel and energy complex) and not in developing the capability to produce it in the enterprises that are converting.

The insolvency of customers and the general decline in financing and its extreme instability (the very lengthy process of budget approval, the transition to quarterly and monthly financing of R&D) have led to a loss of prospects for the defence complex scientific organisations, and this causes personnel problems. Account must be taken of the fact that the reduction of military orders not only concerns the defence sector but also affects higher education in its traditionally strongest area, technical education. Many higher schools in Russia prepared engineers for the defence sector, and conversion of the enterprises raised the problem of demilitarising the higher school. This meant the declassification of the departments where specialists for the military-industrial complex studied and in some cases their reorientation. This requires significant investment for new equipment and for retraining teachers and professors. For example, in the Izhevsk Mechanical Institution, created and developed for the military-industrial complex, the cost of creating a new department was 2 to 2.5 million roubles before January 1992 and 30 to 40 million roubles at the end of 1992. The budget financing of this institute did not increase at that pace, but in fact was cut by half. For the first time on such a scale, the higher schools have had to face the problem of the employment of the young specialists and of creating new jobs in industry and science.

If financial backing for civil priorities cannot be sustained, it may turn out that military orders will be the sole means of avoiding the final collapse of defence complex science. New civil priorities must have more certain resources or there will be a "conversion to nowhere" which threatens the very existence of the defence industry's S&T capacity. In addition to determining civil priorities and working out the mechanism for their realisation, it is necessary to earmark the strategic scientific and technical areas in which military demand has dropped abruptly, and where new stable civil demand has not been created. Under these conditions, a number of projects of key significance for the development of crucial technologies (including dual-purpose technologies) must receive federal status and be developed exactly like long-term technological projects.

In the innovation process (basic research, applied research and development, pilot production and serial production), the decline in military orders puts long-term basic research in a very difficult position. The support of this work is strategically important, as are the priority social programmes that are being realised and have a more applied nature.

The conversion of defence R&D is also an element of industrial policy, which includes the working out and realisation of priorities for structural change and scientific and technical development. In the framework of structural changes in the economy, of which conversion of the defence complex is an important part, the following areas are highlighted: production of equipment for the agro-industrial complex, the fuel and energy complex, public health, ecology, housing, development of the communications network, civil aircraft industry, consumer durables, etc.

Russian priorities for S&T development based on the conversion of defence capacities are, in terms of critical technologies, the following (basic research is retained as a single item, due to the need to retain science management during the transition period):

- basic research;
- micro-electronic circuits, optical electronics, components for radio-electronic devices, computers and communication facilities;
- high-speed computers and peripheral equipment;
- software;
- communications technology;
- new materials, new technologies to process them, manufacturing of parts and constructions;
- flexible automated production technology;
- medical technologies;
- biotechnologies;
- food-processing technologies, production, storage and processing of agricultural products;
- recycling technology;
- aerospace equipment and technology;
- ground and water transport technology;
- energy technology;
- protection and restoration of the environment.

Support and stimulation of the innovative processes to ensure the broad introduction of technologies already in existence or under development into civil production must be the most important part of the state industrial and technological policy for the conversion of defence R&D. It is important both to create general framework conditions for developing investment and innovative activities, irrespective of forms of property, and to create state demand for the science-intensive production of the defence complex.

An example of maximising civilian use of existing S&T capability is the work of the Scientific Research Institute of Measuring Systems (SRIMS) (a radio-electronic institute of the Ministry of Atomic Energy, situated in Nizhni Novgorod). Previously oriented to defence, SRIMS now has about 70 per cent civil orders for science and technical research. Developing automated electro-radio measuring devices and telemetrical systems has taken on an important role. They are used for monitoring and control of atomic energy facilities and gas and oil pipelines. Research themes over the last three years have been oriented to solving problems of the fuel and energy industry. First among them is the development and production of automated control systems for compressor (pump) stations and for systems of linear telemeters to increase the safety of main gas and oil pipelines. The development of instruments and monitoring and control systems for gas mains is carried out at SRIMS in compliance with orders from the production associations of the state concerns Gasprom, Severgasprom, Tyumengasprom, Volgotransgas. In co-operation with AEG (Germany), SRIMS has taken part in the design competition for equipping a 2 000 km gas line with automation systems; as the principal designer, SRIMS is developing modular automation systems and auxiliary equipment, and AEG is working out the advanced software. The SRIMS and AEG project has been adopted by the technical council of Severgasprom as the main design for the equipment of this gas line. In addition to this main project, SRIMS is developing some other types of equipment on orders from the fuel and energy complex: freely programmable microprocessor controllers for checking and control of systems for oil and gas production, transportation and processing; system of underground detection and multi-purpose georadar; technologies concerning the application of corrosion-resistant metallic and non-metallic coatings on various construction materials (technologies that may be used in the enterprises of the oil and gas industry), etc. SRIMS is closely connected with the production plants of the Ministry of Atomic Energy, which traditionally manufacture the products developed in the institute and consequently have technology that allows them to reach full-scale production quickly. SRIMS' contracts with Gasprom have made it possible, two years after the beginning of the work, to fill civil orders for 2 billion roubles in the four production plants of the Ministry of Atomic Energy.

Defence complex structural changes must correspond to organisational measures, including the development of non-state businesses and forms of property, the curtailment of inefficient means of production, and the gradual lifting of restrictions on foreign competition. Such organisational changes in the defence complex, which correspond to the general course of reforms and structural rebuilding of the economy, presuppose a gradual transformation of scientific organisations within defence industries, including changes in the forms of property and the formation of three major groups:

- The very specialised major scientific and research institutes and design bureaus, in which sophisticated and expensive equipment for developing and testing weaponry is concentrated, are not to be privatised. These fundamental military-oriented organisations will have the status of state S&T centres.
- Scientific and design organisations which are part of large corporations that are independent from the state, relatively diversified, and substantially oriented towards civil areas will fulfil military orders under contracts to be awarded mainly on a competitive basis.
- Medium-sized and small scientific and research firms spinning off from the defence complex as a result of privatisation which will fill military orders both under direct contracts with the Defence Ministry and under subcontracts from organisations of the first two groups.

Privatisation in the defence complex

One of the thorniest problems facing the defence complex, where it is even more severe than elsewhere in the economy, is privatisation. The course and efficiency of this process greatly depends on decisions taken at the highest levels concerning the organisational and technological structures of the defence sector (for example, revising mobilisation capacities and withdrawal of conversion enterprises from under direct government control). So far, most problems in this area have yet to be solved.

Therefore, in December 1992, the Russian Committee for Defence Industries stopped the privatisation of several large defence enterprises in St. Petersburg, including the Baltic Plant, the Kirov Plant, etc., even though military orders at these enterprises has fallen to 6 to 8 per cent of their production capacities. Because of the necessity to maintain capacities for military production, the decision was taken not to allow privatisation of enterprises which had applied for it.

Privatisation itself raises many problems. According to the law on privatisation, any department of the enterprise has the right to become independent and to be privatised separately. The main goal is to create favourable conditions for splitting up large enterprises. In order to avoid monopoly, the law also forbids merging of enterprises in the course of privatisation.

However, this could have very severe consequences, especially for defence R&D. Even when the research institute or design bureau is closely connected to the plant, differences in their ability to survive cause them to drift apart. More often, research institute, design bureau and pilot plant, the links in one network of the technological innovation process (and often a single entity in the defence sector), were located sometimes 1 000 km from the production plant. Many industries worked as one large company or as a conglomerate of several companies and sometimes in competition (some aviation scientific and production associations, missile and rocket plants, etc.), although under the rather special conditions of the planned economy.

Separate privatisation in a situation of economic crisis threatens the existence of the scientific base itself. The production plants themselves might survive for several years, but the technological future of the enterprise would be threatened, although it might survive with a lowered technological level, through the purchase of licences, etc. One example is the privatisation of the aviation plant in Voronezh, which builds Ilyushin aircraft, without its design bureau located in Moscow.

One proposed approach is to establish large diversified financial-industrial groups. This would be very difficult from an organisational point of view, and the value of the approach is not evident. On the one hand, bringing together enterprises technologically closely related could improve their ability to enter the world market and maintain a relatively high technological level. On the other hand, there is a danger that because of the military-industrial authorities' high requirements concerning the level of mobilisation capacity, a financial-industrial group would aim to maintain military production at the expense of the civil sector. The inflationary consequences for the economy are evident.

Privatisation in the defence branches has to be preceded by the establishment of organisational structures for commercialising the enterprises. This is very important, because many defence enterprises are supposed to be state-owned, but that does not mean that they would not participate in a market economy.

Chapter IX

Social problems in the S&T sector

1. R&D personnel: social status, employment and quality of living

The social status of researchers and specialists is largely determined by the overall social situation and by the attitude of society and the state to science and the scientific establishment. Russians in general seem to understand the need and importance of state support for science. However, science is widely considered less important than health care, education, ecology, and social insurance. The public tends to accept increases in state expenditure on R&D unless it harms the financial position of the ordinary taxpayer.

A more precise picture can be obtained by analysing a set of social parameters, including level of employment, working conditions, income and spending patterns, level of social risk, and level of social security. In the present social and economic situation in Russia, all these parameters are undergoing substantial changes.

Employment and unemployment

In recent years, the number of R&D employees has decreased steadily. Between December 1991 and December 1992, the total number of R&D personnel dropped by 16 per cent; the figure was 4 per cent for the economy as a whole and 5 per cent for industry, while branches such as management and finance increased by 17 per cent and 13 per cent, respectively. If the absolute losses continue at the 1991-92 level, Russian R&D is likely to disappear by the turn of the century. If the share remains constant, the number of researchers in Russia will be near 700 000, *i.e.* 25 per cent of the 1992 figure, by the year 2000. Russian experts consider the second scenario more realistic, given the present pace of reform.

The greatest loss of jobs in R&D is likely to occur in 1993-95, after which the rate of decrease should slow and the number of personnel should stabilise. Thus, the share of R&D employees in the total number of employees in 2000 will have dropped from 3.4 per cent to 1 per cent.

The decrease in R&D personnel is attributable to the spontaneous outflow of R&D specialists to other sectors of the economy, planned staff reductions, and emigration. The massive outflow (according to estimates, 75 per cent of those who leave do so on their own initiative) is due to low incomes; the loss of prestige of science, scientists and a scientific career; and increasing risk of unemployment. The loss rate is double the rate of new hirings (Figure 9.1). In the first half of 1992, those discharged on grounds of staff reduction accounted for 16 to 21 per cent of the total outflow; the share subsequently lowered somewhat but remains higher than in other sectors of the national economy.

The drop in the R&D labour force is due to a number of economic, social and demographic factors, the most important of which are the general deterioration of the national economy, the decrease in GNP and growth of the budget deficit, and structural shifts connected primarily with the inflation-induced fall in demand for expensive high-technology products. This situation affects primarily the military-industrial complex, where many plants are undergoing a kind of secondary conversion (when contractors do not have enough money to pay for products of military R&D for civil use and the plant has to restructure its production). In 1992, according to the State Committee on Defence Industry, military research institutes and design offices lost 200 000 employees.

The outflow of personnel from R&D results in a decline in the qualifications of R&D staff and a shifting demographic structure. The share of both young and highly qualified personnel is decreasing, because these groups have better opportunities for employment elsewhere in the country and abroad. In military research institutes, the most advanced and experienced specialists have been the first to leave, with a drop of 15 to

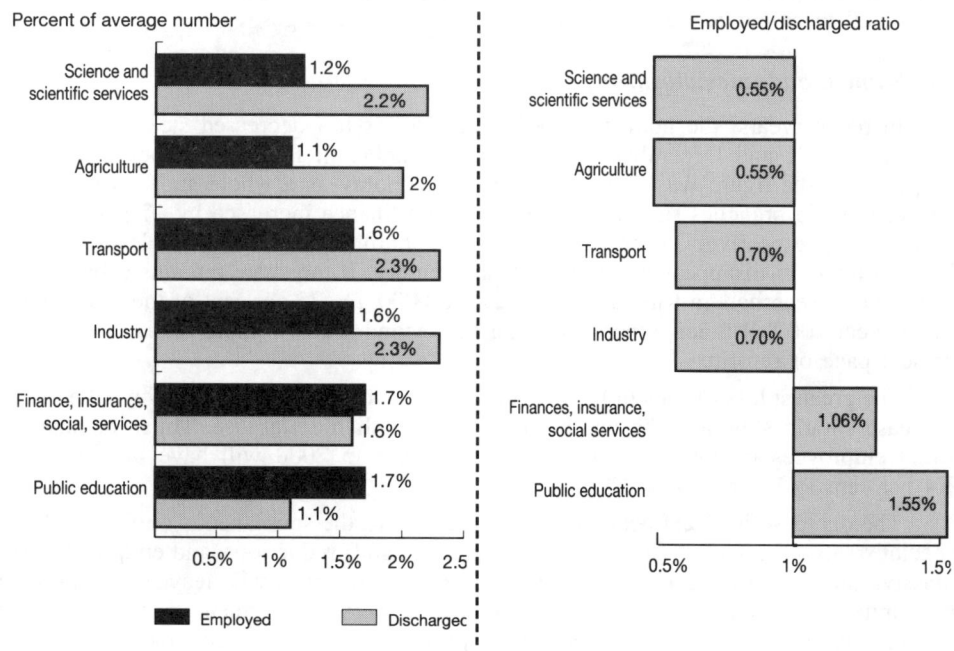

Figure 9.1. **Dynamics of mobility of personnel in branches of the national economy of Russia (employment and discharge) in December 1992**

20 per cent since 1991. The proportion of researchers with academic degrees has also decreased. Academy science shows the same changes. The share of personnel under age 30 is only about 9 per cent, but 50 per cent of those leaving are from this age group. The average age of those who defended their candidate dissertations in 1991-92 was over 36. The most alarming developments are in industrial (branch) research, where the majority of researchers are close to retirement. It is estimated that, by the year 2000, the share of women in the R&D staff will increase from 53 per cent to 65 per cent.

Problems of unemployment in the R&D sphere are especially acute in large cities. In Moscow, according to the Labour and Employment Department, R&D and design organisation personnel account for less than 20 per cent of the total number of employees but about 40 per cent of those dismissed. According to expert estimates, chances of finding a job at the employment bureau are approximately three times lower for R&D specialists than for other categories of workers in Moscow. Industrial R&D personnel are most affected by staff reduction: 94 per cent of researchers who applied for jobs at the employment bureau had previously been employed in industrial R&D institutes, 2.2 per cent came from the academic sector, and 3.4 per cent from higher schools. More than 65 per cent of applicants had higher education, including 1 per cent of candidates of science. Engineers and technicians (48.7 per cent of applicants to the labour exchange) and auxiliary personnel (23.7 per cent) are most affected by staff reductions; the share of researchers proper among the dismissed is relatively low (8.2 per cent).

However, it is not possible to estimate the full extent of unemployment from the available statistical data. First, it is difficult to give a correct evaluation of hidden unemployment, which, according to some estimates, amounts to between 25 and 50 per cent of the total number of researchers. Planned staff reductions registered by the employment bureau account for only a quarter of the total outflow of personnel. Second, in determining the extent of unemployment, account should be taken of the widespread practice of partial employment, involving involuntary unpaid leaves and part-time work. Such measures are widely used in R&D institutions of the military-industrial complex located in small towns where the labour market situation is especially difficult. In 1992, for instance, employees of main divisions of R&D organisations in the city of Kovrov (Vladimir region) had two to three months of involuntary leaves. The same practice was used in many institutes of the Russian Academy of Sciences.

Small business and employment

The growth of small R&D businesses would increase the number of jobs and somewhat lower tensions on the highly qualified labour market by drawing a share of R&D workers to the commercial sector. In the first half of 1992, there were 9 600 known small science and science services firms, with about 421 600 personnel, including part-time and contract workers.

However, the growth of small enterprises in R&D does not solve the problem of providing jobs for dismissed personnel, both because jobs in small enterprises are mainly secondary jobs (there are 2.3 times more of these employees than of staff workers) and because hiring preference is definitely given to men, while the dismissed are mostly women.

Under these conditions, the development of the commercial sector is more a solution to problems of social protection and increased wages than an instrument for improving the labour market situation. According to sociological surveys, 44 per cent of R&D personnel have additional sources of income, and 47 per cent of respondents combine their work in state S&T organisations with employment in the commercial sector.

It should also be recognised that the widespread desire for independence on the part of research teams and their leaders not only can destabilise the R&D structure, since a significant proportion of newly established small independent R&D firms will inevitably lack economic vitality, but may result in greater science unemployment and increased social tension.

Living standards

In 1992, the standard of living of most Russians fell substantially, as rises in income lagged well behind rises in prices, most seriously for public health services, culture, education, science and science services. Salaries of R&D workers in 1991 were 6.8 per cent below the national average, by the end of 1992, 30 per cent, and in March 1993, 32.8 per cent (Figure 9.2). Analysis of Goskomstat data concerning 13 large branches shows that science and science services are in eleventh place for salary levels. The average salary in the R&D sphere is 41 per cent below that in industry, 49 per cent below

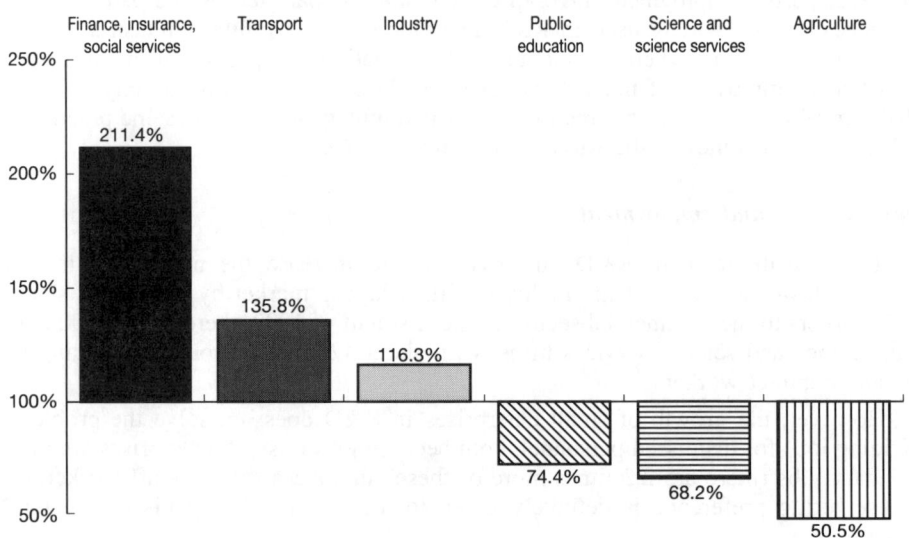

Figure 9.2. **Structure of monthly salaries in various branches of the Russian economy in March 1993 (per cent of the average salary)**

that in construction, 50 per cent below that in transport, 68 per cent below that in banking and insurance, and 75 per cent below that in fishing (Table 9.1). A year ago science was in sixth place.

Since April 1993, following the adoption of the unified wage scale for science and science services (Table 9.2), with its minimum wage of 4 500 roubles, monthly salaries in R&D varied, depending on the position of the worker, from 14 040 to 45 315 roubles. However, the unified wage scale is unable to solve the problem of salaries. The system of indexation does not make it possible to keep pace with the rise in wages and salaries in industry, and even less in the private sector. The very low initial salary levels, together with the low rate of increase, meant that from January to May 1992 R&D workers spent over 70 per cent of their income on basic foodstuffs and obligatory payments, while in industry these expenses accounted for about 40 per cent of income. Most employees in science and science services were unable to save money to buy durable goods.

Thus, the social status of R&D workers has worsened in comparison with other social groups since the reforms began, a situation accompanied by material, social and psychological suffering. Given this situation, the social protection of R&D workers is becoming essential to state science and technology policy.

Table 9.1. **Average monthly wages in branches of the Russian national economy in March, 1993**

	March 1993 (roubles)	March 1992 (roubles)	Rate of growth, per cent	In per cent of average monthly wages in national economy
Total	23 559	2 557	921.4	100
Including:				
Industry	27 410	3 288	833.6	116.3
Agriculture	11 899	1 178	1 010.1	50.5
Forestry	18 166	1 925	943.7	77.1
Fisheries	65 127	4 827	1 349.2	276.4
Transport	31 991	3 553	900.4	135.8
Communications	20 812	2 126	978.9	88.3
Construction	31 344	3 643	860.4	133.0
Information services	23 965	2 172	1 103.4	101.7
Public education	17 518	1 442	1 214.8	74.4
Arts and culture	14 733	1 322	1 114.4	62.5
Science and science services	16 060	1 556	1 032.1	68.2
Finance, insurance and social services	49 798	3 704	1 344.4	211.4
Managerial bodies (state, industry co-operative, public)	32 512	2 123	1 531.4	138.0

Source: State Committee on Statistics (*Goskomstat*) of the Russian Federation.

Table 9.2. **Remuneration categories envisaged by the United Wage Scale for workers in science and science services**

Position	Range of categories	Wage co-efficients
1. Researchers		
Junior research associate	8-11	3.12-4.51
Research associate	10-13	3.99-5.76
Senior research associate	12-15	5.10-7.36
Leading researcher	14-16	6.51-8.17
Chief researcher	16-17	8.17-9.07
2. Experts of R&D units of institutions (organisations)		
Research assistant, probationary researcher	6-8	2.44-3.12
Chief expert of R&D unit of an organisation	12-14	5.10-6.51
Chief engineer (designer, technologist, architect) of a project carried out by a unit	13-15	5.76-7.36
3. Managers		
Head of a structural unit	12-15	5.10-7.36
Head of a main structural unit (division, laboratory, department)	13-16	5.76-8.17
Learned secretary	13-16	5.76-8.17
Chief expert of an institution (organisation)	13-17	5.76-9.07
Head of a branch or a separate department, chief engineer	14-17	6.51-9.07
Deputy director of an institution (organisation)	15-17	7.36-9.07
Director of an institution (organisation)	16-18	8.17-10.07

Note: Salaries are calculated by multiplying the first category wage rate (2 250 roubles from 7 February 1993, 4 500 roubles from 1 April 1993) by an appropriate wage co-efficient.
Source: Ministry of Science and Technological Policy, Social Problems Division.

2. Advanced training and retraining

Because of the economic crisis and structural changes in the economy, the issue of improving skills and retraining personnel in high-technology areas is becoming more urgent.

Advanced training

The principal and most common forms of advanced training are postgraduate studies, doctoral studies, scientific fellowships, leaves for research, and advanced training courses. At the beginning of 1992, 59 300 researchers and teachers were taking postgraduate courses at 1 276 R&D institutions and higher schools (the latter gave courses to 64 per cent of all postgraduates). Over 16 000 had finished their postgraduate studies by the beginning of 1992 (61 per cent of them in higher schools). However, only one out of five students defends his/her thesis during postgraduate studies, and only one student in six in branch R&D institutions.

Since the mid-1980s, the number of postgraduate students has decreased, although a growing number of institutes offer postgraduate courses. In 1991 the number of postgraduate students had decreased by 11 per cent from 1985 (19 per cent in R&D institutions and 4 per cent in higher schools). Because of the growing budget deficit, the state ceased financing advanced training in 1992.

State retraining centres

Personnel discharged from S&T organisations are retrained along with other dismissed workers in retraining courses established under the regional employment centres. As a rule, retraining entails complete reorientation. At present, there are 50 officially registered regional retraining centres. There are also 17 intersectoral centres, 187 centres associated with higher schools, 33 retraining courses, 63 faculties offering new specialties, and 34 institutes of advanced training. However, retraining often does not take account of the regional features of the labour market and offers only a low level of retraining, with the result that the newly trained often do not find employment. Employment bureaus receive many applications from "newly fledged" bookkeepers, secretaries, social workers, etc.

According to the Commission on Professional Training for the Market Economy, priority areas of training and retraining of personnel (and especially for specialists with higher and specialised secondary education) will be directed towards professions such as business administration, marketing, accounting, banking, commercial law, and state management of the economy.

Commercial centres of retraining

According to some estimates, about 300 business schools are active nowadays in the field of training and retraining. However, very few appear to train to a level of real expertise. One is the Higher Commercial School of the Ministry of Foreign Economic Relations. Its mainstays are high quality training and professional consulting activities. Its technical equipment is up to the standards of the best foreign business centres. Another enterprise active in the field is the Centre for Training of Managers at the Russian Economic Academy (Plekhanov Academy). Its task is to train specialists in management, marketing, and finance. The newly established Russian Higher School for Foreign Economies at the Ministry of Foreign Economic Relations has a similar mandate.

At present, those trained in these schools and centres are, as a rule, senior administrators and experts from foreign trade organisations, associations and joint ventures, as well as commercial directors, heads of finance departments, experts of small enterprises and staff members of joint ventures. Retraining centres of this kind operate on a strictly commercial basis and those who have been discharged from S&T organisations are therefore unlikely to be able to afford them. State funding for the unemployed in commercial centres is virtually non-existent because of the limited funds provided for this purpose by the Employment Fund.

International projects

In the framework of the COMNET programme, a centre is planned at the International Institute for Inter-Phase Interactions in St. Petersburg. Its main field of activity is to be improving teaching methods and developing software for training experts (including those dismissed due to conversion) in high-technology commercialisation, in applied mathematics and in computer modelling. The Centre will help introduce advanced high and science-intensive technologies and will contribute to the training of experts recruited from such ill-protected social groups as new graduates of higher schools and personnel dismissed from the military-industrial complex.

In 1993 the Centre, in close co-operation with the Intersectoral Retraining Institute at the St. Petersburg Technical University, is planning to develop tutorial computer programmes and to organise retraining courses based on them.

The lack of proper attention to personnel retraining in Russian employment policy has an especially negative impact on workers discharged from the R&D sphere. The personnel retraining undertaken in existing facilities is very poorly co-ordinated with the reduction of personnel that affects R&D workers in particular. Also, the forms of retraining offered tend to neglect the specific characteristics of this category of workers. This indicates the need to give more emphasis to retraining and advanced training in employment policy and in social policy in general.

3. Internal and external mobility

The mobility of personnel takes at present the form of poorly controlled emigration and other types of "brain drain". It is necessary to distinguish between three main types of migration: from Russia to foreign countries other than the former Soviet republics; between Russia and the former Soviet republics; and within the territory of Russia itself. The three differ as to their intensity, motivations, trends, and consequences for R&D. The ability of the state to influence the flows also differs in each case.

From Russia to distant foreign countries

Currently, the attention of Russian society is largely focused on the problem of "brain drain", which is traditionally identified with emigration of domestic researchers to foreign countries. In 1992, according to the data provided by the Visas and Registration Department of the Ministry of Internal Affairs (which registers only those who left the country for permanent resettlement abroad), 4 572 persons from the field of science and public education (7.8 per cent of all emigrating adults) left the country. These data can be considered an upper estimate of emigration of researchers, since the statistics include not only researchers but also lecturers from higher schools and specialised secondary-education institutions and teachers. One can presume that the share of researchers who have emigrated does not exceed 0.2 per cent of all employees in science and science services. In other words, the estimates of emigration among scientific personnel create the illusion of a relatively serene state of affairs in which personnel losses in Russian R&D are negligible.

However, according to some expert estimates, the number of emigrants in the "active population" category is nearly five times the number of those who leave the country to settle abroad permanently and are counted in the statistics of the Ministry of Internal Affairs. For example, neither the recipients of fellowships to foreign R&D centres nor those offered long-term contracts are reflected in statistics on the emigration of R&D personnel, and there is no comprehensive data on the scale of this phenomenon. Under present conditions, such contracts often become the first stage of real emigration.

According to data provided by the Main Department of External Relations of the Russian Academy of Sciences, one-third of its employees who left the country in 1985-91 to work on a contract basis held research jobs in Russia. Over 58 per cent of these contract emigrants were between 31 and 45 years old. A survey conducted among the researchers of the St. Petersburg Scientific Centre of the Russian Academy of Sciences who worked abroad on a contract basis during the period from January 1990 to May 1992 showed that nearly one-third are doctors of science, and nearly half have candidate of science degrees.

The geographical distribution of the Russian researchers who travel shows that countries with highly developed R&D have priority (Table 9.3). About 60 per cent left for Germany, 25 per cent for Israel, 15 per cent for the United States, and only 1 per cent for the countries of Eastern Europe. In 1992, the number of emigrants to Israel and the United States decreased, while emigration of Russian researchers to Germany and Australia increased.

There is considerable activity on the part of developing countries, which, unlike the United States or Germany, seek personnel with average skills. Brazil, for example, is ready to receive up to 10 000 researchers from the Community of Independent States (CIS), and significant interest is also shown by Paraguay, Bolivia, Chile and Argentina. There is great demand for Russian R&D personnel (primarily for university professors and teachers) on the part of China. Nearly 1 000 Russian researchers are expected to leave for South Korea. Neither Iran nor Iraq conceals its wish to obtain researchers from the CIS, primarily experts in nuclear technologies, and they are ready to pay annual salaries much higher than those of nuclear physicists in the United States.

Between Russia and the former Soviet republics

Migration of R&D personnel between Russia and the republics of the former USSR has some specific features. One is the migration of scientific personnel from the republics of the former USSR to Russia. This largely concerns Russian-speaking persons, a category defined in the republics as all those who are not "titular nationals" (*i.e.* all those whose ethnic identity is not that of the republic) of a given republic. According to independent expert estimates, Russia's positive balance of intellectual migration with virtually all republics of the former USSR was of 140 000 persons in 1991 but dropped to 25 000 in the first half of 1992. This indicates an essential change in migratory trends in the territory of the former USSR.

Another characteristic of migration in the territory of the former Soviet Union is that, in spite of the positive migration balance, those who leave Russia have a higher average level of education than those who enter. According to estimates, of 230 000 per-

Table 9.3. **Number of emigrants who left Russia for permanent resettlement, by countries**

According to the Visas and Registration Department of the Ministry of Internal Affairs of the Russian Federation [1]

Regions and countries	Year	Total	Of which:	
			Industry, power, engineering, communications, transport, construction, material and technical supply	Science and public education
Foreign countries				
Total	1988	20 705		
	1991	90 036		
	1992	103 700		
		58 730 [2]	16 164	4 572
Of which:				
Eastern Europe	1988	1 340		
	1991	1 087		
	1992	454	78	31
Israel	1988	8 137		
	1991	40 417		
	1992	13 972	3 355	1 163
Germany	1988	9 637		
	1991	33 734		
	1992	34 202	10 610	2 765
United States	1988	780		
	1991	11 046		
	1992	n.a.		
Australia	1988	49		
	1991	304		
	1992	514	83	50

1. The Visas and Registration Department provides data on those who received exit permissions. The figures, however, do not differ significantly from the number of those who actually left the country for permanent resettlement, because, as a rule, no more than 2 per cent of applicants change their minds and refuse to emigrate.
2. Adult workers who received exit permissions.

n.a. Not available.

sons who came to Russia in 1991 from the Baltic states and the CIS republics, R&D personnel constituted a minimum of 6.5 to 8.5 per cent. This relatively high proportion of R&D workers in the structure of immigration to Russia is explained by the former practice of sending (with their consent) Russian-speaking graduates, as well as those who had finished their postgraduate studies, to the Union republics, where they sometimes had better prospects for scientific and administrative careers. It was largely due to this practice that academies of sciences, national scientific schools, and research and production centres were created in the republics.

A third feature is the fact that the intensity and trend of intellectual migration between Russia and the other former USSR republics depend on the distribution of the population throughout the territory of former Soviet Union. In 1990, up to 95 per cent of Lithuanians resided in Lithuania, while only 67 per cent of Armenians lived in the territory of Armenia.

One should note that emigration flows into Russia include R&D workers of titular nationalities as well, especially from former republics where national and/or inter-ethnic conflicts are ripening or have already subsided. Today, the share of titular nationals among those who intend to emigrate from national republics shows a clear upward trend, and this is particularly so in the case of the former republics of Middle Asia. However, Russia is not able to absorb the flow of intellectual migrants from the former USSR republics, who sometimes leave the sphere of R&D altogether.

Migration within the territory of Russia

Internal mobility of R&D personnel in Russia has two sides: regional and inter-sectoral mobility. The emphasis is placed here on intersectoral migration, since intersectoral movement of personnel is currently a unidirectional outflow of employees from science to other spheres of activity. The outflow has been increasing constantly since 1988.

The existing level of the outflow from the R&D sphere, its potential consequences, the instability of the process, as well its relation to the general social and economic situation in the country all indicate the urgent need for permanent monitoring of the migration of R&D personnel. The goals, methods and mechanisms of state intervention in the process ought to be clearly identified. A state programme for regulating intellectual migration would help integrate the efforts of state and non-state bodies, international organisations and foundations, the scientific community and the mass media to protect the national intellectual potential. The basic objectives of the programme should be:

- to formulate principles and mechanisms for long-term national policy concerning the migration of researchers and specialists;
- to protect crucial areas of national science and the most valuable research schools against possible collapse resulting from uncontrolled "brain drain";
- to minimise the negative effects of the flow abroad of the intellectual elite in science and the arts. This task may be approached through the creation of adequate organisational, legal, social, and economic conditions for researchers and experts in Russia, as well as mechanisms for their effective participation in the international division of labour.

4. Social policy in S&T: principles and directions

In the transition to the market economy, which is accompanied by a considerable deterioration in the social and economic status of R&D personnel, this category becomes a special target of social policy and of social protection. This means that social policy in the S&T sphere must be aimed not only at the prevention of further reduction in the standard of living of S&T workers, but also at the creation of conditions for the realisation of their professional potential. In this connection, emphasis should be placed on various indirect support measures that favour the preservation and further elaboration of the inherent potential of the R&D sphere, rather than on increased direct financial support in the form of various types of payments.

The legislative basis of social policy

Social policy measures concerning the R&D sphere are based on a series of documents adopted by the Supreme Soviet and/or issued by the Government of the Russian Federation: the Law on Employment, the Main Principles and Directions of Social Policy in the Years 1992 and 1993, and the government decision "On measures for creating jobs under the conditions of massive reductions of personnel" of 5 February 1993. These documents are intended to reinforce state control over the evolution of the labour market situation. The government decision envisages the following measures: granting permission to reduce personnel but making enterprises and organisations bear part of the financial obligations linked to unemployment, in order to slow growth of unemployment; aid for job creation; creation of temporary jobs for public works; organisation of professional training, retraining and improvement of skills of released personnel.

A package of laws and regulations designed to reinforce state control over wages and salaries and to prevent further decrease in the standard of living is being prepared. Among these documents are a draft Law on Control over Salaries, a draft Law on the Minimum Cost of Living, and a draft Presidential Decree "On urgent measures to stabilise the standard of living of the population of the Russian Federation".

However, Russia still lacks a comprehensive legislative basis for regulating the whole spectrum of relations concerning emigration of labour and in particular the recruitment of Russian citizens who have expressed a desire to work abroad. Legislation regulating the return of Russian workers is also lacking.

No integrated system of state control over migration has been formed, nor is there yet any clear distribution of powers and functions among the different state bodies. Rules concerning the activities of agencies that hire Russian citizens to work abroad have not been spelled out, and the interaction between private agencies and state services in regulating emigration of labour does not yet have an appropriate and systematic basis. The Federal Migration Service of Russia has just begun to develop activities aimed at entering into bilateral agreements to regulate these processes.

Social partnership

The President and the Government of the Russian Federation have adopted legislative acts that lay the basis for a system of social partnership, namely, the Presidential Decrees, "On social partnership and settlement of labour conflicts" of 15 November 1991, "On establishing the Tripartite Commission to Regulate Social and Labour Relations" of 24 January 1992, and "On approval of the regulations concerning the procedure for the elaboration and conclusion of the 1992 General Agreement and branch wage agreements and for the settlement of labour disputes" of 15 April 1992.

On the basis of these regulatory acts, working bodies of the social partnership system were created in early 1992. The Russian Tripartite Commission was established to regulate social and labour relations and is composed of representatives of the Government, the Russian trade unions, and employers. The most important result of the activities at different levels of the Tripartite Commission was the signing of the General Agreement between the Government of Russia, Russian trade unions and employers for the year 1992 and of 53 branch wage agreements (43 for industrial production spheres and ten for non-production spheres). So far, however, they have not been effective, since employers and trade unions generally agreed on the demands made to the Government. Therefore, the potential value of social partnership, especially in the sphere of R&D, has not yet materialised.

Many state and non-governmental organisations are emerging whose activities are directed towards the revival of Russian science and the social protection of researchers, such as the Russian Foundation for Fundamental Research, the Nauka insurance society, the Megus company (which insures intellectual property), various intellectual property centres (Dintsis and Kosmoflot), the Informatom association, the Publicist agency, etc.

With the support of the Russian government, a number of international scientific funds and foundations began work in Russia. In particular, there is the Cultural Initiative Foundation, which financed the subscription to 162 scientific journals for the Russian Academy of Sciences, the John and Catherine MacArthur Foundation, the Ford Foundation, and the George Soros Foundation. A number of promising international projects aimed at the preservation of Russian science have been elaborated, such as Stone's project for creating twin institutes in Russia and in the United States.

Objectives of social policy

A number of tasks face the state bodies responsible for pursuing social policy – the Ministry of Social Protection, the Ministry of Labour, the Federal Employment Service, the Federal Migration Service, the Ministry of Science and Technological Policy, and others. They are:
- To create a system for retraining R&D personnel dismissed because of the planned reduction of research and/or due to the conversion of the defence industry. The formation of a central body for retraining R&D personnel in regional departments should be envisaged.
- To elaborate special measures to provide employment for R&D personnel. The measures may include the creation of intellectual employment bureaus, both in the centre and in the regions, and providing jobs for R&D personnel returning to Russia from the former Soviet republics, after postgraduate studies, fellowships, contracts, etc.
- To work out documents for regulating contract payments and for stimulating entrepreneurship.
- To draft legislative acts designed to ensure social protection for researchers, including the creation of a system of supplementary non-state pensions.
- To organise the interaction between various aspects of social policy in the course of solving social problems of the R&D sphere.

Chapter X

Russian science and technology in the international community

1. Scientific and technical co-operation with the CIS

The distribution of R&D resources of the former USSR among the Union republics and the scale of their participation in scientific and technical activities can be estimated from data contained in the tables in Annex 1.

Scientific and technical activities in the republics were long oriented towards participation in the overall scientific effort of the USSR. Today, it is impossible (except in Russia and Ukraine) for the republics to deal independently with the entire spectrum of scientific and technical issues that confront national economies. Further dissociation will lead, and is already leading, to the dismemberment of the previously established scientific and technical base. It will also lead to lowered efficiency of production while maintaining low quality, high and not always justified expenditures for purchase of foreign technologies, and delays in the realisation of their own technological developments, which are generally more appropriate to the technical and organisational characteristics of Russian industry.

Political factors do not markedly affect the scale and structure of research work in science and technology in the Russian Federation. Nonetheless, Russia wishes to develop scientific and technical co-operation as a factor which can contribute to:
- stabilisation of the economic and political situation in the former republics, with preservation of a greater degree of integration and job creation for the Russian-speaking population;
- prevention of ecological disasters near its borders;
- preservation of the possibility of using unique natural sites and scientific installations found on the territories of former Union republics.

For these reasons, it is in the national interest of all the countries of the CIS, from both the scientific and economic perspective, to preserve common scientific and technical work.

Agreements were signed in 1992 at the level of the heads of governments of the Commonwealth states in Moscow, Tashkent and Minsk in the following areas:

- scientific and technical co-operation within the framework of member-states of the CIS;
- co-operation on direct scientific and technical ties within the framework of the CIS;
- co-operation in the training of scientific and scientific-teaching cadres and the acceptation of qualification documents within the CIS framework;
- joint use of scientific and technical installations within the CIS framework;
- co-operation in the field of education;
- exchanges of scientific and technical information.

At the meeting of the Interstate Scientific and Technical Council, which took place in Kiev in September 1992, plenipotentiary representatives of Commonwealth states reaffirmed their intention to broaden and deepen co-operation in the fields of science and education.

Work on the development of bilateral ties in the sphere of science, technology and education between the Russian Federation and the states of the Commonwealth and the Baltic republics, begun in March 1992, is being carried out. A draft agreement on scientific and technical co-operation with the republic of Tadjikistan has already been agreed to, and drafts for similar agreements with the republics of Kyrghystan, Kazakhstan and Turkmenistan have been prepared, while agreements on S&T co-operation and co-operation in the field of higher education have been signed with Armenia. Projects for bilateral agreements on the regulation of relations in the sphere of scientific and technical co-operation have been developed for the Latvian, Lithuanian and Estonian republics and consultations with the governments are being carried out.

In January 1993, a meeting of government representatives from Central and East European countries took place in St. Petersburg. It was agreed during the meeting that further efforts would be made to conclude agreements, treaties and contracts between state organs, research organisations, higher education establishments, innovation centres and individual businessmen of interested countries with the aim of carrying out mutually advantageous scientific and technical co-operation. It was deemed expedient to create an international advisory council to assist in this effort.

Difficulties in the relations between the CIS states at government level sometimes affect the development of scientific and technical co-operation by delaying decision on important problems.

It would be useful in the near future to:
- stimulate direct contacts between actors in innovation activities, different non-governmental associations and scientific unions;
- establish permanent relations between the committees for science and education of the Supreme Soviet of Russia, the Central Asian states and Kazakhstan for the preparation of legal regulations in the area of science and education, intellectual property, privatisation of scientific facilities, and so on;
- conclude agreements destined to preserve the possibility for the Commonwealth countries to use each other's educational facilities as in the past;

- begin the work of "taking stock" of state interests in the scientific and technical sphere, thereby revealing mutually advantageous areas of co-operation, and discuss the possible realisation of projects in conjunction with foreign partners in areas in which Russia and the CIS countries have world standing;
- initiate the preparation of bilateral and multilateral inter-government agreements in the sphere of scientific and technical co-operation, joint use of scientific installations and services, and major innovation projects.

To further strengthen and develop direct contacts among scientists of the republics of the former USSR, organisational and economic measures to help preserve these ties are needed. At present, for example, hotel rates in Russia are about four times higher for residents of the former republics than they are for residents of Russia.

2. Co-operation in basic research

The principle of "self-sufficiency" was fundamental to the state science policy of the USSR and Russia in the sphere of basic research. It meant that research was carried out relatively independently from foreign science and covered all areas of scientific investigation. Research was state property and dependent on distribution of resources from the centre.

Due to the organisational and regional structure of basic research in the USSR, Russia found itself, after the breaking up of the USSR, with almost the totality of all research potential in terms of funding and quality (see Chapters III and IV). However, Russia cannot maintain the former priority, level, and variety of basic research, owing to the present socio-economic situation. Therefore, one aim of current policy is to attract funding for basic research, including resources received from international co-operation. Steps are also being taken to diversify the sources of support and the types of links with foreign structures that support research work.

Among internal efforts to promote international co-operation may be mentioned the Euler International Mathematics Institute opened in St. Petersburg in 1992, the creation by the Landau Institute of Theoretical Physics of branch laboratories in France, Italy and Israel, the formation of the Russian Academy's association of lawyers and specialists in patent affairs, and Science, an international academic publishing company.

General protocol agreements on S&T co-operation have been signed with China, South Korea, India and Taiwan. There is a scientific and technical co-operation agreement (biotechnology, pharmaceuticals, energy, new materials, environmental protection) with the Republic of South Africa. The Soros Foundation has allocated more than $1 million to support research in biology and mathematics and about $100 million within the framework of International Science Foundation for emergency help to scientists, including personal stipends and grants, help for libraries, telecommunications and travel to conferences (more than $10 million), and financing of research (about $80 million). An agreement was signed in November 1992 between the RAS and the US National Academy of Sciences, with 13 priority areas for co-operation.

Despite some success in maintaining traditional international channels and forming new ones, various external and internal factors prevent greater success. The socio-economic situation and the legal framework for international co-operation are the most important internal factors. The current practice of favourable taxation on the foreign currency received from foreign organisations to support basic research requires clarification from the legal point of view and an efficient system of control. At present, such problems are being solved on a case-by-case basis. Thus, while equipment and materials for basic research are not subject to customs duty or to taxes, regulations concerning their delivery have not been formulated. The infrastructure for receiving, accommodating and paying foreign scientists who arrive in Russia to undertake joint work in Russian scientific organisations is inadequate. Laws on intellectual property do not permit unequivocal decisions on the relation between the Russian scientist who receives a grant, or financial or material aid, and the state. Thus, Russian laws need to conform to international practice as quickly as possible.

Among external factors can be counted the lack of knowledge within the foreign scientific community of the state of basic science in many disciplines in Russia. Analysis shows that for some scientific fields (physics, mathematics, and, to some extent, biology and chemistry) Russia is well integrated into the world scientific community. Overall, however, integration indicators are considerably lower than those for other countries that carry out research work on a similar scale. In 1990, Russian scientists took part in only in 15.5 per cent of the conferences indexed in ISTP.[1] In 1991, the year of the greatest number of joint publications, only 8 per cent were prepared in collaboration with foreign scientists. In 1991-92, fewer than 2 per cent of members of the editorial boards of international scientific journals were Russian scientists, while 42 per cent were US scientists. This is one of the reasons for the lack of information about Russian science and scientists. This lack of information narrows possibilities for co-operation, and as a result, there is not even partial compensation for the internal drop in research demand on the part of the state and society.

Another important external factor is ignorance or lack of understanding, on the part of foreign partners, of the internal workings of Russia and Russian science, with the result that they disregard the goals and role of state scientific policy. In particular, most foreign government and non-government organisations engaged in international co-operation with Russia in the field of basic research [the French National Research Centre (CNRS), the US National Academy of Sciences, the Soros Foundation, for instance] offer help to individual scientists but do not give aid to the institutional structures that create the framework of Russian science. The help offered takes two forms: invitations abroad to read papers at conferences, do contract work or undertake practical studies in foreign laboratories, on the one hand; and direct contacts between scientists and direct aid to research teams in Russia, through grants, payment of fixed allowances to certain researchers, links to foreign private firms, delivery of scientific equipment and materials, on the other.

There are some good aspects to this form of co-operation in the present situation. The lack of research possibilities and funding within Russia are being compensated, if only in a narrow spectrum of specialties. Russian scientists are being better integrated into the world community. Their professional level is rising, and the funding improves their material status.

At the same time, avoidance of contact with the institutional framework leads more to negative than to positive results for Russian science. It is important to note some of these negative tendencies. The departure of researchers from Russia on long-term contracts because of the present socio-economic and political situation, is in reality one of the channels of "brain drain". Scientists tend to lose touch with the scientific problems of their own country, and one contract very often leads to another ("contract emigration") and in the end to definitive emigration. Most contract emigration (1985-91) was to the United States (46.3 per cent) and Western Europe (46.1 per cent) and only 8 per cent to the rest of the world. The results are similar to the results of direct emigration: scientific work is curtailed, scientific schools are broken up, and the external and, more importantly, the internal prestige of Russian science is lowered.

The "dollarisation" of science (by which Russian scientists are motivated to work for remuneration in hard currency) means that workers in state scientific organisations, while formally remaining in place, take practically any orders from their foreign partners, even if the work does not correspond to the disciplinary orientation of the institute or laboratory. Owing to the lack of a sufficient legal framework, the materials and equipment of state organisations, and sometimes other scientists' results, are used for this research work.

The distribution of financial and material help to Russian scientists by foreign partners has a negative effect on the psychological climate within the scientific community for several reasons. First, internal and external evaluation of the qualifications of Russian scientists who receive Western aid do not always coincide. Inaccurate information in the foreign scientific community about the overall research work of Russian scientists, on the one hand, and lobbying by Russian scientists who are already known in the West, on the other hand, mean that foreign aid is being channelled to a small number of spheres of knowledge and to a narrow circle of scientific collectives. This situation gives rise to sharp conflicts and "hot spots" within the scientific collectives, affects the level and quality of scientific work, and diverts new scientific leaders from the less prestigious branches of science that do not receive foreign material and financial aid.

The declared amount of aid from foreign bodies, at the current dollar exchange rate, corresponds to the amount of state financing of basic research.[2] Under these conditions, state management of this sphere is weakened and state science policy is losing its ability to be effective.

While it is true that relations between foreign partners and Russian institutional structures (ministries, departments, institutes) have not always been efficient, there are examples of mutually advantageous contacts, in the form of joint research work, aid in the form of equipment and materials for carrying out scientific work, or participation in international conferences. There is co-operation with Germany and France in space research; there is joint work in physics, geology, environmental protection and biology with Germany; there is joint research work with American universities.

International S&T co-operation has recently obtained greater stimulus at the regional level. Western partners are attracted to the idea of establishing technopoles and science parks on Russian territory. Up to now, the interest of Western research and financial institutions in such activities has been largely restricted to regions and territories with a rather well-developed infrastructure and has gravitated to so-called "metropolitan" science. For instance, Italy and the World Bank have already signed documents for funding a number of programmes for the St. Petersburg technopark, and the European Community and the British Know-How Fund have also formed proposals for funding this technopark.

The other region of special interest to Western partners is the Moscow region, which has such internationally recognised centres of basic research as Dubna, Hoginsk-Chernogolovka, Protvino, Pushchino, Troitsk and more than a hundred research and design organisations for developing advanced high technology and science-intensive products. For instance, on the basis of the Noginsk physics and chemistry research centre of the Russian Academy of Sciences, a joint entrepreneurship zone and the Chernogolovka technopole are being developed. The institutes and administration of the Moscow *oblast* have received proposals for founding innovation centres and technoparks on its territory from US universities, California, Washington D.C., and New Jersey. An agreement for establishing a research centre to be developed into a technopark has been signed with Boeing. In December 1991, an Interregional General Agreement on co-operation, including activities in science and education, was signed between the administration of the Moscow *oblast* and the state of Indiana, USA.

In establishing a technopark, the characteristics of the region are taken into account. The local administration, the S&T resources, and the structure of industrial facilities in the region are important considerations.

The 14 international research centres in Siberia, now in different stages of formation, are another example. They operate as voluntary international non-governmental organisations (NGOs) – so-called "open" institutes or laboratories – under the authority of the Siberian Department of the Russian Academy of Sciences. There are nine research centres with about 100 research institutes. In some cases, one of the co-founders of the centre is the Ministry of Science and Technological Policy of the Russian Federation. A number have already been institutionalised and are functioning as international centres. For other on-going collaborative research with foreign partners, the forms taken by international participation in the Centre's activities are being studied. To date, most internationally supported innovation and research centres are in the planning stages, so that it is too early to draw conclusions about the effectiveness of this form of international co-operation. On the whole, international S&T co-operation on the regional level cannot be considered active.

Prospects for developing mutually advantageous co-operation with Russia lie in the sphere of joint use of existing basic research potential (including its educational aspect), unique natural sites (Baikal, Kamchatka), and national instruments (accelerators, telescopes, launching sites, and so on), with the participation of Russian scientists.

The most effective foreign support for basic science in Russia ensures continuing scientific activity by furnishing equipment, materials, and information. In this case, Russia will become integrated quite quickly into the world scientific community, and social tension in the scientific sphere will lessen, as will the danger of "scientific terrorism".

In addition, measures for streamlining international co-operation are needed. In particular, ways must be found to co-ordinate foreign scientists' contacts with the Russian Academy of Sciences and the Ministry of Science and Technological Policy, as well as with scientific collectives, institutes and their branches and, to a lesser degree, with individual scientists.

3. International commercial scientific and technical relations

Obtaining information in this area is complicated by the fact that the central state organs have lost the majority of their regulating and controlling functions in the area of foreign economic activity.

The development of commercial scientific and technical ties takes several directions: trade in scientific and technical production, attraction of foreign investments, import of new technologies, selling of scientific and technical services and information to foreign firms.

Characteristics of the present situation in trade of scientific and technical production and export of new technologies are:

– formation of infrastructure for marketing technologies, such as technoparks and innovation and engineering centres (see also Chapter IV), and commodity exchanges, which work with technologies and R&D products as if they were ordinary goods and commodities.[3]
– poor adaptation of scientific and technical production and technologies (even the most competitive) to world market standards;
– lack of market experience in industrial enterprises and other production and commercial units, which are now autonomous actors in international markets, so that they tend to act without any strategy or co-ordination with respect to profits, thereby negatively affecting results and perspectives for national technology producers as a whole;
– overwhelming efforts by foreign partners to make maximum use of the best Russian scientific and technical achievements, while not allowing Russia full-fledged participation in the world market;
– efforts to change the traditional orientation of international commercial ties towards Third World countries, due to the loss of the East European market;
– considerable potential external demand for the existing reserve of scientific and technical schemes,[4] although their realisation on the world market meets with serious counteraction from Western competitors.

Under current conditions, Russian technology producers often practise dumping to enter the international market or co-operate with foreign firms, using their trading, and marketing, networks and trademarks.[5] This practice lowers economic efficiency and negatively influences the prospects for Russian technologies on the world market. Overall, there are very few successful examples of international trade of scientific and technical production and volume is small.[6]

A Russian Government Decree of 5 July 1992 established the rules regulating the conditions for exporting some kinds of technologies and scientific and technical information. The list includes 13 types of consumer goods and 23 types of technologies, export of which was regulated under licences given in 1992-93 by the Ministry of Foreign Economic Relations of Russian Federation in agreement with the Commission on Export Control (COCOM). This is only a first stage in the process of state regulation of commercial technology transfer and trade of high-technology production.

At present, one priority of state policy is to attract foreign investment, which offers a channel for introducing new foreign technologies or provides mechanisms for adapting Russian technologies for industrial use. In 1987, a first, not very successful, experience of state regulation of foreign investments was connected with the formation of joint ventures.[7] Uncertainty in intellectual property rights legislation led foreign firms to seek out as yet unpatented technologies and R&D products and acquire intellectual property rights for them, which made the operation both cheaper and more advantageous.

However, most Western businesses prefer to act within a strict legal framework. As a result, Russia loses many potential partners and the rights to unique scientific and technical developments. Only when the Russian Federation's Patent Law and supplementary acts took force in September 1992[8] did the rights of inventors become clearer. The patent was introduced as the means of protecting intellectual property. Ideally its existence makes it possible for a scientist or engineer to sell or make a profit from his/her intellectual product. According to the Law on Foreign Investments, enterprises with foreign capital can patent their inventions and industrial samples abroad independently.

A potentially attractive channel for receiving modern technologies is foreign investment in privatisation of enterprises (excluding certain strategic spheres). The Presidential Decree of 3 March 1993, "On the protection of foreign investments in Russia from non-commercial risks", serves to create generally favourable conditions for foreign investments, but it will take time for the decree to take force.

On the whole, state measures for attracting foreign investors are very general in nature. The so-called "permitting-limiting" principle, which simply sets a basic framework, does not stimulate foreign investment and does not aid in the realisation of priority socio-economic and scientific and technical goals.

At present foreign investors are circumspect with regard to entrepreneurial activity in Russia. According to several representatives of private foreign businesses, co-operation with Russia is being impeded not only by economic and political problems but also by technological incompatibility, especially in the field of equipment for material production. They also noted the underdevelopment of private property. On the positive side, they note the availability of highly qualified personnel at relatively low labour cost; reserves of applications that can be advanced to the market realisation stage at relatively low cost; a developed research infrastructure; and a huge potential market. Private foreign investors see as most promising the area of applied science where isolation resulted in approaches different from those taken in the West and often gave outstanding results. In such areas, even modest investment projects in Russia are profitable.

US Department of Defense experts believe that large-scale investment in high technology and the creation of international venture enterprises will only be possible in Russia when there is a modern infrastructure and when demand for consumer goods has been satisfied. The use to which private foreign capital is put in Russia indicates that this is so.[9]

It should also be noted that realising major projects requires solving many scientific and technical, legal, organisational and other questions. Sometimes partners from both sides are not ready to deal with them.[10]

COCOM restrictions are also a limiting factor. At the Paris COCOM meeting in May 1991 the 120 categories of goods and technologies whose export to East European countries and the USSR was prohibited was curtailed by 30 to 50 per cent. Permission was given to export to the USSR metal-working machine tools, civil aviation aircraft and equipment, second and third generation PCs. At the same time, controls on export to the USSR of eight categories was increased: electronic components, new chemical materials, telecommunications systems, sensors and lasers, navigation and aviation/navigation instruments, technologies in the field of aircraft and ship-building, PCs (of the latest models, Intel 80486), and jet engines. These COCOM decisions continue to determine conditions for commercial and investment projects of foreign private firms with Russian partners. The "warming" of the international climate has led to some deviations from the strict observance of such restrictions, in particular for trade in computer equipment and treaties on the creation of telecommunications network. However, concern over the leakage of modern technologies to Russia continues to concern government and business circles of Western countries.[11]

Co-operation in the sphere of scientific information, including scientific and technical and information services offered to Western firms and organisations, is a relatively new form of commercial activity in Russia. In the past, one aspect of Western official policy concerning S&T co-operation with Russia, in which interested private firms, foundations and research centres actively participated, was to find and engage in collaboration with those who possess information on the scientific and technical potential of Russia.[12]

The elimination of the state patent and licence services in Russia (licensing agreements have not been registered since 1991) meant that previously strictly regulated scientific and technical information was leaked abroad, without any control over valuable commercial and defence information. The formerly closed industries of the military-industrial complex and leading institutes have developments and technologies that are competitive on the world market. It was precisely this kind of information that was sought by Western firms.[13]

Overcoming difficulties requires the rapid elaboration of concrete measures, in particular by launching a programme of information monitoring; by forming, with foreign capital, commercial structures for using the research results of Russian research institutes and universities; by creating economic and legal conditions for foreign investors; and by developing a set of legal measures for protecting "national scientific property".

4. Participation in international scientific and technical programmes and organisations

Russia's ability to solve its complex social and economic problems, as well as its future development, depend to a considerable extent on the possibility of preserving its accumulated scientific and technical wealth. In this connection, a national policy is being elaborated, one part of which concerns international scientific and technical co-operation.

Almost immediately upon receiving its new statute, the Russian Federation demonstrated its readiness to be the USSR's successor in respect of international agreements in science and technology. The Russian Ministry of Foreign Affairs, in a note of 13 January 1993, notified all heads of diplomatic missions in Moscow that the Russian Federation continues to have the privileges and obligations arising from the international treaties signed by the USSR.

In its last years, the State Committee of the USSR on Science and Technology (SCST, now the Ministry of Science and Technological Policy) supervised the fulfilling of Soviet obligations for 29 inter-government agreements on economic, scientific and technical co-operation and 25 agreements with corresponding state organisations of foreign countries. Some 150 agreements and protocols on scientific and technical co-operation on specific issues had been signed by the SCST of the USSR with foreign firms and scientific departments throughout the world.

The SCST planned the participation of ministries, organisations and specialists in the work of 237 international organisations. The USSR took part in the activities of about 900 international scientific and technical organisations within the following frameworks:

- 25 international organisations of the United Nations, including UNO, UNESCO, UNIDO, UNEP, IAEA, WIPO, and 30 inter-governmental organisations outside the UN framework;
- multilateral co-operation within the framework of the Conference on Security and Co-operation in Europe (CSCE) and the European Community;
- multilateral co-operation within the framework of international non-government organisations.

Co-operation and membership in international organisations along these lines require membership dues of about 46 million of foreign currency equivalent to roubles.

Branch ministries and departments of the USSR also developed international ties,[14] which have been taken over by ministries and departments of the Russian Federation.[15]

Since the end of 1991, as part of the reorganisation of the former USSR, the organisation of international co-operation in S&T has seen some changes. In 1992, under the direction of the Russian Federation's Ministry of Science, an inventory of agreements and protocols signed by SCST was begun, in order to evaluate them and transfer most of them to interested Russian enterprises and organisations, in the interest of developing further direct ties with foreign partners, while taking into account their commercial merit, the interests of the state, the issue of intellectual property, and the rights of scientists and specialists.

In 1992, the Russian Ministry of Science also began to take stock of membership in international organisations and to renew existing treaties and agreements on behalf of Russia, while stipulating new membership conditions (notably the lowering of dues). In 1992, the scale of Russia's international co-operation did not diminish. Russian organisations and enterprises took part in 432 bilateral projects and multilateral programmes (such as EUREKA, the World Health Organisation), most of them oriented towards high technology, *e.g.* information science, energy and fuel, agrarian and industrial complexes, new materials, machine building, metallurgy and transport, chemistry and biotechnology, public health, and basic research in nuclear physics, ecology, high temperature superconductivity, mass and heat exchange. Thus, international projects covered almost all state scientific and technical programmes, including Mineral Wealth of Russia *(Nedra Rossii)* Russian Public Health, Russian Ecology, and others. In 1993, work continues on 369 projects and financial aid is envisaged for 44 newly formed projects.

The process of widening relations for S&T with the countries of Southeast Asia (South Korea, Singapore), the Middle East (Egypt, Israel), and Africa (South Africa) has begun. Relations with the states of Eastern Europe and China are being restored.

In the past, government and state financing of international S&T co-operation was assured by the responsible administrative bodies (Ministry of Foreign Affairs, former State Committee of Science and Technology, former Ministry of Foreign Trade and its specialised organisations), which allocated funds to Soviet organisations for conducting research, design and experimental work. In the 1992 state budget and in the proposed 1993 budget, corresponding funds were allocated and are being distributed by the Ministry of Science and Technological Policy. In 1992, 809.9 million roubles were allocated for international S&T co-operation, most of which went to fulfil obligations for intergovernmental agreements and to develop the infrastructure of international co-operation, including the use of foreign databases, as well as for scientific conferences, symposia and seminars, organisation of exhibitions, scientific and technical exchanges, and consultancy services by Russian and foreign participants in joint work.

The creation of an independent foundation for scientific and technical projects is being considered. This would mean allocating additional funds to attract national and foreign investors, and would use foreign funds given for scientific and technical research and for technical aid to Russia. There is also the possibility of financing joint research and development with foreign partners from the Russian Fund for Fundamental Research and the non-budget Russian Fund for Technological Development under the Ministry of Science and Technological Policy.

International co-operation will require work in the following directions:
- broaden interaction with S&T organisations of CIS nations and create alliances of scientific capabilities in order to increase the efficiency of Russian science and its ability to fulfil international obligations taken on by the USSR;
- increase participation in West European scientific production programmes, including EUREKA;
- take stock rapidly of agreements and memberships in international organisations in order to renew treaties and liquidate debts to international organisations in which Russia will participate;

- widen S&T co-operation through the establishment and strengthening of ties with countries of Southeast Asia, Latin America, the Middle East, etc.;
- reinstate S&T attachés in the embassies of the Russian Federation and among the permanent representatives of the Russian Federation in international organisations;
- conduct analyses of the S&T activities of foreign countries and the situation of the world markets for technologies;
- organise work on ensuring access to foreign information centres and data banks of scientific and technical information;
- develop a legal base to regulate questions of transfer to foreign partners of the results of scientific and technical activities;
- conclude agreements on information exchange (registration of treaties, agreements, contracts and grants concluded between Russian and foreign organisations).

Notes

1. Index to Scientific and Technical Proceedings, published by the Institute of Scientific Information, United States.
2. See Chapter III for details on state R&D expenditures.
3. Trade on the stock exchange in scientific and technical production is in some sense unlawful, as according to the Russian Federation Law on the Stock Exchanges, objects of intellectual property cannot be a commodity of exchange.
4. According to experts of the US defence and trade departments, the most interesting are: laser technologies; a system to warm the ionosphere; high-turbulence chemical microreactors; metallic materials; nuclear reactors for satellites, with a built-in system of thermoionic conversion; airplane engines run on liquid hydrogen; a high-precision laser microscalpel capable of cutting chains of DNA and RNA; diamond-coated surgical instruments. Foreign firms are very interested in Russia's nuclear welding technologies and surface thermo-reinforcement of metals, milling and drilling of superhard materials, ceramics, treatment of diamonds, machining of plastics, wood and fabrics.
5. Even in fields in which Russian technology excels, as in the production and operation of space technology, firms cannot, on their own, enter the world market. For example, Russia has to compete for the launching of an Argentinean communications satellite through the intermediary of American firms. The case is similar for the agreement between the SPA Energomash and Pratt and Whitney, the American airplane engine construction firm, to build engines on the basis of Russian technologies for sale on the American market. Pratt and Whitney does not invest any money, but it uses the unique scientific and technical capability of a leading Russian association. It obtains a safe technology with a history of successful use which does not require technical testing, since the engines designed and produced by the SPA, the Energy and Buran rockets, launched all Soviet space ships into orbit beginning with the first Earth satellite to the Mir station. According to an agreement of December 1992, the US Lockheed Corporation will invest about $5 million within five years in a joint venture with the Khrunichev production plant. The venture, ownership of which is shared equally by both sides, ensures exclusive rights to the commercial use of the Proton launch rocket, except for launches undertaken by the Russian government. According to US State Department officials, this new joint venture will give the United States the ability to control the use by Russia of its rocket technology. The US position on the market will become stronger as Khrunichev's rocket is more competitive than the corresponding American one.
6. The share of machine-building production exported in the first half of 1992 was less than 8 per cent, and of high and advanced technology 1.5 per cent.
7. Only 5 per cent of registered joint ventures produce goods that correspond to state priorities for development, which should be addressed by this type of foreign investment.

8. On Trademarks, Service Marks and Indication of Places of Origin of Goods, On the Legal Safety of Topologies of Integrated Circuits, and On Security of Computer Programmes and Databases.

9. For example, the international fibre optics communications system began with the creation of Intertelecom, a shareholding firm allied with the Japanese firm KDD and South Korean Telecom. It will unite Russia, Japan and South Korea and is a part of a project of trans-Siberian fibre optics communications lines, in which communications between Denmark and Russia, and between Turkey, Denmark and Russia are envisaged.

10. Two examples are the Russian projects of IBM for education and the creation of an information system for Aeroflot, and the efforts of the Philips Medicine System to organise the production and sales of medical equipment in Russia.

11. Thus, the US government's demand for case-by-case discussion of individual export of American-made satellite equipment to Russia or Kazakhstan. The already mentioned joint project between Lockheed and the Khrunichev plant raised sharp criticism in US government circles (*Space News*, 4-10 January 1993).

12. Thus, major Western firms have had active contacts with the institutes and centres of scientific and technical information, such as the Centre for Scientific and Technical Information, and used their databases. In 1992, the Centre for Processing Geological and Geophysical Information was finished and processes information using modern IBM cluster computers and light software provided by Schlumberger. The centre was formed to process data concerning oil extraction and refining, estimation of oil reserves, and definition of the spatial configuration of oil deposits.

13. Thus, Livermore Laboratory (US) signed contracts with 19 Russian and one Ukrainian research institutes to acquire formerly top secret data on laser technologies. The laboratory paid $25 000 for seven reports on this topic. The price is very cheap for a scientific report of this kind and the information is still strategically valuable (whence Livermore's interest in it). There is serious concern that foreign institutions will buy strategically important S&T information at moderate hard currency prices.

14. Thus, the USSR Public Health Ministry represented the USSR in the World Health Organisation (WHO). In 1991, the USSR concluded an agreement with WHO for an international centre for radiation and related medical problems and contributed to WHO programmes on AIDS and on family planning and reproduction. The Ministry also participated in the programmes of the International Agency for the Study of Cancer (IASC) and was a signatory to the Memorandum of Understanding for co-operation in the area of chemical agents. It also was in charge of 17 bilateral intergovernmental and interdepartmental agreements and took part in ten agreements on scientific and technical co-operation in the framework of SCST programmes and several more under the aegis of the Foreign Ministry. The USSR Ministry of Agriculture carried out co-operation with 97 international organisations, and more than two-thirds of the enterprises, organisations, departments and agricultural units of the agro-industrial complex became part of the Russian Federation.

15. Thus, international agreements and treaties of the former USSR with 51 foreign states in the field of education became the responsibility of the Russian Ministry of Science. These agreements provide long-term and short-term education and practical work and studies for students, teachers and scientific staff abroad and on Russian territory.

Annex 1

Statistical addition to Chapter III

Table A1.1. **R&D personnel by sector of performance**
(in thousands)[1]

	Total R&D personnel			Researchers			Technicians			Supporting staff		
	1990	1991	1991 as a percentage of 1990	1990	1991	1991 as a percentage of 1990	1990	1991	1991 as a percentage of 1990	1990	1991	1991 as a percentage of 1990
Total	1 943.4	1 677.8	86.3	992.6	878.5	88.5	234.8	200.6	85.4	716.0	598.7	83.6
Academy sector	191.9	190.0	99.0	107.5	109.0	101.4	13.8	14.0	101.4	70.6	67.1	95.0
Higher education sector	108.7	90.6	83.3	71.1	60.8	85.5	6.2	5.0	80.6	31.4	24.8	79.0
Industrial R&D organisations	1 500.3	1 278.8	85.2	745.4	649.7	87.2	194.8	165.8	85.1	560.1	463.3	82.7
Enterprise sector	142.5	118.4	83.1	68.6	58.9	85.9	20.0	15.8	79.0	54.0	43.6	80.7

1. Details may not add to total because of rounding.
Source: Centre of Science Research and Statistics.

Table A1.2. **Academy sector researchers by field of science**[1]

(as of 1 January 1991, in percentage)

	Researchers	Doctors of sciences	Candidates of sciences
Total	100	100	100
Physics and mathematics	21.5	26.4	21.9
Chemistry	9.7	9.3	11.2
Biology	14.8	17.0	18.2
Geology and mineralogy	4.4	5.8	4.3
Engineering	16.4	4.6	8.5
Agriculture	9.4	2.1	8.2
History	3.2	7.4	4.6
Economics	4.3	3.3	5.1
Philosophy	0.7	2.3	1.0
Philology	1.5	4.0	2.1
Geography	1.4	1.4	1.5
Law	0.1	0.1	0.1
Pedagogy	0.0	0.0	0.0
Medicine	6.9	11.7	8.5
Pharmacy	0.1	–	0.0
Veterinary	0.6	0.4	0.6
Arts	0.0	0.0	0.0
Architecture	0.0	–	–
Psychology	0.3	0.4	0.4
Sociology	0.6	0.6	0.7
Politics	0.0	–	0.0
Other	4.1	3.2	3.1

1. Including higher education teaching staff working as part-time researchers.
Source: Centre of Science Research and Statistics.

Table A1.3. **Researchers by field of science**[1]

	Researchers		Doctors of sciences		Candidates of sciences	
	1990	1991	1990	1991	1990	1991
Total	1 090 922	968 387	24 027	24 800	183 105	168 649
Physics and mathematics	74 496	67 087	3 672	3 894	21 009	19 969
Chemistry	38 249	34 916	1 495	1 640	11 730	11 416
Biology	31 526	31 428	1 993	2 161	12 337	12 441
Geology and mineralogy	24 523	22 642	1 389	1 288	6 698	6 129
Engineering	653 582	579 919	6 046	6 037	72 550	65 232
Agriculture	23 277	23 144	709	767	7 700	7 438
History	5 294	5 444	638	728	2 442	2 639
Economics	52 351	39 419	994	1 004	10 725	8 679
Philosophy	2 384	2 194	242	258	1 242	1 164
Philology	6 081	5 713	363	413	1 791	1 916
Geography	7 439	7 277	267	302	1 932	2 032
Law	1 083	1 859	52	106	366	732
Pedagogy	4 924	5 270	158	179	1 701	1 813
Medicine	29 524	27 706	3 568	3 479	15 125	13 756
Pharmacy	1 583	1 109	33	34	449	411
Veterinary	3 191	2 804	213	223	1 384	1 234
Arts	2 228	1 406	98	39	546	307
Architecture	3 585	3 992	35	48	470	611
Psychology	1 621	1 624	86	78	677	573
Sociology	1 165	1 038	71	55	407	365
Politics	60	47	14	2	22	19
Other	122 756	102 349	1 891	2 065	11 802	9 773

1. Including higher education teaching staff working as part-time researchers.
Source: Centre of Science Research and Statistics.

Table A1.4. **R&D personnel by economic region**[1]
(in thousands)

	Total R&D personnel			Researchers			Technicians			Supporting staff		
	1990	1991	1991 as a percentage of 1990	1990	1991	1991 as a percentage of 1990	1990	1991	1991 as a percentage of 1990	1990	1991	1991 as a percentage of 1990
Total	1 943.4	1 677.8	86.3	992.6	878.5	88.5	234.8	200.6	85.4	716.0	598.7	83.6
North	22.7	20.0	88.1	11.6	10.5	90.5	3.2	2.8	87.5	7.9	6.7	84.8
North-West	349.2	275.1	78.8	174.6	147.1	84.2	41.4	30.7	74.2	133.1	97.2	73.0
Of which: St. Petersburg	336.8	264.4	78.5	168.8	142.0	84.1	39.2	29.6	75.5	128.9	92.8	72.0
Central	800.6	693.2	86.6	422.5	377.2	89.3	90.9	80.3	88.3	287.1	235.7	82.1
Of which: Moscow	552.9	444.9	80.5	310.2	263.2	84.8	60.3	49.5	82.1	182.5	132.1	72.4
Volga-Viatka	85.2	74.6	87.7	40.3	36.1	89.6	11.8	9.8	83.1	33.1	28.7	86.7
Central-Black Earth	59.5	53.6	90.1	31.4	28.3	90.1	7.3	6.8	93.2	20.8	18.5	88.9
Volga	163.5	145.3	88.9	78.0	69.4	89.0	18.9	15.6	82.5	66.6	60.3	90.5
North Caucasus	93.4	78.9	84.5	48.9	41.5	84.9	12.0	10.4	86.7	32.5	27.0	83.1
Urals	142.5	144.1	101.1	67.5	66.3	98.2	20.5	19.5	95.1	54.4	58.4	107.4
West-Siberian	136.9	117.9	86.1	69.4	60.1	86.6	17.1	14.8	86.5	50.5	43.0	85.1
East-Siberian	43.0	36.5	84.9	23.7	21.3	89.9	4.7	4.5	95.7	14.6	10.6	72.6
Far East	41.7	34.4	82.5	22.5	18.5	82.2	6.1	4.6	75.4	13.2	11.4	86.4
Kaliningrad region	5.3	4.1	77.4	2.3	2.1	91.3	0.9	0.8	88.9	2.1	1.2	57.1

1. Details may not add to total because of rounding.
Source: Centre of Science Research and Statistics.

Table A1.5. **Higher education enrolment, freshmen and graduates by attendance status**
(thousands)

	Student enrolment			Freshmen			Graduates		
	Total	Full-time education	Part-time and distance education	Total	Full-time education	Part-time and distance education	Total	Full-time education	Part-time and distance education
1985	2 966	1 569	1 397	634.6	365.5	269.1	476.6	300.2	176.4
1986	2 907	1 512	1 395	633.3	367.2	266.1	468.6	291.1	177.5
1987	2 835	1 478	1 357	620.9	366.9	254.0	439.4	240.4	199.0
1988	2 795	1 478	1 317	621.0	372.2	248.8	438.1	254.1	184.0
1989	2 861	1 624	1 237	602.7	365.3	237.4	432.8	237.5	195.3
1990	2 824	1 647	1 177	583.9	360.7	223.2	401.1	215.5	185.6
1991	2 763	1 668	1 095	565.9	368.8	197.1	406.8	230.3	176.5
1992	2 638	1 658	980	520.7	359.1	161.6	425.3	252.4	179.9

Source: RF State Committee on Statistics

Table A1.6. **Higher education enrolment by economic region and attendance status**
(thousands)

	Full-time education				Part-time and distance education			
	1985/86	1990/91	1991/92	1992/93	1985/86	1990/91	1991/92	1992/93
Total	1 569	1 647	1 668	1 658	1 396	1 177	1 095	980
North	35	38	39	40	25	20	20	18
North-West	152	150	149	145	140	118	108	94
Of which: St.-Petersburg	141	138	137	133	131	110	100	88
Central	398	416	417	414	483	383	349	310
Of which: Moscow	249	254	252	249	357	275	245	217
Volga-Viatka	71	82	83	83	62	53	50	45
Central-Black Earth	65	76	78	77	58	50	47	43
Volga	173	189	191	189	128	114	109	97
North Caucasus	133	148	152	151	120	104	99	90
Urals	186	188	192	191	134	116	108	97
West-Siberian	179	183	186	182	116	107	100	89
East-Siberian	99	99	101	100	78	67	62	55
Far East	78	78	80	78	52	45	43	38

Source: RF State Committee on Statistics.

Table A1.7. **Percentage distribution of higher education institute graduates by field of study**

	1990	1991	1992
Total	100	100	100
Natural sciences	9.0	8.4	8.7
Humanities	12.1	10.7	10.8
Labour, physical and aesthetic education and training	10.4	11.1	11.2
Health services	6.1	6.1	6.8
Culture and arts	3.2	3.2	2.6
Economics	8.1	8.3	6.9
Applied economics	5.7	5.7	5.5
Geological exploration of mineral resources	0.7	0.8	0.8
Exploitation of mineral resources	1.0	1.3	1.3
Power engineering	1.7	1.8	1.8
Metallurgy	1.0	1.0	1.1
Machinery and metal-working	3.5	3.5	3.6
Aircraft	1.1	1.1	1.1
Shipbuilding	0.6	0.6	0.6
Motor vehicles and tractors	1.9	2.0	2.1
Power engineering machinery	0.4	0.4	0.5
Technological machines and equipment	2.5	2.5	2.5
Electric machines	0.7	0.7	0.7
Instruments	1.0	1.0	1.0
Electric equipment	0.9	0.9	0.9
Automation and controlling	2.7	2.8	3.2
Computers and automated systems	1.8	1.9	2.1
Radio engineering and communications	2.7	3.0	3.3
Transport exploitation	1.1	1.2	1.2
Chemical technology	1.8	1.6	1.7
Timber exploitation and wood processing	0.8	0.8	0.7
Technology of food products	2.1	2.1	1.8
Technology of consumer goods	2.2	2.2	1.9
Construction and architecture	5.6	5.5	5.5
Geodesy and cartography	0.2	0.2	0.3
Agriculture and forestry	7.4	7.6	7.8

Source: Centre of Science Research and Statistics.

Table A1.8. **Postgraduate students by field of science**

	1987	1988	1989	1990	1991	1992
Total, all fields	17 248	16 928	16 695	16 355	16 322	14 857
Physics and	2 124	2 102	1 746	1 815	1 654	1 610
Chemistry	607	636	576	543	527	518
Biology	740	769	758	740	788	740
Geology and	349	300	401	425	412	364
Engineering	6 797	6 480	6 513	6 152	6 232	5 234
Agriculture	624	713	611	594	705	566
History	590	577	558	579	600	543
Economics	1 691	1 659	1 752	1 641	1 611	1 473
Philosophy	459	460	465	413	397	361
Philology	608	649	596	629	586	590
Geography	217	191	195	191	182	175
Law	214	199	245	271	262	216
Pedagogy	501	555	556	580	600	625
Medicine	1 019	1 012	1 043	1 118	1 081	1 116
Pharmacy	46	47	60	72	60	48
Veterinary	135	153	148	122	137	124
Arts	332	210	212	186	203	187
Architecture	87	104	114	91	66	47
Psychology	108	112	114	127	134	123
Sociology	–	–	32	65	74	152
Politics	–	–	–	1	11	45

Source: Centre of Science Research and Statistics.

Table A1.9. **Number of scientific degrees[1] awarded by field of science**

	1990	1991
Total, all fields	35 117	35 040
Physics and mathematics	3 886	3 883
Chemistry	1 576	1 628
Biology	2 289	2 538
Geology and mineralogy	649	555
Engineering	10 520	9 791
Agriculture	1 183	1 215
History	1 421	1 591
Economics	3 038	2 868
Philosophy	1 168	988
Philology	1 398	1 370
Geography	261	294
Law	538	574
Pedagogy	1 323	1 512
Medicine	4 439	4 796
Pharmacy	137	129
Veterinary	249	288
Arts	212	263
Architecture	131	120
Psychology	257	280
Sociology	27	108
Politics	4	25
Other	411	224

1. The total number of degrees also includes degrees awarded to scientists not enrolled among postgraduate students.
Source: RF Supreme Certification Commission.

Table A1.10. **R&D fixed assets by sector**

	All sectors	Academy sector	Industrial R&D organisations	Higher education sector	Enterprise sector
Total R&D fixed assets, million roubles					
1990	31 651.3	6 466.4	21 603.3	2 305.2	1 276.4
1991	34 682.9	7 189.9	23 925.0	2 399.0	1 169.0
Per capita of R&D personnel, thousand roubles					
1990	16.3	33.7	14.4	21.2	9.0
1991	20.7	37.8	18.7	26.5	9.9
Per researcher, thousand roubles					
1990	31.9	60.2	28.9	32.4	18.6
1991	39.5	66.0	36.8	39.5	19.8
Machines and equipment, million roubles					
1990	19 060.1	3 909.6	12 827.3	1 500.9	822.3
1991	20 606.0	4 486.4	13 745.1	1 602.1	772.4
Per capita of R&D personnel, thousand roubles					
1990	9.8	20.4	8.5	13.8	5.8
1991	12.3	23.6	10.7	17.7	6.5
Per researcher, thousand roubles					
1990	19.2	36.4	17.2	21.1	12.0
1991	23.5	41.2	21.2	26.4	13.1

Source: Science and Technology in Russia: 1991, CSRS, 1992, p. 105.

Table A1.11. **R&D fixed assets by economic region**
(million roubles)

	Average annual value of R&D fixed assets			Of which machines and equipment		
	1990	1991	1991 as a percentage of 1990	1990	1991	1991 as a percentage of 1990
Total, all regions	31 651.3	34 682.9	109.6	19 060.1	20 606.0	108.1
North	308.9	327.5	106.0	149.3	172.5	115.5
North-West	5 278.7	5 425.9	102.8	3 369.8	3 378.2	100.2
Of which: St.-Petersburg	4 998.0	5 113.6	102.3	3 185.9	3 191.2	100.2
Central	15 166.6	16 780.9	110.6	9 254.2	9 862.8	106.6
Of which: Moscow	10 465.0	11 088.6	106.0	6 677.2	6 837.8	102.4
Volga-Viatka	1 156.6	1 307.0	113.0	780.2	837.0	107.3
Central-Black Earth	698.1	743.4	106.5	395.6	467.6	118.2
Volga	1 979.3	2 073.5	104.8	1 126.9	1 264.3	112.2
North Caucasus	1 334.4	1 411.0	105.7	720.5	815.3	113.2
Urals	1 851.8	2 398.0	129.5	1097.1	1360.0	124.0
West-Siberian	2 424.2	2 685.1	110.8	1478.4	1658.7	112.2
East-Siberian	653.1	736.4	112.8	377.5	412.5	109.3
Far East	714.9	711.1	99.5	296.5	307.9	103.8

Source: Science and Technology in Russia: 1991, CSRS, 1992, p. 108.

Table A1.12. **R&D equipment by sector and age**
(as of 1 July 1989, in millions of roubles)

	Total	Age				
		1-2 years	3-5 years	6-10 years	11-20 years	Over 20 years
All sectors[1]	15 856.7	3 544.5	4 488.0	4 633.3	2 436.1	754.8
Academy sector	3 116.6	635.2	857.8	945.9	525.2	152.5
Industrial R&D organisations	10 579.0	2 412.8	3 027.4	3 066.1	1 592.3	480.4
Higher education sector	2 161.1	496.5	602.8	621.3	318.6	121.9

1. Excluding the enterprise sector.
Source: Science and Technology in Russia: 1991, CSRS, 1992, p. 119.

Table A1.13. **R&D equipment having cost 30 000 roubles or more, by sector and technical level**

(as of 1 July 1989, in millions of roubles)

	Machines and equipment	Of which: technical level			
		Above the best world level	Equal to the best world level	Below the best world level	Not identified
Total, all sectors[1]	5 370.6	26.1	1 175.3	1 674.5	2 494.7
Academy sector	976.3	2.1	234.0	299.9	440.3
Industrial R&D organisations	3 914.9	23.5	826.5	1 241.4	1 823.5
Higher education sector	479.4	0.5	114.8	133.2	230.9

1. Excluding the enterprise sector.
Source: Science and Technology in Russia: 1991, CSRS, 1992, p. 122.

Table A1.14. **Machines and equipment of R&D institutions by field of sciences and age**[1]

(as of 1 July 1989, in thousands of roubles)

	Total	Age				
		1-2 years	3-5 years	6-10 years	11-20 years	Over 20 years
Total machines and equipment	13 719 127.7	3 052 787.5	3 889 538.3	4 023 707.4	2 119 835.0	633 259.5
Natural sciences	2 875 755.9	567 238.6	805 774.8	842 479.0	505 197.1	155 066.4
Social sciences	240 269.4	48 665.5	68 699.0	85 535.0	28 473.2	8 896.7
Humanities	205 177.2	46 212.0	41 539.4	86 187.9	29 310.9	1 927.0
Engineering	8 863 169.2	2 067 074.3	2 576 856.4	2 533 652.9	1 293 769.4	391 816.2
Agriculture	190 476.4	35 611.7	47 522.4	60 378.9	37 059.5	9 903.9
Medical sciences	446 373.8	72 923.7	105 664.4	146 873.3	96 682.9	24 229.5
Information and information systems	161 078.2	38 405.8	46 842.4	61 372.8	11 963.1	2 494.1
Other	736 827.6	176 655.9	196 639.5	207 227.6	117 378.9	38 925.7

1. Excluding higher education institutes and enterprises.
Source: Centre of Science Research and Statistics.

Table A1.15. **Value of R&D[1] by economic region**
(in millions of roubles)[2]

	1989		1990		1991	
	Total	Of which: performed within R&D institutions	Total	Of which: performed within R&D institutions	Total	Of which: performed within R&D institutions
Russia	26 297.6	18 348.6	26 565.6	18 371.3	32 770.3	23 269.6
North	236.8	198.6	265.3	208.5	390.3	311.2
North-West	4 737.7	3 257.1	4 865.5	3 237.3	5 139.1	3 609.4
Of which: St.-Petersburg	4 655.9	3 184.2	4 783.3	3 168.2	5 035.9	3 521.7
Central	13 215.9	8 353.9	12 984.2	8 239.4	16 081.2	10 360.4
Of which: Moscow	10 291.1	6 226.9	9 794.3	5 975.4	10 736.0	7 101.3
Volga-Viatka	921.1	725.4	925.7	705.3	1 195.9	949.5
Central-Black Earth	551.9	468.6	558.4	452.4	743.7	626.1
Volga	1 595.8	1 295.8	1 626.9	1 328.7	2 067.7	1 692.9
North Caucasus	1 046.4	832.7	979.3	759.1	1 180.3	941.4
Urals	1 355.7	1 082.9	1 553.9	1 225.4	2 271.7	1 854.9
West-Siberian	1 665.5	1 367.0	1 837.6	1 421.5	2 245.3	1 849.2
East-Siberian	401.0	344.7	428.0	371.3	725.8	475.4
Far East	510.4	377.3	477.5	375.9	659.6	541.4
Kaliningrad region	59.4	44.6	3.2	46.4	69.6	57.7

1. Value of R&D includes current expenditure on R&D and profits obtained by R&D institutions from R&D activity during the year.
2. Detail may not add to total because of rounding.
Source: Science and Technology in Russia: 1991, CSRS, 1992, p. 122.

Table A1.16. **Appropriations for R&D from the republic budget through MSTP**
(billions of roubles)

		1991	1992	1993[1]
	Total	13.3	103.8	684.6
I.	Programme of maintaining R&D potential of the Russian Federation (R&D performed by institutions of ministries and departments)			
	Total	10.6	60.0	386.7
	Of which:			
	Russian Academy of Sciences:	2.3	16.0	75.7
	Siberian Branch	0.3	3.3	16.6
	Urals Branch	0.1	1.0	5.0
	Far East Branch	0.1	1.2	6.3
	Russian Academy of Agricultural Sciences	0.3	2.4	13.1
	Russian Academy of Medical Sciences	–[2]	1.8	7.4
	Of which: Siberian Branch	0.0	0.3	1.4
	Russian Academy of Education	0.0	0.4	2.0
	Moscow State University	–	0.3	2.3
II.	Russian Fund for Fundamental Research	0.3	3.1	20.1
III.	Federal S&T programmes Total	2.4	40.7	277.8
	Of which:			
	Government S&T programmes	1.3	27.0	168.7
	Major programmes and projects of the national economy	0.5	9.9	21.0
	International programmes and projects	0.2	1.5	7.9
	State programme to develop research centres	–	–	57.0
	Programme to develop Russian universities	0.2	1.5	5.9
	Programmes to develop S&T innovation infrastructure (technoparks, technopolies, business incubators)	–	–	3.4
	Funds for regional centres and programmes	–	–	6.8
	Programme of integrated information and telecommunications system serving financing and credit bodies of Russia: project "Argonaut – Teleports of Russia"	–	–	2.0

1. Estimated as of 1 July 1993.
2. Financed by the USSR Ministry of Health (MSTP).
Source: Ministry of Science and Technological Policy.

Table A1.17. **R&D budget appropriations for government S&T programmes**
(in millions of roubles)

	1991	1992	1993[1]
Prospective agricultural technologies	158.0	636.4	1 275.0
Prospective technologies for processing agricultural products and food production	36.0	176.9	1 026.0
Prospective information technologies	60.0	210.4	601.0
Prospective telecommunications and integrated communications systems	30.0	104.9	451.0
Informatisation of Russia	60.0	210.5	520.0
Microelectronics, computers and automation	–	60.3	–
Prospective micro- and nanoelectronic technologies and devices	–	60.3	575.0
Of which: Nanostructures in physics and electronics	–	–	175.0
Human genome	32.0	130.5	375.0
Priority objectives of genetics	–	119.8	375.0
Modern bioengineering technologies	40.0	207.8	590.0
Means for research in physico-chemical biology and biotechnology	–	56.2	175.0
New materials	58.0	535.4	1 568.0
Ecologically clean power engineering	66.6	400.6	1 136.0
Resource-saving and ecologically clean technologies in mining and metallurgy	–	125.2	383.5
Prospective technologies for complex exploration of fuel and energy resources of Russia	8.3	70.4	455.0
Ceolites of Russia	–	29.8	–
Nations of Russia: revival and progress	9.8	79.2	224.5
Informatisation of education	–	50.1	–
Higher school of Russia	–	20.3	–
Progress of education in Russia	21.9	27.8	278.5
Ecologically safe and resource-saving technologies in chemistry	43.4	327.1	986.0
Chemical high technologies	–	70.4	–
Priority objectives in chemical research and technologies	–	70.4	–
Secondary processing of polymers without waste	–	20.3	–
New principles and methods of obtaining chemical substances and materials	–	140.8	399.0
High-energy physics	100.0	422.6	1 198.5
Basic space research (solar system, planets)	40.0	200.4	568.0
Basic nuclear physics	–	158.6	450.0
Synchrotron radiation, applications of radiation	–	125.2	320.0
High-temperature superconductivity	130.0	455.4	1 163.0
Controlled thermonuclear synthesis and plasmic processes	30.0	120.0	306.5
National priorities in medicine and health services	71.0	306.4	819.0
Health of population of Russia	15.2	66.5	434.0

Table A1.17. **R&D budget appropriations for government S&T programmes** *(continued)*
(in millions of roubles)

	1991	1992	1993[1]
Prosthetic and orthopedic appliances	–	7.1	–
Creation of new medicines by means of chemical and biological synthesis	–	75.0	439.0
Global environment and climate change	50.0	220.7	667.0
Security of population and national infrastructure in case of natural and technological catastrophes	40.0	180.0	508.0
Complex exploration of the Arctic and Antarctic oceans and seas	80.0	381.2	1 150.0
Progress in construction	50.0	295.0	837.0
Complex utilisation and reproduction of timber	10.0	143.1	598.0
Technology, machinery and production of the future	75.0	421.1	1 083.0
Research-capacious technologies	–	39.9	113.5
High-speed ecologically clean transport	50.0	200.4	568.0
High-efficiency technologies in the social sphere	16.1	55.2	350.0
Federal fund on S&T information	–	–	250.0
Russian space programme	40.0	8 720.0	39 000.0
Civil aviation development programme	–	10 641.0	30 220.0
Ecological security programme	–	–	999.5
Creation and implementation of new medicines and medical supplies in 1992-97	–	–	4 096.0

1. Preliminary estimate as of February 1993.
Source: Ministry of Science and Technological Policy.

Table A1.18. **Value of R&D by sector of performance and type of activity**[1]

	1990				
	Total	Academy sector	Industrial R&D organisations	Higher education sector	Enterprise sector
Total value of R&D	26 565.6	2 626.0	21 422.5	1 250.9	1 266.2
Value of R&D performed within R&D institutions	18 371.3	1 922.1	14 425.8	1 118.3	905.1
Of which: Basic research	1 611.4	1 005.9	384.2	207.5	13.8
Applied research	6 317.8	669.3	4 784.6	697.5	166.4
Development	10 442.1	246.9	9 257.0	213.3	724.9
	1991				
Total value of R&D	32 770.3	3 391.4	26 504.0	1 542.5	1 332.5
Value of R&D performed within R&D institutions	23 269.6	2 751.4	18 252.0	1 282.7	983.4
Of which: Basic research	2 175.2	1 405.4	392.6	368.8	8.4
Applied research	7 761.6	1 094.6	5 815.6	719.0	132.5
Development	13 332.8	251.5	12 043.8	194.9	842.5

1. Detail may not add to total because of rounding. Value of R&D includes current expenditure on R&D and profits obtained by R&D institutions from R&D activity during the year.
Source: Science and Technology in Russia: 1991, CSRS, 1992, p. 78.

Table A1.19. **Average monthly salaries in the sector "Science and scientific services"**

	1970	1975	1980	1982	1985	1986	1987	1988	1989	1990	1991	1992
Average monthly salary in the sector "Science and scientific services" (roubles)	143.2	162.1	184.9	197.3	209.9	215.9	224.9	256.6	314.3	351.9	558.0	4 108.5
As a per cent of that in the national economy												
as a whole (= 100)	113.6	105.8	104.1	105.3	104.2	103.8	104.1	109.1	121.5	118.6	105.3	70.9
in industry (= 100)	105.3	96.5	96.7	97.5	96.3	96.6	97.7	102.5	114.2	113.2	96.2	59.9
in construction (= 100)	92.7	88.5	86.8	86.8	84.8	84.2	83.0	83.7	92.9	93.6	82.3	51.7

Source: Centre of Science Research and Statistics.

Table A1.20. **Average monthly salaries in the sector "Science and scientific services" and in other sectors**

(in roubles)

	1991	1992				
	January	January	March	June	September	December
Total	309.7	1 367.0	2 566.0	5 020.5	7 240.4	15 801.7
Industry	318.6	1 729.7	3 349.9	5 817.4	8 006.1	18 142.9
Agriculture	252.4	879.5	1 323.8	3 463.7	5 618.6	15 283.8
Forestry	235.4	1 079.8	2 104.4	3 977.2	6 353.4	12 702.6
Transport	356.5	1 980.7	3 589.0	8 636.3	10 521.0	21 761.3
Communications	249.3	1 221.2	2 125.8	3 990.0	7 284.6	13 388.0
Construction	370.2	1 699.8	3 856.0	6 648.4	10 282.4	21 049.8
Trade, public catering, material and technical supply, sale, purchase	280.6	1 001.8	2 017.7	3 762.8	6 741.8	12 983.5
Information services	329.9	1 272.4	1 949.1	4 173.3	5 635.8	12 322.0
Housing and communal services, non-productive consumer services	260.7	1 101.9	2 373.0	4 060.8	6 345.3	12 846.3
Health services, physical training and social security	237.5	877.6	1 437.6	3 471.5	5 246.7	9 620.7
Education	272.5	1 042.5	1 279.1	4 176.0	4 849.1	10 987.7
Culture and arts	246.2	816.5	1 270.8	2 899.9	3 746.9	7 071.3
Science and scientific services	373.3	1 014.6	1 958.5	3 434.9	5 175.1	9 855.0
Credit and state insurance	436.4	1 598.2	3 813.9	7 289.0	14 026.8	39 377.2
Administration (state, business, co-operative, public)	378.8	1 351.5	2 250.5	5 028.0	7 520.0	15 831.2
Other	246.3	972.6	1 806.5	4 069.5	10 199.5	12 093.3

Source: Centre of Science Research and Statistics.

Table A1.21. **Scientific discoveries by field of science**

	1989	1990	1991
Total number of discoveries registered (by the end of year)	348	363	372
Discoveries registered during the year	15	15	9
Of which: Nuclear physics	1	2	–
Physical electronics, radiophysics	1	–	–
Astrophysics and physics of atmosphere, physics of Earth-orbital space	1	2	–
Physics of solids	–	1	–
Mechanics of liquid and gas	–	1	–
General chemistry	1	–	1
Physical chemistry, electrochemistry, chemical physics	5	3	–
Geology, geochemistry, geophysics, geomechanics	1	2	2
Biology, biophysics, biochemistry	4	-	4
Health services	1	4	3

Source: Science and Technology in Russia: 1991, CSRS, 1992, p. 131; Russian Patent Office.

Table A1.22. **National applications for protective documents**
(data for the former USSR)

	1985	1986	1987	1988	1989	1990	1991
National applications for protective documents	168 012	171 807	180 563	174 688	148 813	118 843	77 846
Of which: resident applicants	165 648	169 472	178 082	172 218	146 021	115 376	74 517
non-resident applicants	2 364	2 335	2 481	2 470	2 792	3 467	3 329
Applications for author certificates	165 985	169 789	178 341	172 315	145 475	113 434	52 369
Of which: resident applicants	165 625	169 450	178 047	172 057	145 266	113 362	52 345
non-resident applicants	360	339	294	258	209	72	24
Patent applications	2 027	2 018	2 222	2 373	3 338	5 409	25 477
Of which: resident applicants	23	22	35	161	755	2 014	22 172
non-resident applicants	2 004	1 996	2 187	2 212	2 583	3 395	3 305
Dependency ratio[1] for:							
Protective documents of all types	0.014	0.014	0.014	0.014	0.019	0.030	0.045
Author certificates	0.002	0.002	0.002	0.002	0.001	0.001	0.000
Patents	87.130	90.727	62.486	13.739	3.421	1.686	0.149
Autosufficiency ratio[2] for:							
Protective documents of all types	0.986	0.986	0.986	0.986	0.981	0.971	0.957
Author certificates	0.998	0.998	0.998	0.998	0.999	0.999	1.000
Patents	0.011	0.011	0.016	0.068	0.226	0.372	0.870
Inventiveness coefficients[3] for:							
Protective documents of all types	5.942	6.016	6.259	6.006	5.059	3.977	2.56
Author certificates	5.941	6.015	6.258	6.001	5.033	3.908	1.80
Patents	0.001	0.001	0.001	0.006	0.026	0.070	0.76

1. Number of non-resident applications divided by number of resident applications.
2. Number of resident applications divided by total number of national applications.
3. Resident applications per 10 000 population.

Source: Russian Patent Office, CSRS.

Table A1.23. **Registration of inventions**

	1985	1986	1987	1988	1989	1990	1991
Number of author certificates granted to national inventors	47 717	50 529	53 848	52 577	52 853	53 130	52 240
Number of author certificates per 10 000 population	3.33	3.51	3.71	3.62	3.58	3.59	3.51
Number of author certificates per 10 000 employment	6.6	7.5	7.9	7.8	7.9	8.1	–

Source: Science and Technology in Russia: 1991, CSRS, 1992, p. 131.

Table A1.24. **National applications for protective documents by sections of the International Patent Classification**
(data for the former USSR)

	Applications							Protective documents granted						
	Total		Author certificates		Patents			Total		Author certificates		Patents	
	1990	1991	1990	1991	1990	1991		1990	1991	1990	1991	1990	1991
A. Satisfaction of vital human needs	16 311	12 295	15 331	7 805	980	4 490		8 340	10 858	8 187	10 617	153	241
B. Various technological processes	27 749	19 041	26 561	12 840	1 188	6 201		20 984	21 075	20 730	20 764	254	311
C. Chemistry and metallurgy	15 681	10 818	14 440	6 755	1 241	4 063		12 804	11 294	12 380	11 003	424	291
D. Textile, paper	1 771	1 297	1 622	820	149	477		1 096	1 394	1 053	1 357	43	37
E. Construction, mining	9 890	6 482	9 599	4 379	291	2 103		6 549	7 616	6 503	7 552	46	64
F. Mechanics, lighting and heating; engines and pumps; weapons and ammunitions; explosive works	13 540	9 119	12 987	6 188	643	3 001		8 448	8 103	8 342	7 960	106	103
G. Physics	19 740	11 396	19 253	8 349	487	3 047		16 603	15 047	16 553	14 984	50	63
H. Electricity	14 161	7 398	13 731	5 303	430	2 095		9 834	9 190	9 791	9 125	43	65
Total	118 843	77 846	113 434	52 369	5 409	25 477		84 658	84 577	83 539	83 362	1 119	1 215

Source: The Russian Patent Office.

Table A1.25. **External patenting**
(data for the former USSR)

	1985	1986	1987	1988	1989	1990
Number of inventions assigned for patenting during the year	749	751	793	1 273	1 552	1 040
Number of external applications	3 124	3 679	4 058	5 484	7 016	4 737
Rate of diffusion [1]	0.02	0.02	0.02	0.03	0.05	0.04
Number of patents granted	2 021	2 170	2 223	1 424	1 991	1 823
Of which: in developed countries	1 647	1 418	1 523	958	1 127	1 048
Total number of inventions patented (by the end of the year)	8 624	8 686	8 716	9 595	10 142	10 279
Patents suspended during the year	734	698	789	358	702	718
External patents valid (by the end of the year)	20 346	21 066	21 354	15 161	19 417	18 531
Of which: in developed countries	16 699	16 845	16 672	12 070	14 132	2 830

1. Numbers of external applications for protective documents divided by numbers of domestic applications for protective documents.
Source: Research and Development in the USSR. Data Book: 1991, CSRS, 1991, p. 50.

Table A1.26. **External patent applications by patenting country**
(data for the former USSR)

	1980	1985	1986	1987	1988	1989	1990
Europe total	2 950	2 467	2 829	3 097	3 993	5 308	3 430
Austria	90	74	90	86	98	166	111
Belgium	14	5	29	48	64	81	79
Bulgaria	195	339	315	285	384	622	360
Great Britain	222	154	222	218	306	343	276
Hungary	35	90	108	159	226	323	133
East Germany	340	446	384	393	418	655	272
Greece	1	6	7	29	26	15	9
Denmark	16	29	26	27	50	60	56
Ireland	1	5	6	–	1	–	–
Spain	25	18	13	37	53	57	80
Italy	195	144	205	188	235	294	239
Liechtenstein	–	3	–	–	4	5	28
Luxemburg	1	1	6	15	25	15	27
Monaco	–	–	–	–	–	–	1
Netherlands	57	31	42	57	89	125	92
Norway	16	23	24	20	43	44	36
Poland	21	16	23	68	106	117	42
Portugal	3	2	–	4	11	13	10
Romania	15	26	28	41	66	95	43
Finland	75	68	117	126	178	199	151
France	488	183	256	270	327	395	290
West Germany	565	254	310	333	417	475	385
Czechoslovakia	219	343	351	361	380	644	324
Switzerland	89	75	77	100	149	173	147
Sweden	203	105	135	145	219	253	185
Yugoslavia	64	27	55	87	118	139	54
Asia total	602	295	417	500	741	839	645
Vietnam	–	1	1	1	1	2	–
Israel	–	–	–	–	–	–	5
India	67	71	72	106	173	156	93
Iraq	–	6	1	–	6	4	–
Iran	2	–	–	–	1	–	–
Yemen	–	–	–	–	1	–	–
Cyprus	–	–	–	–	–	–	–
China	–	11	54	118	191	221	136
Democratic People's Republic of Korea	–	–	3	–	3	–	1
Kuwait	–	–	1	–	6	1	–
Malaysia	–	–	–	–	2	7	2
Mongolia	62	7	1	3	3	15	8
Pakistan	1	5	4	–	1	5	–

Table A1.26. **External patent applications by patenting country** *(continued)*
(data for the former USSR)

	1980	1985	1986	1987	1988	1989	1990
South Korea	–	–	–	–	–	36	73
Singapore	–	–	–	–	–	–	1
Syria	–	1	2	1	1	1	–
Thailand	–	1	–	1	1	–	1
Turkey	12	6	16	15	15	11	4
Sri Lanka	–	1	–	–	–	–	1
Jamaica	–	1	–	–	–	–	–
Japan	458	184	262	255	337	380	320
Africa total	47	12	9	35	23	16	11
Algeria	5	1	4	4	4	10	7
Ghana	–	–	–	3	1	–	–
Egypt	2	6	4	2	6	4	3
Zambia	–	–	–	3	1	–	–
Zimbabwe	–	–	–	3	1	–	–
Kenya	–	–	–	5	1	–	–
Libya	39	5	–	3	–	2	–
Mali	–	–	–	–	–	–	1
Morocco	1	–	–	1	1	–	–
Nigeria	–	–	1	1	6	–	–
AOIP[1]	–	–	–	3	1	–	–
Somalia	–	–	–	2	–	–	–
Sudan	–	–	–	5	1	–	–
America total	750	311	367	379	630	753	577
South America sub-total	29	48	56	76	106	129	106
Argentina	8	12	21	23	42	28	24
Bolivia	1	–	1	3	1	–	–
Brazil	12	31	29	48	60	97	75
Venezuela	8	5	5	1	–	1	–
Peru	–	–	–	–	1	3	1
Uruguay	–	–	–	1	2	–	6
Central America sub-total	–	–	–	–	1	–	–
Nicaragua	–	–	–	–	1	–	–
North America sub-total	721	263	311	303	523	624	471
Canada	179	61	85	78	147	173	134
Mexico	54	14	20	8	28	27	12
Cuba	–	33	18	25	30	51	40
USA	488	155	188	192	318	373	285
Australia	94	37	54	45	86	93	72
New Zealand	2	2	3	2	10	7	2
Iceland	–	–	–	–	1	–	–
Total	4 445	3 124	3 679	4 058	5 484	7 016	4 737

1. African Organisation for Intellectual Property, including 13 member countries.
Source: Nauka v SSSR: analyz i statistika, CSRS, 1992, pp. 279-280.

Table A1.27. **External patents in force by patenting country**
(data for the former USSR)

	1980	1985	1986	1987	1988	1989	1990
Europe total	12 968	11 491	12 242	12 570	9 230	11 838	11 373
Austria	379	286	286	271	241	241	223
Belgium	394	200	188	172	133	135	90
Bulgaria	212	514	548	639	384	715	873
Great Britain	2 454	1 539	1 468	1 306	1 043	1 020	882
Hungary	249	145	134	130	97	161	164
East Germany	1 116	1 096	1 431	1 553	985	1 789	1 932
Greece	25	28	33	47	44	48	43
Denmark	80	60	56	56	33	42	45
Ireland	15	12	12	13	9	10	5
Spain	187	132	130	136	103	162	171
Italy	1 006	402	493	782	675	776	721
Luxemburg	14	12	11	7	5	6	10
Malta	–	–	2	4	2	3	3
Netherlands	144	136	121	108	86	90	72
Norway	68	56	53	60	47	64	64
Poland	166	104	100	91	59	56	54
Portugal	6	22	20	18	19	18	12
Romania	91	133	135	149	86	92	59
Finland	92	169	183	197	160	200	197
France	2 661	2 215	2 258	2 105	1 521	1 617	1 379
West Germany	1 673	1 875	1 966	1 918	1 409	1 587	1 392
Czechoslovakia	607	1 159	1 350	1 596	1 111	1 951	2 066
Switzerland	485	449	468	465	400	429	374
Sweden	831	729	769	723	564	609	529
Yugoslavia	13	18	27	24	14	17	13
Asia total	1 546	1 275	1 281	1 251	937	1 068	984
Burma	1	–	–	–	–	–	–
India	325	202	212	213	137	198	205
Iraq	4	2	2	2	4	5	5
Iran	86	40	39	24	14	16	15
China	–	–	–	–	1	2	14
Democratic People's Republic of Korea	–	–	–	–	–	–	1
Pakistan	18	10	8	6	7	9	13
Syria	8	3	3	7	–	3	3
Thailand	–	–	–	–	–	1	1
Turkey	13	24	25	23	22	24	27
Sri Lanka	–	–	–	1	2	3	3
Japan	1 091	994	992	975	750	807	697
Africa total	89	18	19	20	10	15	33
Algeria	1	–	–	–	–	2	2
Ghana	–	–	–	–	–	–	3
Egypt	68	8	8	7	2	–	1

Table A1.27. **External patents in force by patenting country** *(continued)*
(data for the former USSR)

	1980	1985	1986	1987	1988	1989	1990
Zaire	2	2	2	–	–	–	–
Zambia	–	–	–	–	–	–	3
Zimbabwe	–	–	–	–	–	–	3
Kenya	–	–	–	–	–	–	3
Morocco	2	1	1	4	4	4	5
Nigeria	–	1	2	3	1	1	1
AOIP[1]	–	–	–	–	–	3	5
Somalia	–	–	–	–	–	2	2
Sudan	–	–	–	–	–	2	5
Tunisia	3	–	–	–	–	–	–
Republic of South Africa	13	6	6	6	1	1	–
America total	5 889	7 362	7 286	7 279	4 787	6 282	5 909
South America sub-total	116	125	131	144	118	157	155
Argentina	70	45	48	49	46	67	63
Bolivia	13	10	10	12	6	9	8
Brazil	8	56	57	62	50	65	65
Venezuela	17	8	10	15	15	15	14
Guyana	1	–	–	–	–	–	–
Colombia	–	–	–	–	–	–	2
Peru	1	2	2	2	1	1	1
Uruguay	1	–	–	–	–	–	2
Chile	5	4	4	4	–	–	–
Central America sub-total	5	–	–	–	–	–	–
Panama	5	–	–	–	–	–	–
North America sub-total	5 768	7 237	7 155	7 135	4 669	6 125	5 754
Canada	1 366	1 845	1 816	1 794	1 250	1 583	1 510
Mexico	54	53	50	55	33	59	52
Cuba	8	7	8	7	6	10	10
USA	4 340	5 332	5 281	5 279	3 380	4 473	4 182
Australia	195	188	227	223	190	207	225
New Zealand	11	12	11	11	7	7	7
Iceland	4	–	–	–	–	–	–
Total	20 702	20 346	21 066	21 354	15 161	19 417	18 531

1. African Organisation for Intellectual Property, including 13 member countries.
Source: Nauka v SSSR: analyz i statistika, CRSR, 1992, pp. 283-284.

Table A1.28. **Number of applications submitted according to the Patent Co-operation Treaty, by country**
(data for the former USSR)

Country of residence of applicants	1989		1990		1991		Total as of 1 January 1992	
	Applications	Of which: designation of the USSR	Applications	Of which: designation of the USSR	Applications	Of which: designation of the USSR	Applications	Of which: designation of the USSR
Australia	562	241	610	289	599	340	4 406	1 454
Austria	112	52	129	60	135	66	910	355
Belgium	52	21	69	36	92	54	395	146
Bulgaria	–	–	–	–	2	2	6	6
Brazil	11	5	25	7	29	13	206	66
Great Britain	1 505	380	2 040	693	2 341	870	11 224	2 946
Hungary	73	41	83	53	54	35	755	410
Greece	–	–	9	8	14	11	23	19
Denmark	314	167	340	233	395	253	2 301	1 054
Spain	–	–	51	43	82	53	133	96
Italy	82	60	106	73	105	63	625	423
Canada	–	–	439	236	472	280	911	516
Democratic People's Republic of Korea	–	–	1	1	2	1	3	2
Luxembourg	1	–	–	–	–	–	11	6
Monaco	–	–	–	1	–	–	5	3
Netherlands	86	32	192	71	251	131	937	317
Norway	137	68	184	119	170	108	1 099	466
Poland	–	–	–	–	15	8	15	8
Republic of Korea	12	5	23	16	34	19	160	59
Romania	–	–	2	1	2	1	27	14
USSR	318	–	265	3	366	24	2 128	27
USA	5 930	1 221	7 310	1 961	9 037	2 509	46 014	9 682
Finland	241	137	309	170	400	228	1 950	1 085
France	703	156	917	254	1 030	262	5 922	1 325
West Germany	799	180	974	255	1 009	255	6 459	1 472
Czechoslovakia	–	–	–	–	2	2	2	2
Switzerland	225	76	291	104	277	94	2 575	738
Sweden	771	284	827	367	929	406	7 420	2 451
Sri Lanka	2	1	–	–	–	–	12	9
Japan	1 357	64	1 716	106	1 815	129	11 289	707
European Patent Office	1 570	354	2 246	627	2 588	743	11 193	2 717
AOIP[1]	1	1	–	–	–	–	2	2
Total	14 864	3 546	19 159	5 787	22 247	6 960	119 118	28 583

1. African Organisation for Intellectual Property, including 13 member countries.
Source: Research and Development in the USSR. Data Book: 1990, CSRS, 1992, p. 58.

Table A1.29. **Export of licences**
(data for the former USSR)

	1980	1985	1986	1987	1988	1989	1990
Total number of licences							
(by the end of the year)	1 202	2 457	2 800	3 190	3 713	4 309	4 582
Of which: during the year	179	343	343	390	523	596	273
Receipts, million roubles	79.8	150.7	169.6	203.7	154.6	182.8	211.1
Of which: in hard currency, million roubles[1]	14.5	20.1	29.6	71.9	20.6	26.3	48.8

1. Converted using the official exchange rates of the USSR State Bank.
Source: Research and Development in the USSR. Data Book: 1990, CSRS, 1991, p. 51.

Table A1.30. **Export of licences by country**
(data for the former USSR)

	1980	1985	1986	1987	1988	1989	Total[1] (by the end of 1989)
Europe total	143	267	270	323	379	470	3 353
Austria	–	1	6	3	5	7	37
Belgium	–	1	1	2	2	–	13
Bulgaria	33	45	49	58	75	123	562
Great Britain	-	3	2	2	3	4	36
Hungary	16	31	29	34	53	26	355
East Germany	14	45	38	53	44	58	487
Greece	–	4	2	4	3	3	19
Denmark	1	1	1	–	1	–	5
West Berlin	–	–	–	–	–	–	2
Spain	1	1	4	1	3	2	29
Italy	6	13	7	15	16	34	144
Liechtenstein	–	–	–	–	–	–	2
Luxemburg	–	–	–	–	–	–	1
Netherlands	–	–	–	1	1	4	9
Norway	–	–	–	1	2	1	9
Poland	19	19	20	33	35	36	304
Portugal	1	1	–	–	–	–	2
Romania	7	12	18	4	10	21	175
Finland	9	14	20	15	23	24	175
France	2	2	2	8	8	10	82
West Germany	3	16	14	19	10	26	150
Czechoslovakia	22	43	29	52	68	60	493
Switzerland	3	3	6	1	5	7	42
Sweden	–	1	2	–	1	–	29
Yugoslavia	6	11	20	17	11	24	191
Asia total	24	41	42	40	96	82	590
Afghanistan	1	1	3	–	3	1	18
Bangladesh	–	2	–	–	–	–	4
Vietnam	–	3	2	–	18	16	46
Israel	–	–	–	1	–	–	1
India	11	11	10	10	10	11	135
Jordan	1	3	–	–	–	1	6
Iraq	2	1	–	1	–	2	29
Iran	–	–	–	–	1	1	17
Yemen	2	–	4	1	13	4	36
Cambodia	–	–	–	–	1	–	1
Qatar	–	–	–	–	–	1	1
China	–	–	2	1	6	6	15
Democratic People's Republic of Korea	–	2	3	3	5	4	22
Laos	1	–	–	–	1	–	2
Mongolia	–	2	1	1	2	2	12

Table A1.30. **Export of licences by country** *(continued)*
(data for the former USSR)

	1980	1985	1986	1987	1988	1989	Total[1] (by the end of 1989)
United Arab Emirates	–	–	–	–	–	–	1
Pakistan	–	3	1	2	–	2	12
Singapore	–	–	–	–	1	–	1
Syria	3	2	3	4	1	1	21
Turkey	2	–	–	–	2	3	23
Sri Lanka	–	–	–	–	–	–	2
Japan	1	11	13	16	32	27	185
Africa total	5	2	1	2	6	11	54
Algeria	2	–	1	1	–	1	9
Egypt	–	–	–	–	2	8	17
Congo	–	–	–	–	–	–	1
Libya	1	–	–	–	–	–	8
Madagascar	–	–	–	–	–	–	1
Mali	–	–	–	1	–	–	1
Mozambique	–	–	–	–	2	–	3
Nigeria	1	1	–	–	–	–	2
Tanzania	1	–	–	–	–	–	1
Tunisia	–	–	–	–	–	–	3
Uganda	–	–	–	–	–	–	1
Ethiopia	–	1	–	–	2	2	7
America total	7	32	29	19	40	31	292
South America sub-total	2	7	12	3	5	6	58
Argentina	–	1	1	1	1	3	15
Bolivia	–	2	–	–	–	–	7
Brazil	–	2	8	–	2	–	18
Venezuela	2	2	3	2	1	3	16
Columbia	–	–	–	–	–	–	1
Peru	–	–	–	–	1	–	1
Central America sub-total	–	–	–	–	–	–	1
Bahamas	–	–	–	–	–	–	1
North America sub-total	5	25	17	16	35	25	233
Canada	–	2	–	1	1	1	13
Mexico	1	–	–	–	3	2	9
Cuba	2	16	13	10	20	11	113
USA	2	7	4	5	11	11	98
Australia	–	1	1	–	1	1	12
CMEA	–	–	–	–	–	1	1
UNESCO	–	–	–	6	1	–	7
Total	179	343	343	390	523	596	4 309

1. Cumulative data.
Source: Nauka v SSSR: analyz i statistika, CSRS, 1992, pp. 288-289.

Table A1.31. **New prototypes of machines, equipment, instruments and means of automation, by type**

	1990	1991	1992
Total number of prototypes developed	1 166	893	997
Machines and equipment	963	742	795
Of which: Power engineering equipment, diesel engines	25	30	15
Equipment for ferrous and non-ferrous metallurgy	9	9	4
Electric equipment and materials	146	100	79
Chemical, pumping and compressor equipment	63	72	55
Metal-cutting lathes	40	57	37
Forge and press equipment	39	44	49
Automated lines, manipulators, industrial robots	16	13	7
Specialised motor vehicles, auto-loaders	35	20	40
Textiles, wearing apparel and leather industry equipment	68	39	17
Food industry equipment	46	30	30
Trade and public catering technological equipment, refrigerators	32	5	11
Medical equipment	40	31	41
Other	404	292	410
Instruments and means of automation	203	151	202
Of which: Technological process control and regulating instruments	70	56	76
Electric measuring instruments	14	10	12
Automated remote-control equipment	1	2	1
Computers	39	26	30
Machines and instruments for measuring mechanical values	23	18	20
Chronometers	5	8	25
Physical research instruments	19	7	1
Optical instruments and apparatus	16	12	9
Other	16	12	28

Source: Science and Technology in Russia: 1991, CSRS, 1992, pp. 139, 141; Computing Centre of the RF State Committee on Statistics.

Table A1.32. Technical level of new prototypes of machines, equipment and apparatus, by type

	Prototypes developed		Of which: a technical level							
			Above the highest world standard		Equal to the highest world standard		Below the highest world standard		Not identified	
	1990	1991	1990	1991	1990	1991	1990	1991	1990	1991
Total	963	742	38	26	749	585	29	31	147	100
Power engineering equipment, diesel engines	25	30	–	–	24	29	1	–	–	1
Equipment for ferrous and non-ferrous metallurgy	9	9	–	–	9	5	–	–	–	4
Electrical equipment and materials	146	100	1	–	131	95	–	–	14	5
Chemical, pumping and compressor equipment	63	72	4	4	50	59	1	4	8	5
Metal-cutting lathes	40	57	–	–	33	47	–	–	7	10
Forge and press equipment	39	44	–	–	25	30	–	2	14	12
Automated lines, manipulators, industrial robots	16	13	–	1	9	12	–	–	7	–
Specialised motor vehicles, auto-loaders	35	20	1	–	25	17	1	–	8	3
Textiles, wearing apparel and leather industry equipment	68	39	3	3	53	27	1	1	11	8
Food industry equipment	46	30	–	1	41	25	2	2	3	2
Trade and public catering technological equipment, refrigerators	32	5	–	–	30	2	–	2	2	1
Medical equipment	40	31	5	3	28	23	–	2	7	3
Other	404	292	24	14	291	214	23	18	66	46

Source: Science and Technology in Russia: 1991, CSRS, 1992, p. 139.

Table A1.33. **Technical level of new prototypes of instruments and means of automation**

	Prototypes developed		Of which: a technical level							
			Above the highest world standard		Equal to the highest world standard		Below the highest world standard		Not identified	
	1990	1991	1990	1991	1990	1991	1990	1991	1990	1991
Total	203	151	8	8	171	117	2	–	22	26
Technological process control and regulating instruments	70	56	2	4	64	41	–	–	4	11
Electric measuring instruments	14	10	1	2	11	8	–	–	2	–
Automated remote control equipment	1	2	–	–	1	1	–	–	–	1
Computers	39	26	1	1	26	20	2	–	10	5
Machines and instruments for measuring mechanical values	23	18	3	–	19	18	–	–	1	–
Chronometers	5	8	–	–	5	7	–	–	–	1
Physical research instruments	19	7	–	–	17	3	–	–	2	4
Optical instruments and apparatus	16	12	1	1	15	10	–	–	–	1
Other	16	12	–	–	13	9	–	–	3	3

Source: Science and Technology in Russia: 1991, CSRS, 1992, p. 141.

Table A1.34. **Machinery production value for export**
(in millions of roubles)

	1990		1991		1992[1]
	In wholesale current prices	Production costs	In wholesale current prices	Production costs	
Production for export	23 000.5	18 467.5	30 962.1	23 972.4	186 624.1
Of which: sold for currency	1 797.6	1 404.4	2 907.8	2 281.9	–

1. In wholesale current prices.
Source: *Science and Technology in Russia: 1991*, CSRS, 1992, p. 162.

Annex 2

The Russian R&D effort in an international perspective

1. Introduction

For many years S&T statistics were based on the concepts of a centrally planned economy and were the only source of R&D data available for the former USSR and other Central and East European countries. These data were founded on a very broad concept of science and technology, which included a variety of activities other than R&D. Attempts to compare these data on R&D with those for OECD countries have brought out many differences in both the definitions of indicators and in the systems of classifications.

The first Russian efforts to approach the guidelines of the OECD's "Frascati Manual"* began in 1989 when a new national R&D survey was launched, using new categories of personnel, new types of R&D activities, etc. In 1993, the Centre of Science Research and Statistics of the Ministry of Science and Technological Policy of the Russian Federation (CSRS) made a first attempt to estimate statistical data on R&D effort for the sectors of performance as defined by the OECD.

As a result of these efforts, data on Russian R&D is more comparable with data for OECD countries, but only from 1989 (and in some cases, 1990); thus, only short-term changes can be analysed at present. However, the CSRS has launched a project to re-estimate earlier data on the basis of OECD standards. Once completed, the revised data, in conjunction with the data for 1992, should allow for a more precise analysis of the structure and trends of Russian science.

Nonetheless, problems of international comparability remain. For example, data on R&D personnel are still reported in terms of headcounts rather than full-time equivalence (FTE), as recommended by the OECD. These data are thus overestimated when compared with personnel data in OECD Member countries.

Other problems arose for calculating some basic R&D indicators such as the ratio of GERD (gross domestic expenditure on R&D) to GDP (gross domestic product). Instead of GDP, the former Soviet Union used the net material product (NMP), calculated on the basis of material product balances. While GDP data have been available for Russia since 1989, they are still only broadly comparable to OECD data because of differences between the two statistical systems, despite intensive efforts to bring them closer together. In addition, the CSRS estimated a GDP deflator for 1992; previously, national income deflator estimates had to be used.

The principal remaining problem for the international comparability of Russian expenditure data is the conversion of expenditure figures into purchasing power parities (PPPs), the accepted conversion rate in OECD countries (see Box A2.1). In this report, the Secretariat has used an

---

* *Proposed Standard Practice for Surveys of Research and Experimental Development* (Frascati Manual), OECD, Paris, 1994.

> **Box A2.1**
>
> The use of PPPs is explained as follows in *Purchasing Power Parities and Real Expenditures (1990)*, Vol. 1, OECD, Paris, 1992:
>
> "**Purchasing Power Parities (PPPs)** are the rates of currency conversion that equalise the purchasing power of different currencies. This means that a given sum of money, when converted into different currencies at the PPP rates, will buy the same basket of goods and services in all countries. In other words, PPPs are the rates of currency conversion which eliminate the differences in price levels between countries. Thus, when expenditures on GDP for different countries are converted into a common currency by means of PPPs, they are, in effect, expressed at the same set of international prices so that comparisons between countries reflect only differences in the volume of goods and services purchased.
>
> "Expenditures converted to a common currency using exchange rates, on the other hand, reflect not only differences in the quantities purchased in the different countries, but also the differences in price levels between the countries. Exchange rates do not reflect the relative purchasing powers of different countries and are not, therefore, the appropriate currency conversion rates with which to make international comparisons of volume. Expenditures on GDP converted at exchange rates remain essentially **nominal measures**; the same expenditures converted using PPPs are real measures."

experimental PPP between the Austrian Schilling (AS) and the rouble, calculated by the Austrian Central Statistical Office, for calculations into US PPP dollars. These experimental PPPs are preferable to "official" exchange rates, especially during the very high inflation of the transition period.

For all the reasons mentioned, this annex contains a rather large number of estimates made by the CSRS and the Secretariat. Hence all comparisons between Russia and the OECD area should be considered as very approximative.

2. Data and indicators on R&D resources

Tables A2.1 to A2.4 present selected data and indicators of R&D resources for Russia and the countries of the OECD area. Data reported for the S&T policy reviews of Hungary and the former Czechoslovakia, which have encountered similar problems in the transition to the market economy, have also been included.

R&D expenditures

Gross Domestic Expenditure on R&D (GERD)

According to CSRS estimates, Russian GERD for 1990 and 1991 was 24 and 20 billion roubles, respectively, in current prices. Expressed in constant prices (using the national income deflator as a substitute for the GDP deflator), GERD decreased by almost 17 per cent from 1990 to 1991. Similarly, after a period of continuous growth, the traditional Russian indicator "gross international expenditure on S&T", which is not comparable to the OECD indicators, decreased sharply from 1989.

Table A2.1. **Gross domestic expenditure on R&D (GERD) – 1990, 1991 (or closest year)**

	Million current PPP $		Percentage of GDP		Per capita current PPPs $		Government financed (%)	
	1990	1991	1990	1991	1990	1991	1990	1991
Russia[a]	23 945.0	20 168.2	2.10	1.54	161.3	135.5	79.4[b,c]	95.0[c]
Australia	3 153.5[d]		1.25[d]		190.9[d]		54.3[d]	
Austria	1 796.7	2 004.4	1.40	1.48	232.8	256.2	44.3	45.9
Belgium	2 751.5		1.69		276.1		27.6	
Canada	7 299.3	7 567.8	1.44	1.46	274.3	280.3	44.3	44.6
Denmark	1 239.6[e]	1 444.4	1.54[e]	1.59	241.5[e]	280.2	45.5[e]	
Finland	1 541.8		1.87		309.2		35.3[e]	
France	23 768.4	25 195.6	2.42	2.42	418.9	441.6	48.3	48.8
Germany	31 585.3	34 813.4	2.73	2.58	499.3	436.2	35.1	37.2
Greece	336.3[e]		0.47[e]		33.5[e]		68.9[e]	
Iceland	43.7	45.6	1.03	1.02	171.5	176.6	65.8	65.5
Ireland	338.8		0.90		96.7		29.0	
Italy	11 964.3	13 446.1	1.30	1.38	207.5	235.4	51.5	52.0
Japan	62 865.0	67 628.2	2.88	2.86	508.9	545.7	16.1	16.7
Netherlands	4 826.8	4 902.2	2.06	2.00	322.8	325.3	45.1	
New Zealand	398.9		0.87		118.6		65.4	
Norway	1 188.7[e]	1 318.5	1.86[e]	1.83	281.2[e]	309.4	50.8[e]	50.9
Portugal	501.8		0.61		51.2		61.8	
Spain	3 888.8	4 342.7	0.85	0.87	99.8	111.3	45.1	
Sweden	3 913.0[e]	3 662.9	2.85[e]	2.54	460.7[e]	425.1	38.4[e]	
Switzerland	3 821.9[e]		2.86[e]		575.0[e]		22.6[e]	
Turkey	885.7		0.47		15.7		71.2	
United Kingdom	20 178.3		2.22		351.5		35.8	
United States	149 225.0	154 348.0	2.77	2.78	597.1	610.8	47.1	46.8
OECD median			1.54		274.3		45.1	
Hungary	1 843.4		1.69		185.0[e]		52.4[e]	
CSFR	2 575.0		2.56		164.0		40.0[c]	
Czech Rep.[f]	1 750.0				169.0			
Slovak Rep.[f]	825.0				156.0			

a) Some military-oriented institutes not included (share estimated by CSRS as 6 to 10 per cent of GERD).
b) Data for the former USSR.
c) Breakdown based on total current expenditure.
d) 1988.
e) 1989.
f) Estimates.
Source: CSRS, OECD/EAS (STIU database), Reviews of National Science and Technology Policy – Hungary – CSFR.

Table A2.2. **R&D expenditure by sector of performance**
(percentage)

	Business enterprise sector		Government sector		Private non-profit sector		Higher education sector	
	1990	1991	1990	1991	1990	1991	1990	1991
Russia[a]	75.6	75.1	16.0	17.7	0.2	0.1	8.2	7.1
Australia	42.0[b]		31.6[b]		1.2[b]		25.2[b]	
Austria	58.6[c]		7.5[c]		1.6[c]		32.4[c]	
Belgium	72.6		6.1		3.9		17.4	
Canada	53.7	53.2	19.5	19.7	1.1	1.1	25.8	26.0
Denmark	55.0[c]		19.1[c]		1.1[c]		24.8[c]	
Finland	62.6		18.8		0.5[c]		18.7	
France	60.4	61.1	24.2	23.5	0.8	0.8	14.6	14.5
Germany	71.4	68.4	13.2	15.2	0.5	0.5	14.9	15.9
Greece	22.3[c]		42.4[c]				35.3[c]	
Iceland	19.4	19.7	49.2	48.4	6.4	6.5	25.0	25.5
Ireland	60.7		16.2		1.7		21.3	
Italy	58.3	55.8	20.9	24.4			20.7	19.8
Japan	75.5	75.3	8.0	8.1	4.4	4.4	12.2	12.2
Netherlands	56.2	55.5	18.1		2.2		23.5	
New Zealand	31.8		49.6				18.6	
Norway	56.6[c]	54.7	19.4[c]	18.5			24.0[c]	26.8
Portugal	26.1		25.4		12.4		36.0	
Spain	57.8	58.4	21.3	21.0	0.5		20.4	20.6
Sweden	64.1[c]	63.2	4.0[c]	3.8	0.1[c]	0.1	31.8[c]	33.0
Switzerland	74.8[c]		4.3[c]		0.9[c]		19.9[c]	
Turkey	20.9		9.9				69.3	
United Kingdom	66.6		14.0		4.6		14.7	
United States	69.9	69.2	11.0	11.1	3.1	3.3	16.0	16.4
OECD median	58.3		18.8		1.1		21.3	
Hungary	45.3[c]		38.2[c]				16.5[c]	
CSFR	69.0		31.0[d]					

a) Breakdown based on total current expenditure.
b) 1988.
c) 1989.
d) Public sector (government sector plus higher education sector).
Source: CSRS, OECD/EAS (STIU database), *Reviews of National Science and Technology Policy – Hungary – CSFR*.

In order to compare Russia and OECD countries, expenditure data were converted into US PPP dollars, using the experimental purchasing power parities mentioned above. Despite its enormous R&D potential, Russian GERD, calculated at the PPP rates, appears much lower than expected, when compared to GERD in the principal OECD economies (Table A2.1). Russia's total domestic R&D effort, approximately 23 945 million PPP dollars, was most like that of France in 1990, but in 1991, owing to the substantial decrease of GERD in Russia (to 20 170 million PPP dollars), its GERD was 20 per cent below that of France, nearly equal to that of the United Kingdom in 1990. The value of the indicator in the United States and Japan was substantially

Table A2.3. **Government budget appropriations or outlays for R&D (GBAORD)**

	Million current PPPs 1991	Percentage of GDP	Defense share of GBAORD (%)
Russia[a]	26 073.3	1.99	48.0
Australia	1 734.2	0.61	9.5
Austria	831.0	0.61	0.0
Belgium	933.2	0.54	0.2
Canada	3 123.6	0.60	7.0
Denmark	664.1	0.73	0.4
Finland	822.6	1.03	1.3
France	14 793.7	1.42	37.4
Germany	14 075.2	1.04	11.0
Greece	209.0	0.26	2.4
Iceland	26.6	0.59	0.0
Ireland	181.9	0.45	0.0
Italy	7 370.6	0.75	7.9
Japan	10 573.8	0.45	5.7
Netherlands	2 143.5	0.87	3.5
New Zealand	251.5	0.53	1.2
Norway	783.8	1.09	5.7
Portugal	411.0	0.46	0.9
Spain	2 706.0	0.54	16.8
Sweden	1 869.8	1.30	27.0
Switzerland	483.9	0.32	18.5
Turkey			
United Kingdom	7 994.2	0.89	44.3
United States	65 897.0	1.19	59.7

a) GBAORD in Russia covers both expenditure and profits of the R&D performing institutions.
Source: CSRS, OECD/EAS (STIU database).

higher. When converted to PPP dollars, Russian GDP was comparable to that of Germany in 1990. However, per capita GDP, for Russia as well as for other Central and East European countries (Hungary and the former CSFR), was of the same magnitude as that of smaller OECD countries such as Greece or Portugal. In the light of these data, the value of GERD converted to PPP dollars in the Russian Federation seems reasonable.

Although in 1991 the increase in R&D expenditure (in constant prices) in several OECD countries was more moderate than in previous years and even negative in some, the situation is very different from the dramatic decline observed in Russia. Downward trends similar to those in Russia were also observed in Hungary and the former Czechoslovakia at the beginning of the transition to the market economy.

GERD as a percentage of GDP

GERD expressed as a proportion of GDP confirms the sharp decrease in resources devoted to R&D in Russia, from 2.1 per cent in 1990 to 1.5 per cent in 1991 (CSRS estimates). In 1991, the value of the indicator for Russia is still very close to the median of the OECD countries, even if its position, which in 1990 was nearly that of the United Kingdom or the Netherlands, was only, in

Table A2.4. **Total R&D personnel and R&D scientists and engineers (RSE) 1990 (or closest year) FTE**

	Total R&D personnel		R&D scientists and engineers		RSE per 10 000 labour force	
	1990	1991	1990	1991	1990	1991
Russia[a,b]	1 943 432	1 677 784	992 571	878 482	114	101
Russia[a,c]	2 041 783	1 767 686	1 090 922	968 384	126	112
Australia	66 041[d]		39 471[d]		49[d]	
Austria	23 084[e]		8 782[e]		25[e]	
Belgium	38 773		18 465		44	
Canada	111 990[e]		62 510[e]		46[e]	
Denmark	24 339[e]	25 800	10 962[e]		38[e]	
Finland	28 516[e]		10 593[f]		41[f]	
France	293 031		123 961		51	
Germany	431 100		176 401[e]		59[e]	
Greece	9 586[e]		5 461[e]		14[e]	
Iceland	1 188	1 221	676	695	53	49
Ireland	8 592[d]		6 477		50	
Italy	144 917		77 876		32	
Japan	794 337	802 820	477 866	491 102	75	75
Netherlands	68 170		26 680[e]		40[e]	
New Zealand	8 288		4 721		30	
Norway	20 217[e]	20 271	12 156[e]	13 460	56[e]	63
Portugal	12 043		5 908		12	
Spain	64 934		37 676		25	
Sweden	53 681[e]	54 200	25 089[e]	25 400	55[e]	56
Switzerland	50 250[e]		14 250[e]		40[e]	
Turkey	16 375		12 361		6	
United Kingdom	277 800[d]		130 000[d]		46[d]	
United States	–		949 300[e]		76[e]	
OECD median					44	
Hungary	36 384		17 550		42[e]	
CSFR[g]	91 976		47 294	37 153	60	51
Czech Rep.[g]	63 231		31 744	24 577	59	49
Slovak Rep.[g]	28 745		15 550	12 576	63	55

a) Calculated in headcounts instead of FTE.
b) Higher education teaching staff partly engaged in R&D activities not included.
c) Higher education teaching staff partly engaged in R&D activities included.
d) 1988.
e) 1989.
f) 1987.
g) Overestimated.
Source: CSRS, OECD/EAS (STIU database), Reviews of National Science and Technology Policy – Hungary – CSFR.

1991, comparable to that of Denmark or Austria. Over this short period, several other countries within the OECD area for which data are available (for example, Japan, Germany, the Netherlands) also report a decline of GERD as a proportion of GDP, but they are usually countries whose GERD to GDP ratio was high and whose decline was not comparable to Russia's (see Figure A2.1).

Figure A2.1. **Gross domestic expenditure on R&D as a percentage of GDP**

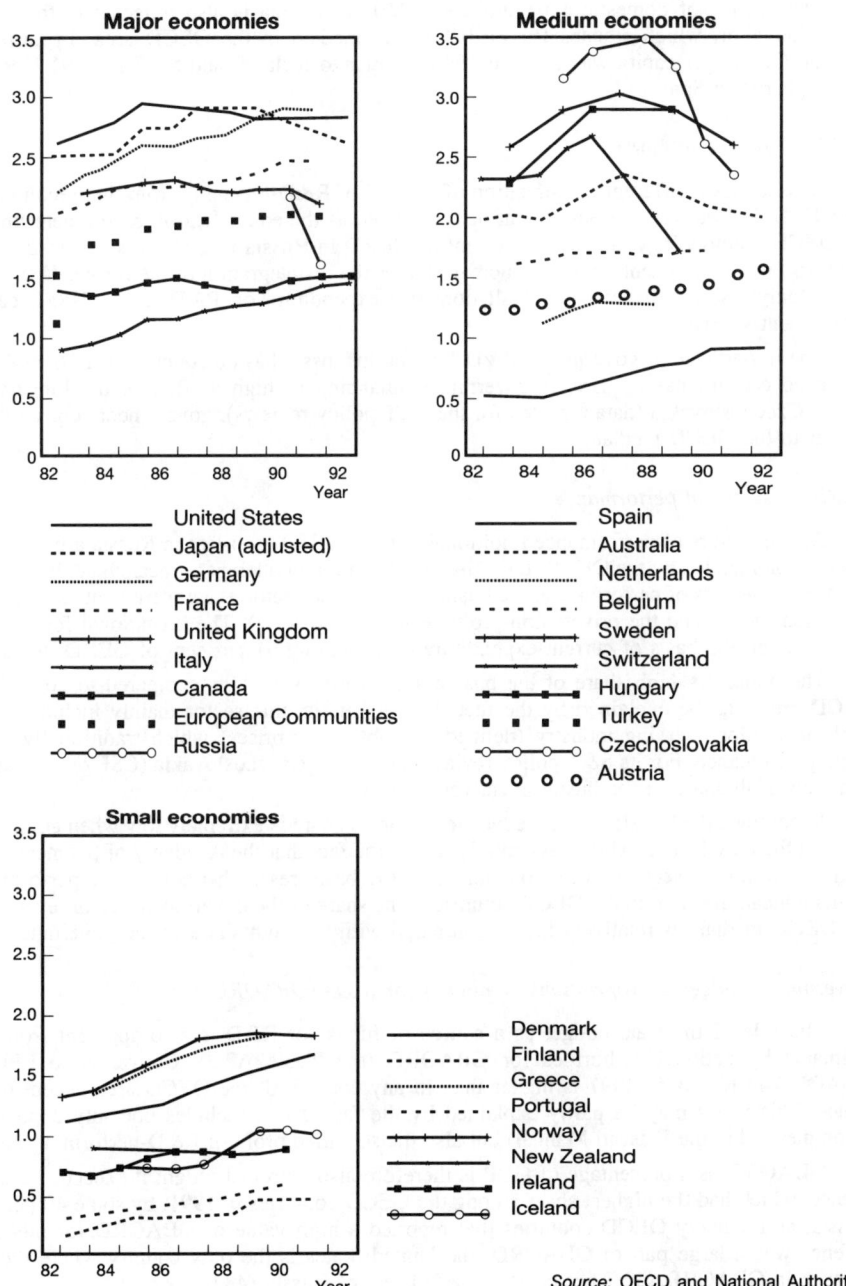

Source: OECD and National Authorities.

GERD per capita (current PPP dollars)

The decline of domestic expenditure on R&D in Russia is also reflected in the GERD per capita indicator, which situates Russia below the median in the OECD area. In current PPPs, Russian GERD per capita was $161 in 1990 (similar to Iceland) and $135 in 1991 (some 20 per cent higher than Spain).

GERD by source of funds

Russia uses a different classification of sources of R&D financing from that recommended by the OECD. If "budget" resources can be considered as the equivalent of government financing in the OECD methodology, about 95 per cent of GERD in Russia in 1991 was financed by government. In fact, government financing increased after the disintegration of the former USSR, since in 1990 "only" some 80 per cent of all domestic expenditure on R&D in the USSR came from government sources.

The importance of government R&D funding in Russia has no counterpart in the OECD area, where no country has a share of government financing as high as Russia. In Hungary and the former Czechoslovakia (data reported for the S&T policy reviews), government contributions were similar to the OECD median.

GERD by sector of performance

As the sectors of performance traditionally used in S&T statistics in Russia are different from those recommended by the OECD, the CSRS made an initial attempt to recalculate the data for four "Frascati" sectors of performance: the business enterprise sector, the government sector, the higher education sector, and the private non-profit sector (Table A2.2). The breakdown for these sectors was made on the basis of current expenditure (representing 91 per cent of GERD in Russia).

The unusually high share of the business enterprise sector, as compared to countries of the OECD area, can be explained by the fact that, in Russia, this sector mainly includes the public R&D institutions serving industry (defined as public enterprises) which traditionally dominated R&D performance. For its S&T policy review, the former Czechoslovakia (CSFR) also attributed a relatively high share of the business enterprise sector.

In contrast, the Russian higher education sector's share is extremely low when compared to its share in the OECD area. This is essentially due to the fact that the Academy of Sciences (classified in the government sector) carries out much of the basic research traditionally performed in the higher education sector in the OECD countries. The share of the government sector, even if close to the OECD median, is relatively low if compared with the high share of the government funding.

Government budget appropriations or outlays for R&D (GBAORD)

The role of the state budget as a source of funds for R&D is also apparent from the data estimated by national authorities for GBAORD (see Table A2.3). Converted to PPP dollars, GBAORD in Russia in 1991 is higher than in any country of the OECD area except the United States. This result may be partly explained by the fact that it includes not only expenditure (as recommended in the Frascati Manual) but also the so-called profit of R&D-performing institutions.

GBAORD as a percentage of GDP is therefore also extremely high; it exceeded the ratio for France, which had the highest share among the OECD countries in 1991, by some 40 per cent. For Russia, as for many OECD countries that reported a high value of GBAORD for this indicator, defence was a large part of GBAORD; the United States is the only country where the share of defence in GBAORD (59.7 per cent) exceeded that of Russia (48.0 per cent).

Preliminary estimates for 1992 indicate reduced resources for R&D from the state budget (approximately 180 billion roubles, or $12 500 million calculated with the experimental PPP rate), with a lower share for defence (42 per cent) and a drop in GBAORD as a percentage of GDP (1.17 per cent) from 1991.

R&D personnel

Comparisons of R&D personnel data for Russia with similar figures for the OECD Member countries are affected by remaining differences in the definition of R&D personnel; Russia uses headcounts instead of the full-time equivalent (FTE) used by OECD countries. As a result, Russian data overestimate personnel, and comparisons with OECD countries should be regarded as very approximate (Table A2.4).

The dominant feature of the evolution of the labour force engaged in R&D activities in Russia from 1989 until 1991 is the decrease of 24.1 per cent (533 000) in total R&D personnel, which particularly affected research scientists and engineers (RSE) (237 000) and supporting staff (226 000). On the contrary, over the most recent period for which data are available, most OECD countries saw a rise in human resources for R&D.

The decline of R&D personnel in Russia is due both to the unfavourable financial situation of most sectors of R&D performance and to the process of conversion of defence-oriented R&D resources. As a result, the CSRS expects a continuing reduction of R&D personnel in 1992. The R&D labour force has a very low salary level compared to other sectors (with culture and education the only exceptions), partly as a consequence of the dominant role of the government budget in R&D funding and its limited resources. Therefore, R&D personnel, often the most qualified and talented, are leaving R&D for positions in more prosperous sectors of the economy. On the other hand, CSRS estimates indicate that the external brain drain is less serious than expected, as the annual number of R&D personnel emigrating from the country during the 1990-91 period did not exceed 2 100.

A decrease of the R&D personnel was also observed in Hungary and the former Czechoslovakia at the time of the S&T policy reviews. In the former CSFR, the decline was partly explained by the privatisation process, as R&D staff transferred from formerly "public" units to "new" institutions had not yet been registered as R&D staff.

The structure of R&D personnel in Russia shows a growing share of RSE, an evolution similar to the short-term evolution in major OECD economies.

The breakdown by sectors indicates that higher education had only 8.1 per cent of R&D personnel in 1991 (CSRS estimates), a share lower than that of all OECD countries. This is essentially due to the structure of R&D, which is concentrated in other sectors: the government sector has a very high share (similar to that of France), as does the business enterprise sector (similar to that of the United States). Another reason is that university teachers devoting only part of their activity to R&D are not counted in these calculations.

If the share of RSE in the total labour force is compared with the same data for OECD countries, the overestimation and/or the "overemployment" of R&D personnel, which is a common feature in Russia as well as in Central and Eastern Europe, is also apparent. Despite a significant decline in 1990-1991, the share in Russia is still substantially higher than that of any OECD country or even Hungary or the former Czechoslovakia.

3. R&D output indicators

The ex-USSR traditionally used certain indicators – such as the number of scientific discoveries and inventions, the "use of inventions", the number of prototypes and bibliometric data – to measure output in science and technology.

It is rather difficult to use these data to make international comparisons, because of the very different concepts of intellectual or industrial property in Central and East European countries and OECD countries. For example, the USSR granted intellectual property rights mainly in the form of the "author certificate", which remunerated the inventor for giving the State the right to use his/her invention. In most cases, patents were only granted to foreign inventors. This system is now being revised to make it compatible with a market economy. A new law on inventions was put in force in the USSR on 1 July 1991. It is not yet possible to obtain data on the recent developments in Russian R&D output as a result of patenting.

External patenting

The European Patent Office (EPO) publishes annual data, by country of origin, on applications it receives through the Patent Co-operation Treaty (PCT). In 1991, they show a decrease in the number of applications from the USSR after a regular growth during the previous years (Table A2.5). Hungary shows the same downward trend. The decline certainly reflects changes related to the transition period. Russia appears in the EPO statistics for the first time in 1992, with 7 Euro-PCT applications. Until 1990, Soviet applications through the Euro-PCT system broadly compared with those of Hungary, Israel or Taiwan but were far below those of the United States, Japan or Canada.

In the United States, the number of patents granted to Soviet inventors declined regularly during the 1980s, but began to rise in 1989 and 1990 (Table A2.6). Numbers of patent granted to the USSR were broadly comparable to numbers for Hungary, Denmark, Spain, or Norway but far below those of most OECD countries.

Machinery, electric and electronic equipment, chemicals and allied products as well as professional and scientific instruments are the product areas for which the former USSR had the highest number of patents granted in the United States (Table A2.7). Excluding electric and electronic equipment, the same holds true for the former CSFR.

Table A2.5. **Euro-PCT patent applications**

	1988	1989	1990	1991
USSR	106	162	194	90
Hungary	109	114	103	72
Israel	124	137	176	156
Taiwan	74	87	117	127

Source: European Patent Office and OECD.

Table A2.6. **Number of patents granted in the United States**

	1975	1980	1985	1986	1987	1988	1989	1990
East European countries								
USSR	421	463	148	117	121	97	160	176
Czechoslovakia	120	55	54	35	46	34	34	38
Hungary	52	87	108	131	126	94	131	94
Poland	37	38	10	15	14	11	17	19
North America								
United States	46 551	37 213	39 548	38 101	43478	40 451	50 121	47 293
Canada	1 325	1 103	1 333	1 305	1 581	1 487	1 949	1 850
European Economic Community								
Germany	6 044	5 767	6 651	6 806	7 817	7 312	8 277	7 575
France	2 366	2 096	2 400	2 367	2 870	2 647	3 139	2 857
Italy	736	806	915	994	1 182	1 078	1 297	1 260
United Kingdom	3 043	2 416	2 504	2 411	2 781	2 592	3 102	2 795
Ireland	16	19	29	26	38	45	66	54
Belgium	285	250	237	240	300	297	370	314
Luxemburg	16	14	37	31	22	30	32	19
Netherlands	628	659	768	729	929	813	1 080	970
Denmark	148	160	191	181	205	152	219	158
Spain	98	65	78	98	117	124	132	128
Portugal	7	2	4	2	5	5	10	6
Greece	9	4	6	11	4	9	10	8
Other OECD countries								
Australia	254	270	341	379	387	418	502	436
Austria	313	265	322	358	349	342	405	392
Finland	98	122	203	209	275	233	231	304
Japan	6 358	7 136	12 756	13 220	16 570	16 157	20 167	19 499
New Zealand	28	50	33	52	69	54	58	51
Norway	105	80	92	80	136	121	128	109
Sweden	916	827	856	886	950	780	841	772
Switzerland	1 469	1 279	1 235	1 219	1 380	1 246	1 365	1 294
Turkey	1	2	1	9	2	2	3	2

Source: Computer Horizon, Inc., and OECD.

4. Conclusion

The former USSR was traditionally known for its R&D potential and still possesses a large number of S&T personnel, despite the decline of the very recent past. The reduction in personnel and expenditures, as well as the reorganisation of the S&T system, are similar to those occurring in other Central and East European economies. The government of the Russian Federation, which

Table A2.7. **USSR: Number of patents granted in the United States**

US standard industrial classification	1975	1980	1985	1986	1987	1988	1989	1990
Food and kindred products	3	3	0	1	0	3	0	1
Textile mill products	1	2	0	0	0	1	2	0
Chemical and allied products	69	64	14	15	15	12	20	16
Petroleum/nat. gas extract./refining	4	2	0	2	1	0	2	2
Rubber and miscellaneous plastic prod.	6	13	2	2	0	3	1	3
Stone, clay, glass, concrete products	9	15	3	1	1	2	2	4
Primary metals	20	16	6	3	1	0	5	6
Fabricated metal products	22	18	10	6	4	1	5	6
Machinery (exc. electrical)	165	151	49	53	54	47	58	60
Elec., electronic mach., equipment, etc.	71	105	25	10	13	12	36	25
Transportation equipment	6	7	5	1	1	2	2	4
Professional and scientific instruments	41	56	30	23	27	13	21	26
Unclassified patents	0	0	0	0	0	0	1	16
All other industries	3	11	4	1	5	3	6	6
All product fields combined	421	463	148	117	121	97	160	176

Source: Computer Horizon, Inc., and OECD.

finances 95 per cent of R&D, is still very much engaged in S&T, even if it has other more important short-term priorities. Russian science can be expected therefore to play an important role at the international level, once economic conditions have stabilised.

MAIN SALES OUTLETS OF OECD PUBLICATIONS
PRINCIPAUX POINTS DE VENTE DES PUBLICATIONS DE L'OCDE

ARGENTINA – ARGENTINE
Carlos Hirsch S.R.L.
Galería Güemes, Florida 165, 4° Piso
1333 Buenos Aires   Tel. (1) 331.1787 y 331.2391
                    Telefax: (1) 331.1787

AUSTRALIA – AUSTRALIE
D.A. Information Services
648 Whitehorse Road, P.O.B 163
Mitcham, Victoria 3132   Tel. (03) 873.4411
                         Telefax: (03) 873.5679

AUSTRIA – AUTRICHE
Gerold & Co.
Graben 31
Wien I   Tel. (0222) 533.50.14

BELGIUM – BELGIQUE
Jean De Lannoy
Avenue du Roi 202
B-1060 Bruxelles   Tel. (02) 538.51.69/538.08.41
                   Telefax: (02) 538.08.41

CANADA
Renouf Publishing Company Ltd.
1294 Algoma Road
Ottawa, ON K1B 3W8   Tel. (613) 741.4333
                     Telefax: (613) 741.5439
Stores:
61 Sparks Street
Ottawa, ON K1P 5R1   Tel. (613) 238.8985
211 Yonge Street
Toronto, ON M5B 1M4   Tel. (416) 363.3171
                      Telefax: (416)363.59.63
Les Éditions La Liberté Inc.
3020 Chemin Sainte-Foy
Sainte-Foy, PQ G1X 3V6   Tel. (418) 658.3763
                         Telefax: (418) 658.3763

Federal Publications Inc.
165 University Avenue, Suite 701
Toronto, ON M5H 3B8   Tel. (416) 860.1611
                      Telefax: (416) 860.1608
Les Publications Fédérales
1185 Université
Montréal, QC H3B 3A7   Tel. (514) 954.1633
                       Telefax : (514) 954.1635

CHINA – CHINE
China National Publications Import
Export Corporation (CNPIEC)
16 Gongti E. Road, Chaoyang District
P.O. Box 88 or 50
Beijing 100704 PR   Tel. (01) 506.6688
                    Telefax: (01) 506.3101

DENMARK – DANEMARK
Munksgaard Book and Subscription Service
35, Nørre Søgade, P.O. Box 2148
DK-1016 København K   Tel. (33) 12.85.70
                      Telefax: (33) 12.93.87

FINLAND – FINLANDE
Akateeminen Kirjakauppa
Keskuskatu 1, P.O. Box 128
00100 Helsinki
Subscription Services/Agence d'abonnements :
P.O. Box 23
00371 Helsinki   Tel. (358 0) 12141
                 Telefax: (358 0) 121.4450

FRANCE
OECD/OCDE
Mail Orders/Commandes par correspondance:
2, rue André-Pascal
75775 Paris Cedex 16   Tel. (33-1) 45.24.82.00
                       Telefax: (33-1) 49.10.42.76
                       Telex: 640048 OCDE

OECD Bookshop/Librairie de l'OCDE :
33, rue Octave-Feuillet
75016 Paris   Tel. (33-1) 45.24.81.67
              (33-1) 45.24.81.81
Documentation Française
29, quai Voltaire
75007 Paris   Tel. 40.15.70.00
Gibert Jeune (Droit-Économie)
6, place Saint-Michel
75006 Paris   Tel. 43.25.91.19
Librairie du Commerce International
10, avenue d'Iéna
75016 Paris   Tel. 40.73.34.60
Librairie Dunod
Université Paris-Dauphine
Place du Maréchal de Lattre de Tassigny
75016 Paris   Tel. (1) 44.05.40.13
Librairie Lavoisier
11, rue Lavoisier
75008 Paris   Tel. 42.65.39.95
Librairie L.G.D.J. - Montchrestien
20, rue Soufflot
75005 Paris   Tel. 46.33.89.85
Librairie des Sciences Politiques
30, rue Saint-Guillaume
75007 Paris   Tel. 45.48.36.02
P.U.F.
49, boulevard Saint-Michel
75005 Paris   Tel. 43.25.83.40
Librairie de l'Université
12a, rue Nazareth
13100 Aix-en-Provence   Tel. (16) 42.26.18.08
Documentation Française
165, rue Garibaldi
69003 Lyon   Tel. (16) 78.63.32.23
Librairie Decitre
29, place Bellecour
69002 Lyon   Tel. (16) 72.40.54.54

GERMANY – ALLEMAGNE
OECD Publications and Information Centre
August-Bebel-Allee 6
D-53175 Bonn   Tel. (0228) 959.120
               Telefax: (0228) 959.12.17

GREECE – GRÈCE
Librairie Kauffmann
Mavrokordatou 9
106 78 Athens   Tel. (01) 32.55.321
                Telefax: (01) 36.33.967

HONG-KONG
Swindon Book Co. Ltd.
13–15 Lock Road
Kowloon, Hong Kong   Tel. 366.80.31
                     Telefax: 739.49.75

HUNGARY – HONGRIE
Euro Info Service
Margitsziget, Európa Ház
1138 Budapest   Tel. (1) 111.62.16
                Telefax : (1) 111.60.61

ICELAND – ISLANDE
Mál Mog Menning
Laugavegi 18, Pósthólf 392
121 Reykjavik   Tel. 162.35.23

INDIA – INDE
Oxford Book and Stationery Co.
Scindia House
New Delhi 110001   Tel.(11) 331.5896/5308
                   Telefax: (11) 332.5993
17 Park Street
Calcutta 700016   Tel. 240832

INDONESIA – INDONÉSIE
Pdii-Lipi
P.O. Box 269/JKSMG/88
Jakarta 12790   Tel. 583467
                Telex: 62 875

ISRAEL
Praedicta
5 Shatner Street
P.O. Box 34030
Jerusalem 91430   Tel. (2) 52.84.90/1/2
                  Telefax: (2) 52.84.93
R.O.Y.
P.O. Box 13056
Tel Aviv 61130   Tél. (3) 49.61.08
                 Telefax (3) 544.60.39

ITALY – ITALIE
Libreria Commissionaria Sansoni
Via Duca di Calabria 1/1
50125 Firenze   Tel. (055) 64.54.15
                Telefax: (055) 64.12.57
Via Bartolini 29
20155 Milano   Tel. (02) 36.50.83
Editrice e Libreria Herder
Piazza Montecitorio 120
00186 Roma   Tel. 679.46.28
             Telefax: 678.47.51
Libreria Hoepli
Via Hoepli 5
20121 Milano   Tel. (02) 86.54.46
               Telefax: (02) 805.28.86
Libreria Scientifica
Dott. Lucio de Biasio 'Aeiou'
Via Coronelli, 6
20146 Milano   Tel. (02) 48.95.45.52
               Telefax: (02) 48.95.45.48

JAPAN – JAPON
OECD Publications and Information Centre
Landic Akasaka Building
2-3-4 Akasaka, Minato-ku
Tokyo 107   Tel. (81.3) 3586.2016
            Telefax: (81.3) 3584.7929

KOREA – CORÉE
Kyobo Book Centre Co. Ltd.
P.O. Box 1658, Kwang Hwa Moon
Seoul   Tel. 730.78.91
        Telefax: 735.00.30

MALAYSIA – MALAISIE
Co-operative Bookshop Ltd.
University of Malaya
P.O. Box 1127, Jalan Pantai Baru
59700 Kuala Lumpur
Malaysia   Tel. 756.5000/756.5425
           Telefax: 757.3661

MEXICO – MEXIQUE
Revistas y Periodicos Internacionales S.A. de C.V.
Florencia 57 - 1004
Mexico, D.F. 06600   Tel. 207.81.00
                     Telefax : 208.39.79

NETHERLANDS – PAYS-BAS
SDU Uitgeverij Plantijnstraat
Externe Fondsen
Postbus 20014
2500 EA's-Gravenhage   Tel. (070) 37.89.880
Voor bestellingen: Telefax: (070) 34.75.778

NEW ZEALAND
NOUVELLE-ZÉLANDE
Legislation Services
P.O. Box 12418
Thorndon, Wellington   Tel. (04) 496.5652
                       Telefax: (04) 496.5698

NORWAY – NORVÈGE
Narvesen Info Center – NIC
Bertrand Narvesens vei 2
P.O. Box 6125 Etterstad
0602 Oslo 6　　　　　　Tel. (022) 57.33.00
　　　　　　　　　Telefax: (022) 68.19.01

PAKISTAN
Mirza Book Agency
65 Shahrah Quaid-E-Azam
Lahore 54000　　　　　Tel. (42) 353.601
　　　　　　　　　Telefax: (42) 231.730

PHILIPPINE – PHILIPPINES
International Book Center
5th Floor, Filipinas Life Bldg.
Ayala Avenue
Metro Manila　　　　　　Tel. 81.96.76
　　　　　　　　Telex 23312 RHP PH

PORTUGAL
Livraria Portugal
Rua do Carmo 70-74
Apart. 2681
1200 Lisboa　　　　　Tel.: (01) 347.49.82/5
　　　　　　　　Telefax: (01) 347.02.64

SINGAPORE – SINGAPOUR
Gower Asia Pacific Pte Ltd.
Golden Wheel Building
41, Kallang Pudding Road, No. 04-03
Singapore 1334　　　　　Tel. 741.5166
　　　　　　　　Telefax: 742.9356

SPAIN – ESPAGNE
Mundi-Prensa Libros S.A.
Castelló 37, Apartado 1223
Madrid 28001　　　　　Tel. (91) 431.33.99
　　　　　　　　Telefax: (91) 575.39.98

Libreria Internacional AEDOS
Consejo de Ciento 391
08009 – Barcelona　　　Tel. (93) 488.30.09
　　　　　　　　Telefax: (93) 487.76.59

Llibreria de la Generalitat
Palau Moja
Rambla dels Estudis, 118
08002 – Barcelona
　　　　　(Subscripcions) Tel. (93) 318.80.12
　　　　　(Publicacions) Tel. (93) 302.67.23
　　　　　　　　Telefax: (93) 412.18.54

SRI LANKA
Centre for Policy Research
c/o Colombo Agencies Ltd.
No. 300-304, Galle Road
Colombo 3　　　Tel. (1) 574240, 573551-2
　　　　　　Telefax: (1) 575394, 510711

SWEDEN – SUÈDE
Fritzes Information Center
Box 16356
Regeringsgatan 12
106 47 Stockholm　　　Tel. (08) 690.90.90
　　　　　　　　Telefax: (08) 20.50.21

Subscription Agency/Agence d'abonnements :
Wennergren-Williams Info AB
P.O. Box 1305
171 25 Solna　　　　　Tel. (08) 705.97.50
　　　　　　　　Téléfax : (08) 27.00.71

SWITZERLAND – SUISSE
Maditec S.A. (Books and Periodicals - Livres
et périodiques)
Chemin des Palettes 4
Case postale 266
1020 Renens　　　　　Tel. (021) 635.08.65
　　　　　　　　Telefax: (021) 635.07.80

Librairie Payot S.A.
4, place Pépinet
CP 3212
1002 Lausanne　　　　Tel. (021) 341.33.48
　　　　　　　　Telefax: (021) 341.33.45

Librairie Unilivres
6, rue de Candolle
1205 Genève　　　　　Tel. (022) 320.26.23
　　　　　　　　Telefax: (022) 329.73.18

Subscription Agency/Agence d'abonnements :
Dynapresse Marketing S.A.
38 avenue Vibert
1227 Carouge　　　　Tel.: (022) 308.07.89
　　　　　　　　Telefax : (022) 308.07.99

See also – Voir aussi :
OECD Publications and Information Centre
August-Bebel-Allee 6
D-53175 Bonn (Germany)　Tel. (0228) 959.120
　　　　　　　　Telefax: (0228) 959.12.17

TAIWAN – FORMOSE
Good Faith Worldwide Int'l. Co. Ltd.
9th Floor, No. 118, Sec. 2
Chung Hsiao E. Road
Taipei　　　　Tel. (02) 391.7396/391.7397
　　　　　　　　Telefax: (02) 394.9176

THAILAND – THAÏLANDE
Suksit Siam Co. Ltd.
113, 115 Fuang Nakhon Rd.
Opp. Wat Rajbopith
Bangkok 10200　　　Tel. (662) 225.9531/2
　　　　　　　　Telefax: (662) 222.5188

TURKEY – TURQUIE
Kültür Yayinlari Is-Türk Ltd. Sti.
Atatürk Bulvari No. 191/Kat 13
Kavaklidere/Ankara　Tel. 428.11.40 Ext. 2458
Dolmabahce Cad. No. 29
Besiktas/Istanbul　　　　Tel. 260.71.88
　　　　　　　　　Telex: 43482B

UNITED KINGDOM – ROYAUME-UNI
HMSO
Gen. enquiries　　　　Tel. (071) 873 0011
Postal orders only:
P.O. Box 276, London SW8 5DT
Personal Callers HMSO Bookshop
49 High Holborn, London WC1V 6HB
　　　　　　　　Telefax: (071) 873 8200
Branches at: Belfast, Birmingham, Bristol, Edinburgh, Manchester

UNITED STATES – ÉTATS-UNIS
OECD Publications and Information Centre
2001 L Street N.W., Suite 700
Washington, D.C. 20036-4910 Tel. (202) 785.6323
　　　　　　　　Telefax: (202) 785.0350

VENEZUELA
Libreria del Este
Avda F. Miranda 52, Aptdo. 60337
Edificio Galipán
Caracas 106　　Tel. 951.1705/951.2307/951.1297
　　　　　　Telegram: Libreste Caracas

Subscription to OECD periodicals may also be placed through main subscription agencies.

Les abonnements aux publications périodiques de l'OCDE peuvent être souscrits auprès des principales agences d'abonnement.

Orders and inquiries from countries where Distributors have not yet been appointed should be sent to: OECD Publications Service, 2 rue André-Pascal, 75775 Paris Cedex 16, France.

Les commandes provenant de pays où l'OCDE n'a pas encore désigné de distributeur devraient être adressées à : OCDE, Service des Publications, 2, rue André-Pascal, 75775 Paris Cedex 16, France.

9-1994

OECD PUBLICATIONS, 2 rue André-Pascal, 75775 PARIS CEDEX 16
PRINTED IN FRANCE
(14 94 12 1) ISBN 92-64-14239-8 - No. 47435 1994